Digital Computer Principles

Digital Computer Principles

BURROUGHS CORPORATION

Technical Training Department

Military Field Service Division

Radnor, Pennsylvania

McGRAW-HILL BOOK COMPANY
New York   Toronto   London

Foreword

This book, in its original form, was written for the General Computer Fundamentals Course which is conducted by the Military Field Service Division of the Burroughs Corporation. The course was specifically designed to prepare the prospective computer technician, engineer, or programmer for the more advanced computer concepts which he will encounter when he studies different types of computer equipment.

The staff of instructors who have conducted the General Computer Fundamentals Course have collaborated in the preparation of this book. The training material which serves as the foundation of this book has been completely revised, and information concerning recent developments and new concepts in the computer field has been incorporated into the present text to increase its usefulness. We are grateful for the critical examination to which each chapter was subjected by the authors and other members of the instructional staff; their individual contributions enabled us to improve the presentation of each subject.

E. S. JUNKER, *Manager*
Technical Training Department

Preface

This book provides a nonmathematical explanation of digital computers: their operations and the components that make them work. The components of the digital computer are in a constant state of evolution as a consequence of the quest for greater speed and compactness. The extensive use of semiconductors in modern computer circuitry has resulted in computer reliability, miniaturization, and speed previously unattainable with the earlier relay and vacuum-tube versions. As a result of these innovations, the computer is decreasing in bulk and increasing in renown. Commercial applications are numerous. They range from relatively simple tasks such as mail sorting to more intricate ones that include automatic accounting and check processing in the larger banking institutions and automatic control of chemical and mechanical processes in industrial plants and laboratories. Military applications range from automatic land surveillance to gun laying and missile guidance. Future applications of computers are practically limitless.

The main objective of this book is to evaluate the underlying concepts of computer logic and circuitry. It has been written primarily for the computer engineer, programmer, and technician.

This book is divided into three sections to facilitate the study of computer elements and/or computer operational units. These sections are:

    I. Computers and Transistors (Chap. 1 through 7)
   II. Computer Circuits (Chap. 8 through 15)
  III. Computer Units (Chap. 16 through 24)

Section I provides the background information necessary for comprehension of the material in the two following sections. Topics covered in this section include basic concepts of computer logic, symbolic notation, number systems, and a general introduction to computer components. Much emphasis is placed on the theory of semiconductor devices, especially transistors since they are extensively used as gate elements in modern computers.

Section II provides an analysis of basic computer circuits. This is accomplished by first analyzing each circuit with the vacuum tube as the active element and then proceeding to analyze the transistorized version of the circuit. The description of logical circuits in this section will give a deeper insight into the "how" of computer operations and was included mainly for the prospective computer technician. The reader whose prime concern is the logical operation of the computer may bypass this circuitry section.

Section III shows how the logical elements described in the two previous sections are connected to perform major computer operations. Data flow and the basic essentials of programming are also described to acquaint the reader with methods of controlling the computer.

A comprehensive chart of computer symbols used by the various computer manufacturers is included in Appendix I, a general bibliography of books, articles, and periodicals is to be found in Appendix II, and a glossary of computer terms are given in Appendix III.

B. L. LOGAN
Training Projects Coordinator

Contents

Computers and Transistors

Chapter 1

Introduction to Computers

Throughout the ages, man's progress has been measured by the implements he has invented to ease his mental and physical burdens. Perhaps the greatest single invention has been the written word, for with this, man has been able to record his discoveries and pass them on to future generations. In much of his scientific research, man has relied upon mathematical computations to predict the outcome of his multitudinous experiments and to test an abundance of new ideas. This has been probably the greatest stimulus to production of the outstanding developments in the field of automatic computation and electronic data processing in the last few years.

Electronic computers have made possible scientific and industrial advances that were unattainable only two decades ago. The mathematics required to orbit the sun with a satellite, for example, would tax the capabilities of teams of mathematicians for an entire lifetime. Now, with the aid of the electronic computer, the conquest of space is rapidly becoming a reality.

Currently, computers are employed wherever repetitious calculations or the processing of voluminous data becomes routine. Computers find their greatest applications in the commercial, scientific, and military fields. They are used in many varied projects, ranging from mail sorting through engineering design calculations to air traffic control. The beneficial aspects of computers include speed, accuracy, and the reduction of manpower in clerical and routine jobs.

The digital computer is a familiar member of a family of machines known as electronic data processors, which range in size from the desk-size computer used in most banking applications to the room-size machines used in air traffic control. Digital computers solve mathematical problems

1

by performing simple arithmetic operations. Although the basic opera-iton is addition, digital computers also subtract, multiply, divide, and extract square roots by modification of the addition process. Following a sequence of instructions known as a *program*, a computer can solve prob-lems in algebra, in geometry, and in calculus in a fraction of the time required by a human mathematician. Because they are capable of per-forming thousands of basic arithmetic operations each second, digital computers can relieve the scientist of lengthy numerical calculations and free his mind for more creative activities. Since the computer is a product of man's ingenuity, it can be only as versatile as its designers and pro-grammers make it.

Another important type of computer that will be introduced at this time is the analog computer. Although not so renowned as the digital computer, the analog computer finds exclusive use in some applications. For the sake of clarity, the characteristics of both types of computers will be compared in the following paragraphs.

Data is applied to digital computers in the form of electric pulses of two discrete levels; hence this type of machine is highly adaptable to numerical calculations. The information is represented by the number of pulses and the spacing between them. There must be an intermediate device, between the operator and the data-manipulating portions of the computer, that will translate the information from numerical data to pulse data. This device is usually in the form of a typewriter that punches the information on cards or produces an input tape for the computer. This intermediate step is necessary since the computer can arrive at a solution in a fraction of the time it takes to insert the information and the medium must therefore be prepared well in advance. The computer then accepts the information from the medium as it is required, usually at a high rate of speed. After computations have been performed, the results are translated into a form that a human operator can read and understand.

Data is applied in the analog computer in the form of variable voltages representing quantities by analogy. The input voltages originate at sources such as thermocouples, potentiometer arms, or other electro-chemical or electromechanical devices. The input data is then manipu-lated within the analog computer by linear voltage amplifiers, voltage dividers, and other circuits or mechanical devices to produce the required output. The output is one (or sometimes more than one) voltage or graph which represents by its magnitude a number consisting of several digits. The analog computer is adaptable to solving problems of the calculus that involve rate of change or integration of minute quantities. In brief, the analog computer performs specialized functions, whereas the digital computer finds a more general use. Depending upon application, the analog computer under specific circumstances may outperform or be more economical than the digital computer. The converse is also true.

This chapter presents a brief history of digital computers and the events that led to their present stage of development, a detailed account of computer applications, and a description of the basic elements of computers. More detailed information is presented in the chapters that follow.

History of Digital Computers

Early man counted on his fingers and measured size and quantity with parts of his anatomy, such as the foot, hand, and palm. Another unit of measure based on the human body is the cubit (the length of the forearm from the elbow to the end of the middle finger). The familiar decimal system used for expressing quantity originated with the use of the fingers (digits) of the hand for computation; hence the word "digital" is used to describe any device which uses numbers to express quantity.

Eventually, the human hands proved inadequate for counting the quantities man needed to express, and he resorted to such devices as scratches in stones, notched sticks, and knotted string. The earliest known device made with a provision for denoting carries was the abacus, which originated in the Far East about 600 B.C. The abacus is a wooden frame with beads strung on wire columns (Fig. 1.1). Each column of beads represents an order, or place, in the decimal system, such as units, tens, hundreds, and thousands. The abacus is still used in some parts of the world, and skilled operators can manipulate it at a speed comparable to that of a desk calculator.

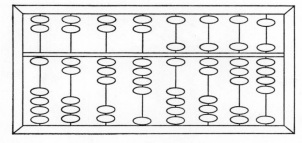

Fig. 1.1 Abacus.

The next significant contribution to the field of computation was made in 1614 by John Napier, who invented and published tables of logarithms. Working with John Briggs, Napier was able to convert the logarithms to the base of 10 and introduce the use of the decimal point in this method of calculation. These logarithms were used by William Oughtred of England, who inscribed them on ivory in originating the slide rule. In 1617 Napier devised a system of computation known as "Napier's Bones," which consists in manipulation of numbered squares of bone arranged to form whole numbers and fractions.

About 1642 Blaise Pascal constructed the first desk-calculator type of adding machine (Fig. 1.2). This device used gears with 10 teeth to represent numbers from 0 through 9. In its original form the machine

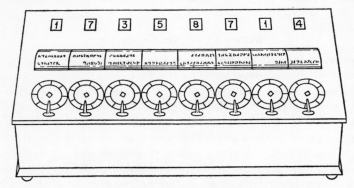

Fig. 1.2 Pascal's calculator.

performed addition and subtraction. It was later modified by other scientists to perform multiplication by repeatedly adding a given number for the required number of times. The principle of using repeated addition and subtraction is currently used in modern electronic computers to multiply and divide large numbers.

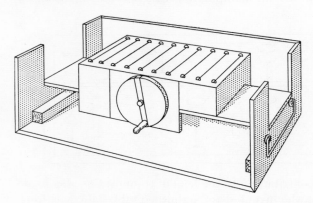

Fig. 1.3 Stepped reckoner.

Baron von Leibnitz constructed a machine called a *stepped reckoner* (Fig. 1.3) in the latter part of the seventeenth century. This machine was gear-operated, and it provided a carry from one order to the next. The various calculating machines just discussed were the forerunners of modern adding machines.

During the early part of the nineteenth century, Charles Babbage attempted to build a calculator that would solve problems and print answers. Babbage envisioned a machine that could automatically follow stored instructions and store a thousand numbers of 50 digits each. For an input to this analytical engine, Babbage planned to adapt the punched card that Joseph Marie Jacquard had invented in 1801 for the control of looms. Babbage's machine was never completed because the British Government withdrew its support and because the machine tools of the

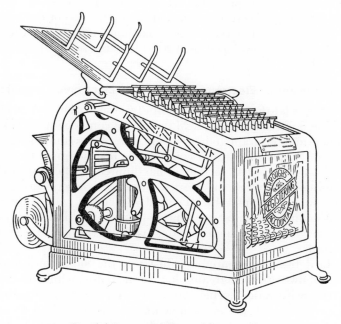

Fig. 1.4 Burroughs's first adding machine.

day were incapable of the precision required to construct the components. Babbage's ideas were advanced for the technology of that time, and they included many of the features found in modern computers.

Charles Xavier Thomas of Alsace invented the first successful calculating machine in 1820. This machine, which was widely sold, contained units for setting, counting, and registering. In Europe Arthur Burkhardt began manufacturing in 1878 a Thomas type of machine known as the *arithmometer*. In 1875 Frank Stephen Baldwin and W. T. Odhner each designed a calculating machine that modified the stepped reckoner so that a variable number of teeth protruded from the periphery of the wheel. The thin Odhner wheel made possible a more compact design, which has been used in several more recent adding-machine designs. In 1850 D. D. Parmalee obtained a patent for the first keydriven adding machine in the United States. It could add only a single column of digits at a time. It was not until after the turn of the century that Dorr Eugene Felt introduced parallel operation of keys and carry.

Although E. D. Barbor incorporated a printing device with an adding machine in 1872, the first commercially practical adding-listing machine was invented by William Seward Burroughs, who was granted a patent on it in 1888. The company for which Burroughs worked (the Boyer Machine Company) received a contract to produce 50 of the calculating machines (Fig. 1.4). Thus the business machine industry was established. Special motors were developed in 1920 so that the desk calculators could be electrified.

Development of Electromechanical and Electronic Computers

The first special-purpose relay computer was originated in 1940 by the Bell Telephone Laboratories. Many of the components developed by the telephone and telegraph industry were suitable for computing-machine construction. A special-purpose computer is one designed to perform a specific job and no other, so that it has limited applications. The first general-purpose computer, the Mark I, or automatic sequence-controlled calculator, was developed by Harvard University and International Business Machines Corporation jointly. Designed by Dr. Howard Aiken of the Harvard faculty, this computer used electromagnetic relays and punched cards.

While the debt of the computer industry to the communications industry is great, it owes an even greater debt to the pulse techniques developed in connection with radar during World War II. During this period when industry turned to automation, applied mathematics gained momentum. In fact, the general development of electronic computers had its real beginning in government projects during World War II.

Perhaps the greatest single advance in automatic computing came in 1945 when Dr. John von Neumann introduced the idea of storing the computer's instructions internally. Previous computers had been controlled by means of plugboard wiring or instructions stored in some external medium such as punched paper tape or cards. The new development in storage was first used in the design of the electronic discrete variable automatic computer (EDVAC). The computer was developed in 1946 by the Moore School of Engineering of the University of Pennsylvania for use by the United States Army at Aberdeen Proving Grounds in Maryland. In this machine the program of instructions was inserted directly into the memory so that an instruction was immediately accessible when the previous one had been performed. The Standards eastern automatic computer (SEAC) was constructed at the National Bureau of Standards following the logical design of the EDVAC. The SEAC was the first computer to make extensive use of a-c techniques.

The electronic numerical integrator and computer (ENIAC) was developed by J. W. Mauchly and J. P. Eckert of the University of Pennsylvania for the Ordnance Department of the United States Army. Completed in 1946, this machine represented both an advance and a step backward from the technological level of the EDVAC. The ENIAC was the first computer to be completely electronic in internal operation. However, it had no stored program, utilizing instead a complex external switching arrangement.

These computers were followed in rapid succession by others that featured improvements in speed, storage, and reliability. A. W. Burks, Dr. John von Neumann, and Dr. H. H. Goldstine developed a whole family of computers that used electrostatic memories. These computers were developed largely for military, scientific, and statistical purposes in various government projects. Soon after the close of World War II, such leaders in the computing machine field as the International Business Machines Corporation, Burroughs Corporation, National Cash Register Company, and Remington Rand (now Sperry Rand Corporation) developed electronic computers for general purposes. The UNIVAC, built in 1951 by Remington Rand, was the first mass-produced electronic computer.

Modern computers use transistors and miniature magnetic elements for compactness and reliability. They compute with speeds and accuracies that far outstrip the capabilities of the human brain. Today computers and other electronic data processors not only relieve man of many tedious tasks but also help him to understand his environment.

Description of a Typical Computer

Basically, electronic digital computers are composed of five units (see Fig. 1.5): input, storage (or memory), arithmetic, control, and output. The following paragraphs briefly describe these units.

Input unit. The purpose of the input unit is to accept the initial input data which is required to solve the problem. This input data must be prepared in a form that the computer can understand. The information is then said to be *encoded* into machine language. Typical input units are punched-card readers, tape readers (paper or magnetic), and keyboards. The input and output units are often slower in operation than the rest of the computer, which makes it necessary to store unworked and partly processed data in the storage unit.

Storage unit. To solve a complex problem, the storage unit, or memory, must first retain the steps for solution and the initial input data and, later, the intermediate and final results. All information that enters or leaves the computer passes through this unit.

Full-scale digital computers being manufactured today generally have either the magnetic-tape, revolving-drum, or magnetic-core type of memory, although other types now in development may supersede these.

Arithmetic unit. The arithmetic unit performs all mathematical computations upon receiving instructions from the control unit. These operations take place sequentially. If multiplication is required, the unit obtains the result by repeated addition. The arithmetic unit receives its inputs from the storage unit and, after carrying out the appropriate calculation, sends the answers back to the same unit. The design of modern vacuum-tube or transistorized arithmetic units permits exacting, high-speed requirements to be met.

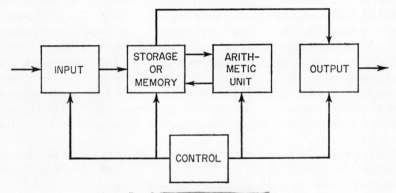

Fig. 1.5 Basic computer units.

Output unit. The output unit accepts final results from the storage unit and usually translates them from machine code to a form that may be interpreted by the operator. Common forms of output units are card punches, magnetic-tape writers, and paper-tape punches or printers.

Control unit. The control unit performs the most vital function in the computer. It actuates the other units and controls the data flow between them to solve a problem. In other words, it accepts the problem and directs the order of operation.

Manual Problem Solving

The way an electronic digital computer solves a problem may probably best be illustrated by first analyzing the manner in which a typical business problem is solved manually. Then in the next section, Computer Problem Solving, the corresponding steps taken by a computer to solve this problem will be described.

The problem taken for analysis is that of computing and recording an employee's pay and deductions, and the method of solution follows.

Step 1. If this is the first time that the accountant has prepared a payroll for this particular firm, he will first consult a procedure manual or else obtain instructions from his fellow workers.

Step 2. The next step is to accumulate the basic factors of the problem, namely, hours worked, hourly rate, overtime, tax deduction tables, employee tax status, and any other applicable deductions.

Step 3. Next, the accountant will carry out the proper arithmetic calculations with a pencil and paper or with a desk calculator.

Step 4. The final answers are then transferred to the regular company payroll form.

Computer Problem Solving

An electronic digital computer will solve this payroll problem in a manner closely paralleling that of the accountant. The method follows.

Step 1. In digital computer procedure the loading of the program into the storage unit by way of the input unit corresponds to the accountant's obtaining the proper instructions for his job.

Step 2. The loading of raw data into the computer's storage unit through the input units corresponds to the accumulating by the accountant of the basic factors of the problem (hours worked, etc.).

Step 3. In this step the computer begins actually to calculate the desired payroll data, guided always in a step-by-step manner by the control unit. Here the storage unit serves three functions: it holds raw data until the arithmetic unit is ready for it, it holds partially processed data, and it holds the final answers.

Step 4. When the output unit is switched on, it prints out or otherwise records the final answers on a sheet of paper, a punched card, or a tape.

This payroll problem illustrates a highly useful characteristic of a digital computer, namely, that it can solve any problem, no matter how complex, which can be broken down into simple logical steps.

The payroll problem is only one of many now being solved by computers. The chapters that follow will cover all the basic decision and storage elements of computers in detail and will show how these elements are connected to compose the operational units described in this chapter.

Applications

It has been previously stated that computers are employed widely in the commercial, scientific, and military fields. The commercial field is the largest of the three. Nearly all large businesses use computers and data processors for calculating payrolls and billings, for processing inventories, and for reducing huge piles of statistics to comprehensible terms.

Data processors are used in the New York Stock Exchange to (1) inform stockbrokers of stocks available, (2) determine whether stock values are increasing or decreasing, and (3) compute Dow-Jones averages to show prevailing market tendencies. Several large transportation companies also use data processors to direct trains and airplanes along the most favorable routes.

Banking applications. Because banks are swamped with millions of checks daily, their clerical staffs have grown to almost unmanageable proportions with work loads continually increasing. Computers can

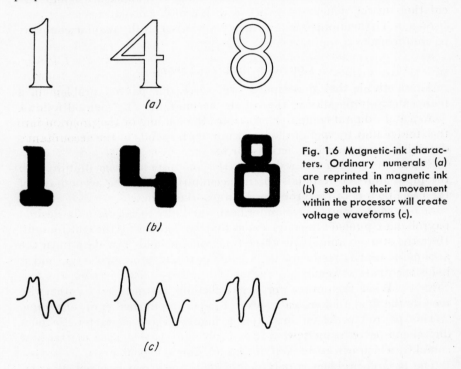

(a)

(b)

Fig. 1.6 Magnetic-ink characters. Ordinary numerals (a) are reprinted in magnetic ink (b) so that their movement within the processor will create voltage waveforms (c).

(c)

solve this problem by taking the checks after the teller has typed in the amount, sorting the checks into the proper bins at the rate of thousands per hour, and recording the transactions on permanent records.

The American Bankers' Association, working with engineers and printers, has developed a standardized set of symbols for the numbers 0 through 9, along with four other symbols meaning "transit number," "on us," "amount," and "dash." These 14 symbols include all the information required for banking that is completely automatic except for writing the amount on the check. The numbers or symbols used for processing are written in magnetic ink across the bottom of each check. The technique applied in processing a check is indicated in Fig. 1.6. The three digits 148, normally printed as in Fig. 1.6a, are printed on the check with magnetic ink in the special forms shown in Fig. 1.6b. When the check is moved through the sensing (reading) mechanism of the processing machine, these magnetized digits produce magnetic flux densities of the magnitude, polarity, and duration indicated in Fig. 1.6c. This data is recorded in the memory, where it will be available for further processing or for activating sorting equipment for proper disposition of the check.

Other commercial applications. Manufacturing plants use computers for the control of industrial tools and processes, machine loading, and production scheduling. Accounting and sales applications include payroll and royalty computations, sales analysis, inventory control, and cost accounting. Among the many uses that engineers have found for computers are highway and canal cut-and-fill calculations, instrument-response studies, and gas-plant design.

Scientific applications. Businesses and institutions in scientific fields use digital computers and data processors for developing and testing new alloys and compounds, for finding weak and strong areas of newly designed devices, and for determining the effects of natural forces on man and his machines. Computers used for these purposes do not solve complete problems, but they do reduce the boredom and especially the time involved in solving the simple, repetitive portions of the problems. Many scientific institutions reduce the cost of operating their computers by solving problems for companies that can neither afford nor justify the cost of a full-time computer. Further examples of scientific applications of computers are molecular-vibration studies, optical-ray tracing, and high-energy-physics research. Among the many scientific applications of digital computers are physical, mathematical, chemical, astronomical, and biological research; nuclear physics; and biometrics. The future of the digital computer in science is promising, for the computer helps to open up new areas for scientific exploration.

Military applications. The armed forces also use many digital computers and data processors to (1) supply materials to combat units, (2) detect hostile aircraft and ships, and (3) conduct retaliatory attacks at peak efficiency. Digital computers are used to determine the best place to store cargo in ships and airplanes, for both weight distribution and convenience, and they calculate the quantities of supplies required for combat units. Data processors are employed in early-warning-radar systems to arrange information in a form easily interpreted by the officers who assign and direct missiles and aircraft to the target. Compact airborne digital computers are used in supersonic aircraft for aiming rockets at targets and in intercontinental ballistic missiles for accurate guidance. Computers are also used aboard ships and submarines to calculate positional data. Thus, the computer can be used in both offensive and defensive military applications.

The computer uses presented in this chapter are representative of the many ways in which digital computers and data processors have been employed in commercial, scientific, and military applications. As technology expands, more and more uses for computers will be found in these and other fields.

Summary

In the fields of science and industry there has been a growing need for high-speed computing devices. Long, tedious calculations that take months to perform have impeded to a considerable extent the progress of scientific research and development. Time-consuming computations that might take a human being years to do can be accomplished in a matter of minutes with modern high-speed computers.

Automatic electronic digital computers are relatively new, dating back to about 1944. Since then, about 200 types of computers have been built. Of the two general types of computers, analog and digital, the digital type has become more prevalent. The advantages of digital computers over analog computers are that greater accuracy may be obtained for the same cost, computations are performed with discrete values, and higher-speed operation is possible. Computers range in size from small desk calculators to those used in high-capacity nationwide data-processing systems.

The chief characteristic of analog computers is that quantities or magnitudes are determined by incremental variations of voltages rather than by step changes. For control use this type of computer has the advantage that the output can be used as a continuously variable voltage source to drive electrical mechanisms.

This chapter has surveyed the wide applications of digital computers in the commercial, military, and scientific fields. Also, operation of computers and typical computer problem-solving methods have been described in simplified form. The remarkable future potential of these machines should be apparent. It can certainly be said that, in general, the future of those trained or experienced in the computer field appears bright.

QUESTIONS

1.1 What advantages do computers offer over conventional methods of problem solving?

1.2 What are the two major classifications of computers?

a. Which type is more adaptable to numerical calculations? Why?

b. Which type is more adaptable to controlling a process? Why?

1.3 Draw a block diagram showing the five basic units of a digital computer and briefly describe the function of each unit.

1.4 Can a digital computer arbitrarily solve any type of problem? What are the factors involved?

1.5 List the applications for which computers can be used.

Chapter 2

Computer Elements and Symbology

A first glance at the circuitry of a digital computer has the tendency to reinforce the assumption of the observer that this machine is, in all actuality, a giant brain containing masses of exotic circuits, the operation of which is beyond the comprehension of the average technician. It is the purpose of this chapter to dispel this assumption, to show that this is not the case. By definition, a computer is a mechanical or electronic machine which is capable of performing sequences of reasonable operations upon information—mainly arithmetic and logical operations. The term "computer logic" indicates the manner in which the basic computer elements are connected to provide the reasoning and decision-making activity of the computer. A simplified mathematical expression of computer logic termed *Boolean algebra* has been adopted by the digital computer industry; this system of mathematics removes the computer from design-equation level and simplifies the operational analysis to the point where it can be comprehended readily by well-informed laymen. A more extensive treatment of Boolean algebra is given in Chap. 4.

As the material in this book is assimilated, the seemingly intricate operations will become clear and sometimes surprisingly simple. A computer is constructed from only a few types of basic circuits, modified to suit a particular need (compactness, circuit reliability, stability, etc.). These circuits are then grouped together to process information. The purpose of this chapter is not to give a complete theory of computer operation but to acquaint the reader with computer language, computer components, and the logical symbols used.

Basic Principles of Computer Design

Computer design is divided into two areas: logical design and electrical design. Logical design involves the use of mathematical logic to provide

13

equations for all the operations a computer must perform. Electrical design provides electric circuits corresponding to the logical equations. The four basic requirements for computer design are as follows:

1. A system of numbers that can be easily adapted by the machine to perform arithmetic operations
2. A system of mathematics that can determine and describe all the operations to be performed by a computer
3. A means of representing all commands, information, and numbers in a computer by electrical quantities
4. A system of electric circuits to execute all the operations to be performed by a computer

Each of these requirements will now be discussed.

Number Systems for Computers

The arithmetic operation of a digital computer is dependent on counters for computations and data synchronization and upon gating devices for decision making. The early computers, such as the Harvard Mark I

Table 2.1 Binary Representation of Decimal Digits

Decimal Number	Binary Equivalent	
	8421	Position value
0	0000	
1	0001	
2	0010	
3	0011	
4	0100	
5	0101	
6	0110	
7	0111	
8	1000	
9	1001	
10	1010	

calculator constructed by the International Business Machines Corporation in 1944, used many standardized calculator parts. This electromechanical computer used relays and mechanical counters, and it had a storage capacity of 1,728 decimal digits. The basic time cycle of the machine was 300 msec for the addition of two numbers. Its mechanical drive was a 4-hp motor. The total assembly weighed approximately 5 tons.

The high driving power required and the speed limitations of relays and mechanical counters, caused by inertia, led to the utilization of vacuum tubes for counting and temporary storage and to the abandonment of the decimal system of numeration in the computers that followed. The 10 digits used in the decimal system were too cumbersome for a computer of reasonable size. In order to use the decimal system, either 10 storage devices or a device with 10 distinct levels was required for each order. Since a signal of two discrete levels is less subject to deterioration than a multilevel signal, modern digital computers operate with the binary (two-value) system. The binary system uses only two digits: 0 and 1. The equivalent counts in the binary system for the decimal numbers 0 through 10 are shown in Table 2.1. The binary 1 can be represented by a conducting tube and the binary 0 can be represented by a cutoff tube. In the binary system, five tubes could represent a decimal value of 31 (binary 11111 = decimal 31). A complete explanation of the binary system is given in Chap. 3, Number Systems.

Although the binary system is cumbersome for pencil-and-paper manipulation, the fact that only two digits are involved makes this system ideal for computer manipulation.

Mathematical Logic for Computers

The most widely used system of mathematics for describing the logical sequences of operation a computer must perform is Boolean algebra, which was developed by George Boole, a philosopher and mathematician who wished to express philosophical logic in mathematical terms. Boolean algebra is not an algebra involving customary numerical values; rather, it is an algebra of "classes." Only two of the classes in Boolean algebra are of importance in computer design. These are the universal class, in which everything is a member $(1 + 0 = 1)$, and the empty class, in which nothing is a member $(1 \times 0 = 0)$.

The concept of classes in its pure sense, however, is of importance only to the mathematician and the philosopher. For computer design purposes, the important factor is that only two discrete values are involved: a quantity either exists or does not exist.

In a computer, the universal class is mechanized by what is termed an AND gate. The simple switch-and-lamp configuration shown in Fig. 2.1 illustrates the function of an AND gate.

If the lamp L is to light, series switches A and B must be closed at the same time. The Boolean expression for this function uses the multiplication sign and can be expressed in either of three forms: $A \times B = L$, $AB = L$, or $A \cdot B = L$, read as "A AND B equals L." If a closed switch were to represent a 1, or "true," condition and the open switch were to represent a 0, or "false," condition, a table could be constructed showing all possible conditions of the two variables. Such a table is called a *truth table*. Although the table shown in Fig. 2.1 is simple and self-explanatory, truth tables are quite useful when a large number of variables are used.

The empty class is mechanized by an OR gate. The switch-and-lamp configuration is again used to illustrate the OR function as shown in Fig. 2.2. The truth table for this function is also shown. If either of the parallel switches (A or B) is closed, the lamp will light. The Boolean expression for the OR function is simply $A + B = L$, read as "A OR B equals L."

The diagrams illustrate the important AND and OR functions in their purest form. In actual computer circuitry, these gates are composed of diodes or of amplifying devices such as transistors or vacuum tubes. The

$AB = L$

A	B	L
0	0	0
0	1	0
1	0	0
1	1	1

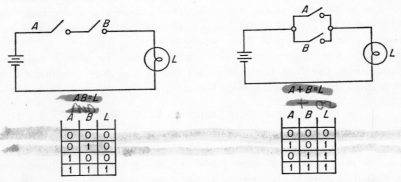

Fig. 2.1 Switches performing the AND function.

$A + B = L$

A	B	L
0	0	0
1	0	1
0	1	1
1	1	1

Fig. 2.2 Switches performing the OR function.

AND gate is the actual "decision" element in a computer and the OR gate is the "mixer" element.

The following example shows how computer operations are expressed in Boolean notation. In Chap. 1, two of the main computer units described were the arithmetic unit and the memory unit. Quite often it is desired to transfer a sum from the arithmetic unit to the memory unit. There are two conditions that must exist before the transfer may occur:

1. The addition process must be complete.
2. A position must be available in the memory unit to accommodate the sum.

To express these conditions for transfer in Boolean notation, let T designate the transfer command, signal A indicate that addition is complete, and signal B indicate that a position exists in the memory. The equation for transfer is written as follows:

$$A \cdot B = T$$

This equation states that a transfer command will occur when addition is

completed and a position is available in the memory. The dot in the
equation indicates that an AND circuit is used.

Consider another example, using the OR circuit. Prior to any arithmetic
operation, the arithmetic unit must be cleared. Let C designate the clear
command, signal A indicate an add instruction, S indicate a subtract
instruction, M indicate multiplication, and D indicate division. The
equation for the clear instruction is written as follows:

$$C = A + S + M + D$$

Boolean algebra expresses all the logical operations performed in a
computer in terms of the existence or nonexistence of specific conditions.
A more detailed description of Boolean algebra is given in Chap. 4.

Representing Information by Electrical Quantities

Boolean algebra and the binary number system have one important
common characteristic: only two discrete quantities exist in each system.
In Boolean algebra these quantities are "present" and "not present,"
and in binary arithmetic they are 1 and 0.

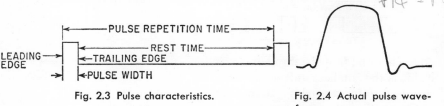

Fig. 2.3 Pulse characteristics.   Fig. 2.4 Actual pulse waveform.

Since, in each case, only two values are used, an electric pulse is the
most suitable means of representing these values. All numbers, commands,
and information are contained in the computer in the form of pulses. This
is the internal language of the computer.

Pulse characteristics. An electric pulse is either a voltage or a current
that undergoes an almost instantaneous change in amplitude from one
constant level to another. Pulse characteristics are shown in Fig. 2.3.
The time between the leading edge of one pulse and the leading edge of
the following pulse is known as the pulse repetition time (PRT). The
pulse repetition frequency (PRF) is the reciprocal of the PRT. For example, if the time between pulses is 0.002 sec, the PRF is 1/0.002 or
500 pulses per second.

The pulses shown in Fig. 2.3 are idealized. An actual pulse seen on an
oscilloscope would appear similar to the pulse shown in Fig. 2.4. Pulse-
amplifying and -shaping circuits are used in the computer so that the
ideal waveshape is approached.

Pulses perform a variety of functions in a digital computer: they provide basic timing, indicate information, and control the sequence of operation of the computer. Each function will now be discussed.

Timing pulses. The speed of computer operation is dependent upon the PRF of the basic timing pulses. A digital computer is a sequential machine in that all tasks performed by it are accomplished in a sequence of basic, and often repetitive, operations. Each operation a computer performs is done in coincidence with a timing pulse.

Timing pulses are generated by a stable pulse-generating circuit, or *timing oscillator*. The width of the timing pulse is short, usually about 2 μsec. Timing pulses are often called *clock pulses*.

Information pulses. Information in a computer includes coded data such as numbers, letters, and symbols. This information is represented in the computer by a configuration of 1s and 0s. For example, decimal 10 is represented as binary 1010. The pulse representation of this number is shown in Fig. 2.5.

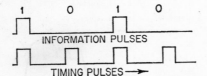

Fig. 2.5 Pulse representation of binary 1010.

Each 1 and 0 in the number is a BInary digiT, often contracted to *bit*. A bit is the smallest unit of information, that is, a Yes or a No. The bits are used to form machine characters.

Characters. A character can be a decimal digit 0 to 9, a letter A to Z in either uppercase or lowercase, a punctuation mark, or a symbol. Characters are the basic pieces of intelligible machine information, and they are usually of fixed length. The pulses shown in Fig. 2.5 illustrate a four-bit machine character, representative of the decimal number 10. The same configuration could also be used to represent either the letter J or a symbol; this is determined by the character code used by the computer.

Words. Machine characters are used to construct computer "words." An analogy may thus be drawn between the machine character and a written letter and between the machine word and a spoken word. In both cases, an elemental unit of a language (character) is used to compose a unit of intelligence that has meaning. The characters represent letters, numbers, and symbols.

When space in the computer is not at a premium, each word contains a fixed number of characters. Characters are grouped into words and handled by the computer as a single piece of information.

Blocks. In the majority of digital computers it is expedient to process information in larger units than the word. Since the internal storage capacity of a computer is limited, voluminous and seldom-used information, such as records and accounts, is generally stored externally in large magnetic-tape-handling units. Since thousands of words can be stored on a reel of tape, this type of unit is usually preferred for permanent bulk storage because of the low cost per character stored and the fairly short access time. Before the external data is actually needed by the computer, the tape units are actuated by signals from the computer to search for the required information. Information is applied to the computer in units of several words each, termed *blocks*. The blocks of information are thus transferred to internal storage, to which the computer has a shorter access time (in the order of microseconds). Figure 2.6 illustrates a segment of an information block of 20 four-character words using four-bit characters.

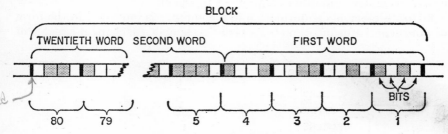

Fig. 2.6 Typical information block.

More details on block information selection from external storage are presented in Chap. 22, Computer Memory Systems, and Chap. 23, Input-Output Equipment.

Computer Circuits

The digital computer is a complex machine in its entirety; however, it is still no more than an aggregate of simple devices that perform a few basic operations. The two most commonly used devices are bistable switching circuits and gates.

A bistable device is one having two stable states of conduction or being. A typical example of a bistable device is an ordinary push-button light switch. When the switch is pushed to the ON position, it makes a rapid transition from the OFF state to the ON state and "remembers" that position until it is depressed again to the OFF position. A rapid transition is highly desirable in bistable switching circuits because it determines the maximum speed at which the computer can operate.

The two types of gates used in computers are the linear gate and the logical gate. The linear gate is defined as one from which the output is an approximate replica of at least one of the inputs. The logical gate is defined as one in which the output is a pulse which may have no resemblance to any of the inputs, except that the pulse occurs during an interval selected by the control voltages. The term "logical" is applied to these gates because the input-output characteristics of these circuits are suggestive of logical operations. Every computer operation is implemented by bistable switching circuits, gates, or a combination of these items. Gates and switching circuits are generally used in conjunction with other devices such as delay lines, multivibrators, inverters, and amplifiers to control the movement of pulse information throughout the machine. The function and the representative symbol of each type of basic computer circuit are described in the following paragraphs. The emphasis will not be upon the electrical characteristics, but rather on how the circuit performs its function. The electrical operation of each type of circuit will be described in detail in other chapters of this book.

Bistable elements. Information in a computer is indicated in the form of words consisting of 1s and 0s. A bistable element, an element capable of

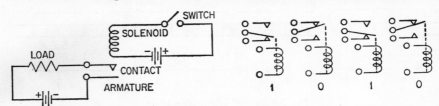

Fig. 2.7 Simple relay.   Fig. 2.8 Relays indicating 1010.

indicating a 1 or a 0, must be used to indicate each bit in a word. The relay was the bistable element used in earlier computers, and it is still useful in many applications today. Figure 2.7 shows the simplified diagram of a relay. A relay is a switch that operates electromagnetically. The relay closes or opens a circuit if the current through its exciting coil is started or stopped. If the operating switch is closed, current flows through the coil, energizing the electromagnet and drawing the armature upward to the contact.

If the relay contact is closed, a 1 could be indicated; if the relay contact is open, a 0 could be indicated. Of course, the opening and closing of the switch is controlled by other relays or control elements.

Since words rather than individual bits are processed in a computer, the bistable elements are grouped together as a unit to accommodate a word. This is the reason that words contain a fixed number of characters. For example, four relays would be required to hold the word 1010. In Fig. 2.8 the positions of the relay contacts are shown as they would appear when the word 1010 is indicated.

A typical relay has a life expectancy of nearly a billion cycles and operates in the order of milliseconds. The operational speed of the electro-mechanical relay restricted the computational speed of the relay-equipped computer to the range of hundreds of cycles per second. To overcome speed limitations, the relays were supplanted with high-speed electronic switches.

Flip-flops. The most commonly used bistable element in modern computers is the Eccles-Jordan multivibrator, usually referred to as a *flip-flop*. The Eccles-Jordan type of multivibrator utilizes vacuum tubes or transistors, and it has two stable states. A simple description of the vacuum-tube flip-flop follows.

A schematic diagram of a flip-flop is shown in Fig. 2.9. The values of the resistors and the grid-bias voltage are chosen so that the circuit will

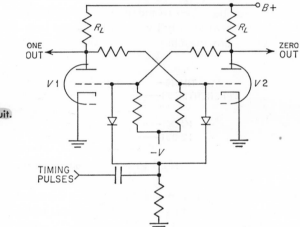

Fig. 2.9 Flip-flop circuit.

be stable when one tube is conducting and the other is cut off. Hence, the circuit has two stable states: tube V_1 conducting and V_2 cut off, or V_2 conducting and V_1 cut off. The circuit can be changed from one stable state to the other by applying a positive voltage pulse to the grid of the cutoff tube or by applying a negative voltage pulse to the grid of the conducting tube.

The output from the plate of each tube consists of pulses of opposite voltage levels. When V_1 is cut off, no plate current flows and the plate voltage is high at the B+ level; simultaneously, V_2 is conducting and its plate voltage is low, being the difference between the B+ voltage and the voltage dropped across the load resistor R_L. The voltage levels, along with the timing pulses, are shown in the timing diagram of Fig. 2.10.

The timing pulse is differentiated so that a positive spike is developed at the leading edge of the pulse and a negative spike is developed at the trailing edge. The positive spike is eliminated, and the negative spike is applied to the grid of the conducting tube. Hence, the flip-flop will change state at the trailing edge of each input pulse.

The two stable states of the flip-flop represent the two bits. If V_1 is chosen to be the ONE side, then V_2 is automatically labeled the ZERO side. If the B+ level is chosen to represent a 1, the flip-flop will indicate a 1, or "be in the ONE state," when V_1 is cut off and V_2 is conducting. The flip-flop will indicate a 0, or "be in the ZERO state," when V_2 is cut off and V_1 is conducting. When the more positive of the two levels used is chosen to indicate a "true" condition, the device or system uses a *positive logic level*. When the more negative of the two levels is used to indicate a "true" condition, a *negative logic level* is being employed.

The fact that the upper level appears at the output of V_2 when V_2 is cut off should not be taken to mean that the ZERO side is holding a binary 1. A 1 can be indicated only by the side chosen to be the ONE side. It will be seen in the following chapters that the output from the ZERO side must

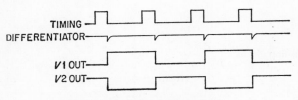

Fig. 2.10 Flip-flop voltage levels.

also be used to perform the electrical operations required by the computer. Many refinements have been made in the basic circuit to increase its switching speed and circuit reliability; however, its main purpose is merely to store a 1 or a 0. Newer computers use transistorized flip-flops, but their operations are essentially the same as those of vacuum-tube flip-flops. More details on flip-flops are given in Chap. 10, The Bistable Multivibrator.

Magnetic Cores. The development of magnetic materials possessing high retentivity and a nearly square hysteresis loop has made it possible to construct magnetic cores for use as bistable switching devices. Their small physical size and their ability to store binary information at the expense of very little energy make these core devices ideally suited for computer data-storage applications.

Consider the arrangement illustrated in Fig. 2.11. The type of core shown is similar to a ring-transformer core, but it is much smaller in size, ranging from ⅛ to 1 in. in diameter, depending upon its application and method of construction. Assume that a pulse of current of sufficient amplitude to saturate the core is applied to coil winding W_1. The direction of the lines of force in the core depends upon the direction of the current that flows through W_1. After a current pulse has passed, the core remains magnetized in the same direction at a point close to saturation. If a current pulse is again applied to W_1 in the same direction, there will be only a slight increase in the number of flux lines; consequently, only a small voltage is induced in the output winding W_3. If, on the other hand, the current pulse is applied to W_2 in a direction opposite to the current pulse applied to W_1, the direction of the lines of force changes and a large output appears in the detect network.

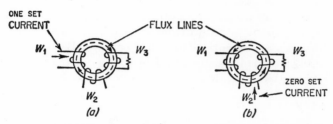

Fig. 2.11 Use of a magnetic core as a bistable element. (a) ONE state. (b) ZERO state.

The core can be regarded as storing a 1 when magnetized in a given direction, and storing a 0 when magnetized in the opposite direction. W_1 can be referred to as the *write* winding, since it "writes" a 1 into the core. W_2 may be referred to as the *read* winding since the current through it changes the direction of the lines of force if a 1 is present in the core, thereby indicating to the output winding W_3 that a 1 is present in the core. When the core is "read," it is set to the ZERO state.

Logical gates. Many electric devices are used in the construction of logical gates. Semiconductors find extensive usage in this application

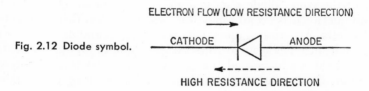

Fig. 2.12 Diode symbol.

because of their low power requirements. The most commonly used type of semiconductor device is the diode. A diode is characterized by a high resistance in one direction and a low resistance in the other. The diode symbol is shown in Fig. 2.12.

The arrow of the diode symbol indicates the anode, and the bar perpendicular to the arrow represents the cathode. Electrons will flow from the cathode to the anode as long as the anode is a few tenths of a volt more positive than the cathode. Electrons encounter a high resistance if they attempt to flow from anode to cathode; hence, electron flow through the diode is negligible if the cathode becomes more positive than the anode.

Diode AND *Gate.* The AND gate is used to detect coincidence of pulses. Figure 2.13 shows a diode AND gate for pulses whose upper levels indicate a "true" signal (binary 1).

Each diode input is connected to a common point (C). The output voltage at C will be equal to the lower voltage level applied at the inputs (A and B). Assume that the pulses applied to the input have an upper voltage level of $+50$ volts and a lower voltage level of $+10$ volts. From time t_0 to t_1, the input to both diodes is $+10$ volts. The diodes conduct and the difference of potential (40 volts) between B+ and the input is dropped across the load resistor R_L. The voltage at C is then $+10$ volts (less the few tenths of a volt dropped across the diodes). At time t_1, the

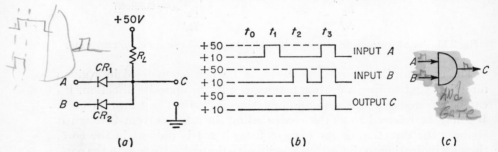

Fig. 2.13 Diode AND gate. (a) Electrical diagram. (b) Timing diagram. (c) Logical diagram.

voltage at A is $+50$ volts and the voltage at B is $+10$ volts. Diode CR_1 now cuts off, but the anode of CR_2 is still positive with respect to the cathode; therefore, diode CR_2 maintains conduction. The difference of potential between B+ and input B is across R_L, and the output remains at $+10$ volts. At times t_2, diode CR_1 will conduct and diode CR_2 will cut off. The output remains at 10 volts. At time t_3, both inputs are $+50$ volts. Neither diode conducts, and the B+ voltage ($+50$ volts) is present at the output. Hence, the output will go to its upper level only when both inputs are at their upper levels simultaneously.

Diode OR *Gate.* The OR gate provides the pulse-mixing function. Figure 2.14 shows a diode OR gate for pulses whose upper levels indicate a "true" signal.

Notice that, in this case, the input is applied to the *anodes* of the diodes and the gate supply voltage is returned to a *negative* voltage. The output follows the higher voltage level applied to either input. Assume again that the input levels are $+10$ and $+50$ volts. From time t_0 to t_1, inputs A and

B are at the $+10$-volt level. Both diodes conduct, and the output is $+10$ volts. At time t_1, diode CR_1 conducts harder than diode CR_2, and the $+50$ volts is impressed across the output. The $+50$-volt potential applied to the output makes the cathode of diode CR_2 40 volts positive with respect to the plate, and diode CR_2 cuts off. At time t_2, diode CR_2 conducts and diode CR_1 is cut off; the output is again at $+50$ volts. At time t_3, both diodes conduct, and the output rises to $+50$ volts. Hence, the OR gate produces a "true" output when a "true" input is present at A or B.

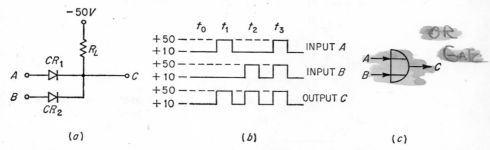

Fig. 2.14 Diode OR gate. (a) Electrical diagram. (b) Timing diagram. (c) Logical diagram.

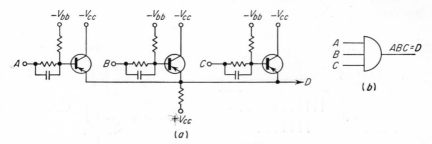

Fig. 2.15 PNP emitter-follower AND circuit. (a) Electrical diagram. (b) Logical symbol.

It has been assumed in the previous discussion that the upper level of a pulse indicates a 1 and the lower level indicates a 0. This choice of levels is somewhat arbitrary. The lower level could have been chosen to indicate a 1, and the upper level could have been chosen to indicate a 0. If the latter choice were taken, the roles of the AND and OR gates just described would be exchanged. The AND gate shown in Fig. 2.13 is an OR gate for low-level "true" signals, and the OR gate in Fig. 2.14 is an AND gate for low-level "true" signals.

Transistor AND *Gate.* Because of their amplifying properties, transistors are sometimes preferred to diodes. Figure 2.15 shows a typical PNP-transistor AND gate to be used in a system of positive logic. The capacitors which parallel the input resistors to the base connections enable the pulse to retain a steep leading edge; this provides faster and more reliable switching action. The transistors are connected as parallel emitter followers. This circuit will produce a "high" output at D only when all inputs (A, B, and C) are high.

Transistor OR *Gate.* Figure 2.16 shows a PNP-transistor OR gate for positive systems of logic. The series transistors each respond in the manner of an open switch when a positive pulse is applied to the base connection. Therefore, across the common-emitter resistor, the output voltage is at its upper level whenever A, B, or C is present.

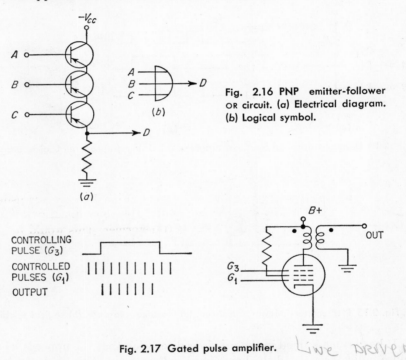

Fig. 2.16 PNP emitter-follower OR circuit. (a) Electrical diagram. (b) Logical symbol.

Fig. 2.17 Gated pulse amplifier.   Line DRIVER

As with the diode AND and OR circuits, the transistor configurations in Figs. 2.15 and 2.16 are interchanged for systems using negative logic.

Vacuum-tube Gates. Another type of gating circuit used in computers to perform the AND function is the gated pulse amplifier. This circuit consists of a special type of pentode vacuum tube wherein the suppressor grid exercises approximately the same amount of control over plate current as the control grid. The most commonly used tube for this application is the 6AS6. In Fig. 2.17 the essential components of the gated pulse amplifier are shown.

The OR function can be mechanized by using triodes as illustrated in Fig. 2.18. The triodes are connected as cathode followers utilizing a common-cathode resistor which is returned to a source of negative voltage. If a positive pulse is applied to either input (A or B), the pulse will appear at the output (C).

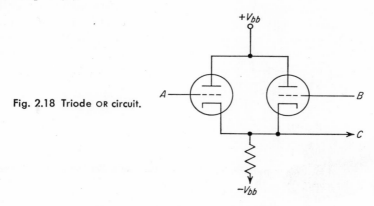

Fig. 2.18 Triode OR circuit.

Inverters

Quite often it becomes necessary to invert the polarity of a pulse. Inversion may become necessary to perform a logical function or to obtain the correct level to perform an electrical operation. Inversion is usually performed by an amplifier stage whose output is 180° out of phase with the input or by a phase-inverting pulse transformer. This would include either a grounded-cathode vacuum-tube amplifier stage or a grounded-emitter transistor amplifier stage as shown in Fig. 2.19.

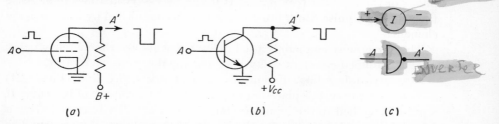

Fig. 2.19 Inverter circuits. (a) Vacuum-tube inverter. (b) Transistor inverter. (c) Logical symbol.

An example of inverter usage is shown in Fig. 2.20. It is desired to produce an output D when a situation F exists and a situation E does not exist. This is expressed as $F \cdot \bar{E} = D$. Since this is an AND function, output D must occur only when F is true and E is not true. If upper levels are chosen to represent a "true" signal, the F input to the AND gate will be at its upper level and the E input will be at its lower level. However, the E input goes through an inverter stage before it is applied to the AND-gate diode; hence, the correct levels are present at the gate inputs to produce output D.

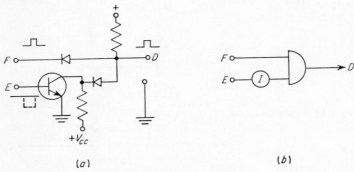

Fig. 2.20 Use of inverter to perform logical operations. (a) Simplified electrical diagram. (b) Logical diagram.

Observe that output D can exist only if the input at E is at its lower level. If E were true, the input to the diode would be at the lower level and output D would not occur. Output D can exist only when the condition $F \cdot \bar{E}$ occurs. The gate is also called an *inhibit gate* since a "true" input at E will inhibit the output.

Delay Devices

It is often necessary to delay a train of timing pulses or a binary word as it is routed through the machine, without affecting the widths of the pulses or the time between pulses. It is also necessary at times to increase the width of a pulse. Both functions can be accomplished by using a delay element.

The three most commonly used delay elements are the mercury delay line, the lumped-constant delay line, and the delay multivibrator.

Mercury delay line. Essentially, a mercury delay line (Fig. 2.21) consists of two crystals placed at opposite ends of a column of mercury. If a pulse is applied to the input crystal, the crystal will vibrate, creating a wave of energy that traverses the length of the column of mercury. The delay encountered depends upon the delaying properties of mercury and the length of the tube. When the pulse of energy reaches the other crystal, the crystal vibrates and a pulse is produced at the output side.

Figure 2.22 shows how the word 1101 may be delayed for a period of 4,000 μsec. Observe that even though each bit in the word has been delayed for 4,000 μsec, the pulse widths and the time between pulses are unaffected.

Lumped-constant delay line. The lumped-constant delay line performs the same function as the mercury delay line. This type of delay line is composed of a group of inductors and capacitors, arranged in a manner similar to that shown in Fig. 2.23.

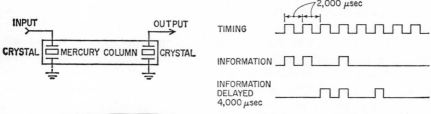

Fig. 2.21 Mercury delay line.

Fig. 2.22 Binary word delayed 4,000 μsec.

The specific amount of time required for a pulse to traverse each inductor-capacitor section depends upon the values of the components. The desired delay is accomplished by choosing the correct sizes of components and the required number of sections. For short delays only inductors are required; the distributed capacitance existing between the windings provides the shunt capacitance.

Fig. 2.23 Lumped-constant delay line.

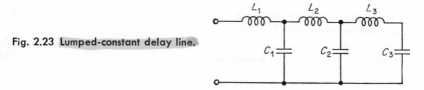

Delay multivibrator. A delay multivibrator is a one-shot type of multivibrator that is modified to delay a pulse. The explanation of the circuit is somewhat lengthy and is beyond the scope of this chapter. However, it is explained in detail in Chap. 9.

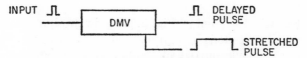

Fig. 2.24 Delay multivibrator; input and outputs.

The amount of time an input pulse applied to the circuit will be delayed depends upon the circuit components. Two outputs may be taken from the circuit; one is the delayed pulse, and the other is a "stretched" pulse whose duration is equal to the delay time of the multivibrator. Figure 2.24 shows the input and outputs of the delay multivibrator.

Amplifier and Waveshaping Circuits

When the logical building blocks are connected in various combinations to perform logical operations, the output pulses from these devices decrease in amplitude and their waveforms become distorted. Also, the output from a gate or a flip-flop is usually applied to several other inputs. These devices may not provide enough power to drive all the necessary inputs. Circuits must be interspersed between logical blocks to reshape the pulses and provide driving power and the necessary isolation between stages. Pulse amplifiers and buffer amplifiers are used throughout a system for these purposes. Although they provide no logical function, they are necessary for reliable electrical operation of computers.

Logical Symbols and Diagrams

A digital computer diagram that used electrical schematic diagrams of every circuit and component in the computer would be difficult to trace and would make troubleshooting difficult. Since most logical elements in the computer are used over and over and since the input and output characteristics are known, each element can be represented by its particular logical symbol. Then, by showing the connections between symbols, the complete operation of the computer can be traced. The most frequently encountered symbols are given here. The symbols shown are typical of those used by the different computer manufacturers.

Flip-flop symbols. Logical symbols for the flip-flop are shown in Fig. 2.25. The input and output terminals are indicated on the logical

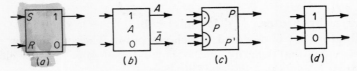

Fig. 2.25 Flip-flop symbols.

diagrams. The logical symbol of Fig. 2.25a is in its simplest form. Some diagrams designate flip-flops by letters, such as A, B, and L. Figure 2.25b shows that the ONE-side output of flip-flop A is designated A and the ZERO-side output is designated $\bar{A}$ (A NOT). Most flip-flops have internal gating circuits so that the flip-flop will change state only when specified input conditions are met. Internal circuits are also provided to allow a series of clock pulses to be applied alternately to each side of the flip-flop, provided that all other gating conditions are satisfied. Then one input pulse will set the flip-flop to a particular stable state, and the following input pulse will set it to the opposite stable state. A flip-flop having such an arrangement is called a *complementing* or *complemented* flip-flop. The logical symbol of a complemented flip-flop is shown in Fig. 2.25c. The symbol shown in Fig. 2.25d is used mainly in systems of transistor logic.

Core logic. The bimag (bistable magnetic) cores discussed in this chapter have various uses. Figure 2.26 shows a bimag core and its logical symbol; this type of core is used for temporary storage and shifting applications.

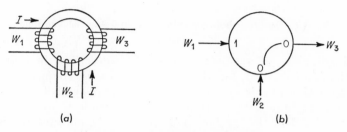

(a)   (b)

Fig. 2.26 (a) Bimag core and (b) symbol.

The first input pulse applied to the winding W_1 in Fig. 2.26b will set the core to the ONE state if it is in the ZERO state. The second input pulse applied to winding W_2 will set the core to the ZERO state if it is in the ONE state when the pulse is applied. The line with the arrow going away from the 0 indicates that an output pulse will be developed when the core changes from the ONE state to the ZERO state.

Gate symbols. Symbols for the four types of gates discussed in this chapter are shown in Fig. 2.27.

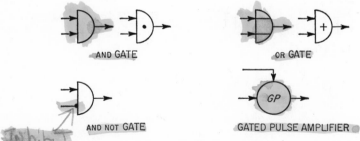

AND GATE   OR GATE

AND NOT GATE   GATED PULSE AMPLIFIER

Inhibit

Fig. 2.27 Gate symbols.

The OR gate differs from the AND gate in that the input lines are continued through the gate symbol. The dot at the lower input to the AND-NOT gate shows that the input is inhibited. The gated pulse amplifier shows the gating input on the top and the gated input (individual pulses) on the side. The same gating symbols may be made for vacuum tubes, transistors, diodes, magnetic cores, or relays.

Delay symbols. A delay symbol is shown in Fig. 2.28. The delay time is usually indicated.

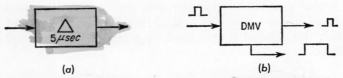

(a)   (b)

Fig. 2.28 Delay symbols. (a) Delay line. (b) Delay multivibrator.

Standardization of symbols. The symbols described here are but a few of the symbols used, but they are the ones most frequently encountered. At the time of this writing, no standard set of symbols exists for use throughout the industry, but steps have been made to establish standardization. A list of the symbols most likely to be encountered is given in Appendix I.

Logical diagrams. A logical diagram shows the manner in which the building blocks are connected to perform logical operations. An example is given in Fig. 2.29.

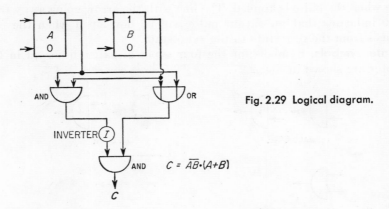

Fig. 2.29 Logical diagram.

$$C = \overline{AB} \cdot (A+B)$$

A logical diagram and the Boolean equations that describe computer operations are the most useful means of analyzing the complete operation of a computer. Notice that no voltage levels are shown on the logical diagram. The primary concern is merely to show the logical sequence of operation. Another diagram may be provided to show input and output levels along with the location of pulse and buffer amplifiers and other necessary circuitry. A diagram such as this is very useful in troubleshooting in order to isolate a fault to a specific block.

Summary

The purpose of this chapter is to describe the basic requirements of computer design, to show how pulses are used to perform logical operations, and to describe the basic types of pulse circuits required to perform computer operation. The basic circuits are called building blocks and are used repetitively to perform the various logical operations. Logical diagrams employing symbolic representations of the basic blocks may be used to trace the complete operation of the computer without considering the electrical characteristics of each circuit.

None of the explanations given in this chapter have been complete. Rather, an overall view has been given describing the essential topics to be discussed in the book. Number systems, Boolean algebra, pulse circuits, and logical operations will be discussed in detail in subsequent chapters.

QUESTIONS

2.1 What system of numeration was used by the first electromechanical computers? Why was it later abandoned?

2.2 Make up a table showing the binary equivalents of decimal numbers 1 through 10.

2.3 What are the two basic logical gates used in digital computers? Which is the decision-making gate and which is the mixing gate? Make up a truth table showing all possible input and output conditions of a two-input gate of each basic type.

2.4 What is the purpose of computer timing pulses? Information pulses?

2.5 Briefly explain the following terms: bit, character, word, and block.

2.6 List as many components as you can that could be used as bistable elements in digital computers.

2.7 What are positive logic levels? Negative logic levels?

2.8 Draw the electrical diagram for a two-input diode AND gate for negative-logic systems.

2.9 Why is the transistor sometimes preferred to the diode as a gate element?

2.10 What is the purpose of a logical diagram?

Chapter 3

Number Systems

Bistable devices for counting and storing pulses are used extensively throughout digital computers and data processors. These devices produce outputs of two levels which are equivalent to either 1 or 0. This mode of counting can be expressed by the binary number system. Therefore, in order to grasp the concept of computer operation, it is necessary to become familiar with computer number systems. Although digital computers can and do utilize several number systems, the most commonly used system is the binary because of the nature of the electronic and electromechanical components available to digital computer designers. This chapter describes the basic principles of number systems, with emphasis on the binary.

History

Quantity is perhaps one of the most abstract concepts that civilizations have had occasion to develop. Comprehension of the significance of numbers such as 10, 5, or 20 is relatively easy. However, comprehension of the true value of numbers on the order of billions is difficult. The history of number systems is the history of man's efforts to find a notation that would overcome this difficulty and also simplify the rules for manipulating numbers arithmetically.

Making a single vertical mark for each item to be counted was probably the first approach to systematic counting or record keeping. This is known as a tally system, and it was soon found to be too cumbersome for the representation of large numbers. An improvement came with the making of four vertical marks, with a diagonal fifth mark to complete a set of five items. Many believe this was the beginning of a crude form of decimal counting, and it is attributed to the fact that we have five fingers on each hand and five toes on each foot. The decimal system of counting by tens naturally evolved from this and the fact that we have two hands and two feet.

The greatest forward step in the development of the decimal system came with the adoption of Arabic symbols and positional notation. The Arabic symbols 0, 1, 2, 3, 4, 5, 6, 7, 8, and 9 are easy to write and recognize visually compared with other symbols that might be used, such as Roman numerals. When written in the above order, each Arabic symbol has a value of one more than the symbol preceding. These symbols, and the idea of giving each symbol yet another value depending on its relative position, brought about the concept of the decimal system.

Basic Ideas

In the decimal system, each symbol has a dual value. When standing alone, each symbol has a fixed value assigned to it; but when combined with other symbols, each has a varying value assigned to it depending on its relative position. When two or more symbols are combined to represent a single quantity, each symbol is referred to as a *digit*, and the position of each symbol is referred to as a *digit position*. The digit position at the extreme right is the one of least value, or lowest order, with the value of each digit position increasing by a power of 10 to the left. Thus, the digit of highest order, or the most significant digit (MSD), appears at the extreme left; and the digit of lowest order, or the least significant digit (LSD), appears at the extreme right. This order, rather than the reverse thereof, was chosen because in English-speaking countries it is customary to read from left to right. With this convention, and the proceeding order of digit positions, the MSD meets the eye first, making numbers easier to read.

As an illustration of positional notation, consider the number 5,287. The notation 5,287 really means

$$5{,}000 + 200 + 80 + 7 = 5{,}287$$
or
$$5 \times 10^3 + 2 \times 10^2 + 8 \times 10^1 + 7 \times 10^0 = 5{,}287$$

The concept of units, tens, hundreds, and thousands has been in use for a long time, but few have considered its real significance. Note that each position of a digit has a base value of a power of 10 according to Table 3.1. The presence of a 0 as a digit within a number merely means that the power of 10 represented by its positional location is not used. For example, the number 402 means

$$4 \times 10^2 + 0 \times 10^1 + 2 \times 10^0 = 4 \times 10^2 + 0 + 2 \times 10^0$$
$$= 400 + 2$$
$$= 402$$

Table 3.1 Positive Powers of 10 and Decimal Equivalents

Thousands	Hundreds	Tens	Units
1,000	100	10	1
10^3	10^2	10^1	10^0

Thus far, only decimal integers or whole numbers with the decimal point assumed to be to the right of the LSD have been considered. When a decimal fraction is written, each digit position to the right of the decimal point has a negative power of 10 assigned in ascending negative powers of 10 to the right. For example, the number 0.6834 is

$$6 \times 10^{-1} + 8 \times 10^{-2} + 3 \times 10^{-3} + 4 \times 10^{-4}$$
$$= \frac{6}{10} + \frac{8}{100} + 3/1{,}000 + 4/10{,}000$$
$$= (6 \times 1{,}000 + 8 \times 100 + 3 \times 10 + 4)/10{,}000$$
$$= (6{,}000 + 800 + 30 + 4)/10{,}000$$
$$= 6{,}834/10{,}000$$
$$= 0.6834$$

The mixed decimal number 529.78 really means

$$5 \times 10^2 + 2 \times 10^1 + 9 \times 10^0 + 7 \times 10^{-1} + 8 \times 10^{-2}$$

In writing 529.78, the decimal point is used merely as a reference to show where the positive powers of 10 end and the negative powers begin.

In the decimal system, 10 is called the *base*, or *radix*, of the system. In any number system employing a single radix, the radix of the system is equal to the number of different symbols that can be used in any digit position. For example, in the decimal system there are 10 Arabic symbols that can be used in any digit position. In the quaternary system, only four symbols (0, 1, 2, and 3) are used in any digit position. These symbols have the same significance as in the decimal system in that they represent no units, one unit, two units, or three units, respectively. In the quaternary system, however, there are no symbols representing four or more units; and the radix of the system is 4. For example, the quaternary number 213.23 means

$$2 \times 4^2 + 1 \times 4^1 + 3 \times 4^0 + 2 \times 4^{-1} + 3 \times 4^{-2}$$

This is equivalent to the decimal number 39.6875.

In addition to the number systems employing a single radix, such as the decimal and quaternary systems, number systems having more than one radix have been used in digital computers. That is, it is possible to construct number systems in which certain digit positions have one radix and other digit positions have a different radix. Number systems employing other special rules have also been constructed. Some of these will be discussed later.

For applications other than in digital computers, the choice of a number system depends on economy and ease of reading. Since recognizing the magnitude of quantities written in decimal has become customary, it is difficult to recognize the same magnitudes written in some other notation. For everyday use, then, only the decimal system is employed. In general, however, a system having a smaller radix will also have a simpler addition and multiplication table. That is, it would be easier to do arithmetic computations with a system having a smaller radix because it would not be necessary to memorize as large an addition or multiplication table; hence, such a system would be more economical from that point of view. On the other hand, with a system having a smaller radix, a larger number of digits is required to represent a given quantity than would be required with a system having a larger radix; hence, the smaller radix system would be less economical from that point of view. For general application, then, the choice of a number system is not a simple one.

In digital computer applications, the choice of a number system depends primarily on the physical components available to the computer designer. Electronic devices capable of assuming 10 discrete stable states could be constructed to count units. The basic counting capability could then be increased by increasing the number of these tens-counters, but the use of these devices necessitates voltage levels of 10 distinct values. Incorporation of these levels into a pulse system presents problems not only of design but also of expense and space. This is primarily due to the "all-or-nothing" quality of pulse signals. Because of this, the smaller-radix number systems—in particular, the binary system—have been found to be most economical in computer applications.

The important point to remember here is that the basic ideas presented in the preceding paragraphs with respect to the decimal system apply, in general, to any other system.

Binary System

The binary system employs only one of two symbols (0 or 1) in any digit position. Therefore, 2 is the radix, or base, of the system.

The binary system is sometimes called *true binary* to distinguish it from binary-coded systems such as binary-coded decimal. Some of these binary-coded systems will be discussed later.

In the binary system the symbols 0 and 1 have the same significance as in the decimal system. That is, they represent no units and one unit, respectively; and the positional location of a binary digit has the same significance as in the decimal system, except that the base is 2 instead of 10. The positive and negative powers of 2 and their decimal equivalents are listed in Table 3.2.

Table 3.2 Positive and Negative Powers of 2 with Decimal Equivalents

Positive power of 2	Decimal equivalent	Negative power of 2	Decimal equivalent
2^0	1		
2^1	2	2^{-1}	$\frac{1}{2}$
2^2	4	2^{-2}	$\frac{1}{4}$
2^3	8	2^{-3}	$\frac{1}{8}$
2^4	16	2^{-4}	$\frac{1}{16}$
2^5	32	2^{-5}	$\frac{1}{32}$
2^6	64	2^{-6}	$\frac{1}{64}$
2^7	128	2^{-7}	$\frac{1}{128}$
2^8	256	2^{-8}	$\frac{1}{256}$
2^9	512	2^{-9}	$\frac{1}{512}$

The presence of a 1 in any digit position of a binary number indicates that the corresponding power of 2 is to be used in expressing a quantity. A 0 indicates that the power of 2 is not required. For example, the binary number 11011 means

$$1 \times 2^4 + 1 \times 2^3 + 0 \times 2^2 + 1 \times 2^1 + 1 \times 2^0$$
$$= 1 \times 16 + 1 \times 8 + 0 \times 4 + 1 \times 2 + 1 \times 1$$
$$= 16 + 8 + 0 + 2 + 1$$
$$= 27$$

The binary number 11011 is equivalent to the decimal number 27. This example illustrates not only the method of representing a quantity in binary notation but also the most convenient method of converting a binary number to its decimal equivalent.

When fractional quantities are represented in binary notation, the same general rules apply as in decimal notation. For example, the binary number 0.1101 means

$$1 \times 2^{-1} + 1 \times 2^{-2} + 0 \times 2^{-3} + 1 \times 2^{-4} = \frac{1}{2} + \frac{1}{4} + 0 + \frac{1}{16}$$
$$= 0.5 + 0.25 + 0.0625$$
$$= 0.8125$$

This also illustrates the most convenient way of converting a binary fraction to its decimal-fraction equivalent. In binary notation, the dividing point between whole and fractional integers is called the *binary point* rather than the decimal point. Also, in the preceding example a terminating binary fraction was converted to a terminating decimal fraction.

In general, however, this will not be the case. Some terminating binary fractions yield a nonterminating decimal fraction and vice versa.

A final example will illustrate the meaning of a binary number and the way it may be converted to its decimal equivalent. In this example the mixed binary number 101101.0101 is considered. Although not necessary, it is perhaps more convenient in the case of a mixed number to convert the whole number and fractional parts separately and then combine the two parts after conversion. In this example, the whole-number part is 101101, and the fractional part is 0.0101. Converting the whole-number part to decimal first shows that 101101 in binary is

$$1 \times 2^5 + 0 \times 2^4 + 1 \times 2^3 + 1 \times 2^2 + 0 \times 2^1 + 1 \times 2^0$$
$$= 1 \times 32 + 0 \times 16 + 1 \times 8 + 1 \times 4 + 0 \times 2 + 1 \times 1$$
$$= 32 + 0 + 8 + 4 + 0 + 1$$
$$= 45$$

The whole-number part is equivalent to 45 in decimal. Converting the fractional part to decimal shows that 0.0101 in binary is

$$0 \times 2^{-1} + 1 \times 2^{-2} + 0 \times 2^{-3} + 1 \times 2^{-4} = 0 + \tfrac{1}{4} + 0 + \tfrac{1}{16}$$
$$= 0.25 + 0.0625$$
$$= 0.3125$$

The fractional part is equivalent to 0.3125 in decimal. Combining the two decimal parts produces a result of 45.3125, the decimal equivalent of 101101.0101.

When binary is converted to decimal it is, perhaps, easier to write and sum the powers of 2 by columns. For example, the binary number 10011 might be converted to decimal as follows:

$$1 = 1 \times 2^4 = 16$$
$$0 = 0 \times 2^3 = 0$$
$$0 = 0 \times 2^2 = 0$$
$$1 = 1 \times 2^1 = 2$$
$$1 = 1 \times 2^0 = \underline{1}$$
$$19 = \text{sum}$$

The even shorter notation following might be used:

$$1 = 16$$
$$0 = 0$$
$$0 = 0$$
$$1 = 2$$
$$1 = \underline{1}$$
$$19 = \text{sum}$$

Another method of converting a binary integer to decimal is known as the *double-dabble* method. The rules for using this method are as follows:

1. Double the highest-order binary digit, add this doubled value to the next lower-order binary digit, and record the sum.
2. Double the sum obtained, add this doubled value to the next lower-order binary digit, and record the new sum.
3. Continue step 2 until the last, or lowest-order, binary digit has been added to the previous doubled sum and a final sum has been obtained. This final sum is the decimal value sought.

For example, convert the binary integer 110101 to decimal. The method is outlined as follows, with the successive sums listed beneath the binary digits:

Binary digits:	1	1	0	1	0	1
Sums:		3	6	13	26	53

The final sum, 53, is the decimal equivalent sought.

Decimal-to-binary integer conversion. Two methods have been found most useful for converting a decimal integer to binary. The first is the direct method, and the second is called the double-dabble method since it is, arithmetically, the reverse of the double-dabble method previously mentioned.

In the direct method, the largest possible power of 2 is subtracted from the decimal number. From this result the largest possible power of 2 is again subtracted. This is continued until there is no remainder. Then a 1 is written for each power of 2 subtracted, and a 0 is written for those powers of 2 not used, in the order in which the subtractions were performed. The four examples following illustrate the method.

1.		2.		3.		4.	
	25		17		31		10
	$-16 = 2^4$		$-16 = 2^4$		$-16 = 2^4$		$- 8 = 2^3$
	9		1		15		2
	$- 8 = 2^3$		$- 1 = 2^0$		$- 8 = 2^3$		$- 2 = 2^1$
	1		0		7		0
	$- 1 = 2^0$				$- 4 = 2^2$		
	0				3		
					$- 2 = 2^1$		
					1		
					$- 1 = 2^0$		
					0		

or	or	or	or
$1 \times 2^4 + 1 \times 2^3$	$1 \times 2^4 + 0 \times 2^3$	$1 \times 2^4 + 1 \times 2^3$	$1 \times 2^3 + 0 \times 2^2$
$+ 0 \times 2^2$	$+ 0 \times 2^2$	$+ 1 \times 2^2$	$+ 1 \times 2^1$
$+ 0 \times 2^1$	$+ 0 \times 2^1$	$+ 1 \times 2^1$	$+ 0 \times 2^0$
$+ 1 \times 2^0$	$+ 1 \times 2^0$	$+ 1 \times 2^0$	

or	or	or	or
11001	10001	11111	1010
or	or	or	or
decimal 25	decimal 17	decimal 31	decimal 10

In the first example, 1 is written to represent the subtraction of 2^4. Since 2^3, the next lowest power of 2, was also subtracted, another 1 representing that subtraction is written. Since 2^2 and 2^1, the next lowest powers of 2, were not used, a 0 is written for each. Then a 1 is written to represent the subtraction of 2^0, the next lowest power of 2. From this is obtained 11001, the binary equivalent of 25. The same process is used in the other three examples.

Although this method is direct and easy to apply, it has one disadvantage. To convert large decimal integers it is necessary to carry or memorize a large table of powers of 2 or to compute the powers of 2 to be subtracted. The double-dabble method requires neither tables nor memorization, except of the method itself.

In the double-dabble method the decimal number is successively divided by 2, the quotients being placed directly beneath the dividend and the remainders opposite the quotients. The equivalent binary number is composed of the remainders, with the last remainder being the MSD. In the three examples shown in Table 3.3, the decimal numbers 26, 18, and 32 are converted to binary by this method.

Table 3.3 Double-dabble Conversion from Decimal to Binary

1. Quotients	Remainders	**2.** Quotients	Remainders	**3.** Quotients	Remainders
26		18		32	
13	0 (LSD)	9	0 (LSD)	16	0 (LSD)
6	1	4	1	8	0
3	0	2	0	4	0
1	1	1	0	2	0
0	1 (MSD)	0	1 (MSD)	1	0
				0	1 (MSD)
26 = 11010		18 = 10010		32 = 100000	

In the first example, the decimal number 26 is divided by 2, yielding a quotient of 13 and a remainder of 0. The quotient 13 is recorded and, opposite it, the remainder 0. Next, the quotient 13 is divided by 2, yielding the quotient 6 and the remainder 1. The quotient 6 is recorded and, opposite it, the remainder 1. This process is continued until a quotient of 0 is obtained. The remainders are then written in horizontal succession, beginning with the one at the bottom of the column and going to the top. This is the binary number sought.

When the division process is performed, it is necessary to remember that 1 divided by 2 yields a quotient of 0 and a remainder of 1.

This is the most used method of converting a decimal integer to binary, since even large decimal integers can be converted with little effort and without tables.

Decimal-to-binary fraction conversion. While a decimal integer is converted to binary by successively *dividing* by 2, a decimal fraction is converted by successively *multiplying* by 2. The successive products are placed directly beneath the multiplicand. If at any time a product has an integer part, the integer part is ignored when performing the next multiplication by 2. This is continued until the fractional part of any

Table 3.4 Conversion of Fractions to Binary Notation

1. Product	Integer part	2. Product	Integer part	3. Product	Integer part
0.8125		0.7893		0.218	
1.6250	1	1.5786	1	0.436	0
1.2500	1	1.1572	1	0.872	0
0.5000	0	0.3144	0	1.744	1
1.0000	1	0.6288	0	1.488	1
		1.2576	1	0.976	0
		0.5152	0	1.952	1
		1.0304	1	1.904	1
				1.808	1
				1.616	1
				1.232	1
				0.464	0
0.8125 = 0.1101		0.7893 = 0.1100101+		0.218 = 0.00110111110+	

product is 0 or, in the case of a nonterminating binary fraction, until the required number of binary digits is obtained. The binary fraction is then the integer parts of the successive products, with the first integer part being the MSD of the binary fraction. In the three examples in Table 3.4, the decimal fractions 0.8125, 0.7893, and 0.218 are converted to binary by using the described method.

In the first example, the decimal number 0.8125 is multiplied by 2, yielding a product of 1.6250. The integer part (1) is recorded, and the fractional part (0.625) is multiplied by 2, yielding the product 1.2500. The integer part (1) of this product is recorded, the fractional part (0.2500) is multiplied by 2, and so on, until the product 1.0000 is obtained. Since the fractional part of the product 1.0000 is 0, it indicates that the process is complete and, also, that the required binary number is a terminating binary fraction. Then after the binary point, the integer parts are written in horizontal succession, beginning with the one at the top and going to the bottom. This is the required binary fraction. The same process is used in examples 2 and 3, except that in these the resultant binary number is not a terminating fraction, as indicated by the + sign at the end. The assumption is made that in examples 2 and 3, seven and eleven binary places are required, respectively; hence, the multiplication process is carried out until that number of binary digits is obtained in each case.

When a decimal mixed number is converted to its binary equivalent, the integer and fractional parts are converted separately by using any of the above methods, and the separate results are then combined. For example, to convert the decimal mixed number 528.27 to binary, the integer part (528) and the fractional part (0.27) are converted separately as shown in Table 3.5. Combining the results gives 1000010000 + 0.010001 as the binary equivalent of 528.27.

Table 3.5 Conversion of Mixed Numbers to Binary

Integer Part		*Fractional Part*	
	528		0.27
	264—0		0.54—0
	132—0		1.08—1
Division by	66—0	Multiplication	0.16—0
2 method	33—0	by 2 method	0.32—0 Integers
	16—1 Remainders		0.64—0
	8—0		1.28—1
	4—0		
	2—0		
	1—0		
	0—1		
	= 1000010000		= 0.010001+

This adequately illustrates binary-to-decimal and decimal-to-binary conversion. Proficiency in performing these conversions should be developed before the subject of binary arithmetic is undertaken.

Binary arithmetic. The mechanics of binary addition are the same as those for decimal addition. When the limit of any digit position is reached and one more unit is added, then counting in the same digit position must begin again at 0 with a carry of 1 to the next higher-order digit position. In the binary system there are only two symbols, 0 and 1. The limit of any digit position is therefore reached when a 1 is present. Adding one more unit to that digit position then results in a sum of 0 and a carry of 1 into the next higher-order digit position. The rules for binary addition are summarized in Table 3.6.

Table 3.6 Summary of Rules for Binary Addition

1. 0 plus 0 equals 0 with no carry.
2. 0 plus 1 equals 1 with no carry.
3. 1 plus 0 equals 1 with no carry.
4. 1 plus 1 equals 0 with a carry of 1.

Four examples of binary addition follow:

	1.		**2.**		**3.**		**4.**	
	1000		1010		1101		1111	
	111		101		1001		111	
	1111		1111		10110		10110	

Examples 1 and 2 are self-explanatory since there are no carries. In example 3 if the lowest-order digits are added, 1 plus 1 equals 0 with a carry of 1 into the next higher-order digit position. Adding the next higher-order digits, 0 plus 0 equals 0 plus a carry of 1 equals 1 with no carry. Adding the next higher-order digits, 1 plus 0 equals 1 with no carry. Adding the highest-order digits, 1 plus 1 equals 0 with a carry of 1 into the next higher-order digit position. Since there are no higher-order digits to be added, the last sum 0 is written with a 1 to the left of the 0 to indicate the final carry of 1 into the next higher-order digit position, and the addition is complete. In example 4 if the lowest-order digits are added, 1 plus 1 equals 0 with a carry of 1 into the next higher-order digit position. Adding the next higher-order digits, 1 plus 1 equals 0 plus a carry of 1 equals 1 with a carry of 1 into the next higher-order digit position. Adding the next higher-order digits, again, 1 plus 1 equals 0 plus a carry of 1 equals 1 with a carry of 1 into the next higher-order digit position. Adding the highest-order digits, 1 plus 0 equals 1 plus a carry of 1 equals 0 with a carry of 1 into the next higher-order digit position. Since there are no higher-order digits to be added, the last sum 0 is written with a 1 to the left of the 0 to indicate the final carry into the next higher-order digit position, and the addition is complete.

These same rules of addition apply to binary fractions and mixed numbers. That is, the binary point of the augend is placed beneath the binary point of the addend, and the addition is then carried out according to the rules given.

Although three or more binary numbers can be summed simultaneously, as in summing a column of three or more decimal numbers, the propagation of carries becomes complex, and the process has little application in digital computers. Should it become necessary to sum three or more binary numbers, it is suggested that the appropriate quantities be added two at a time to reduce the likelihood of a mistake in the carries.

Unfortunately, arithmetic operations which are simple when performed on paper become complex when a mechanical means of solution is sought. When subtraction is performed on paper, the direct method (the method commonly used with decimal numbers) is the simplest. However, in a digital computer, use of the direct method would complicate the circuitry required; so methods that involve complementing are used. These methods will be described after direct binary subtraction and decimal complementing have been discussed.

When direct decimal subtraction is performed each digit of the subtrahend is subtracted from the corresponding digit in the minuend. If the digit in the subtrahend is larger than the corresponding digit in the minuend, then a 1 is borrowed from the next higher-order digit of the minuend, and that digit is reduced by 1. If, in borrowing, the next higher-order digit of the minuend is 0, then a 1 is borrowed from the next higher-order digit of the minuend that is not 0; that digit is reduced by 1, and the 0s thus skipped in the minuend are replaced by 9s. The same rules apply in performing direct binary subtraction, except that, in borrowing, the 0s that are skipped in the minuend are replaced by 1s. In decimal a unit which has a value of 10 is borrowed, while in binary a unit which has a value of 2 is borrowed. The rules for direct binary subtraction are summarized in Table 3.7.

Table 3.7 Summary of Rules for Binary Subtraction
1. 0 minus 0 equals 0 with no borrow.
2. 1 minus 1 equals 0 with no borrow.
3. 1 minus 0 equals 1 with no borrow.
4. 0 minus 1 equals 1 with a borrow of 1.

It is wise in performing direct binary subtraction to remember that the binary number 10 is equivalent to 2 in decimal and that rule 4 in Table 3.7 really means $10 - 1 = 1$.

$$
\begin{array}{ll}
\textbf{1.} & \begin{array}{r} 1101 \\ -1001 \\ \hline 0100 = 100 \end{array}
\qquad
\textbf{2.} & \begin{array}{r} 1001 \\ -1000 \\ \hline 0001 = 1 \end{array}
\end{array}
$$

The first two examples need no explanation since borrowing was not necessary. The two examples that involve borrowing are as follows:

3.	1011011	Minuend after borrowing	1	0 0	10	10	1	1
	−1001111							
	0001100	Minuend before borrowing	1 0 1	1 0 1 1				
		Subtrahend	1	0 0	1	1 1	1	
		Remainder	0	0 0	1	1 0	0	

4.	1100010	Minuend after borrowing	0	10 1	1	10 1	0
	−100100						
	111110	Minuend before borrowing	1	1 0	0	0 1	0
		Subtrahend		1 0	0	1 0	0
		Remainder		1 1	1	1 1	0

Example 3 illustrates the case where a 1 is borrowed from a digit (the fourth from the right), reducing that digit to 0; and then, because of that borrow, another borrow must be made from the next higher-order digit in order to perform the next subtraction.

Example 4 illustrates the case where a 1 is borrowed from a digit (the sixth from the right), reducing that digit to 0; but in the process of borrowing, 0 digits are skipped and are replaced by 1s in performing succeeding subtractions.

These same rules for direct binary subtraction apply when binary fractions and mixed numbers are involved. Again, the binary point of the subtrahend is placed beneath the binary point of the minuend, and the subtraction is then carried out according to the rules.

Several problems in direct subtraction should be solved before continuing.

Because of the nature of the electronic components available to digital computer designers and the fact that subtraction is the reverse of addition, a relatively complex circuit is required if it is to perform both operations, while a relatively simple circuit is required if it is to perform only one of these operations. Therefore, in a digital computer the arithmetic circuits are usually designed to perform addition only, and the operation of subtraction is reduced to one of addition by using numerical complements.

In the decimal system every number has two complements, called the "10's complement" and the "9's complement." The 10's and 9's complements are essentially the same in that they serve the same purpose in digital computer applications and they differ by only 1 numerically. That is, the 9's complement of a number is 1 less than the 10's complement.

The 10's and 9's complements are most conveniently defined in terms of the arithmetic registers of a computer. In general, the 10's complement of a number N is $10^n - N$, where n is the number of digits that can be contained in the arithmetic registers of a computer. For the purposes of illustration, it is assumed that the arithmetic registers of a computer can contain 10 digits. The 10's complement of a number N is then $10^{10} - N$. According to this definition, then, the 10's complement of 325 is

$$10^{10} - 325 = 9999999675$$

or

$$\begin{aligned}
10000000000 &= 10^{10} \\
-0000000325 & \\
\hline
9999999675 &= \text{10's complement of 325}
\end{aligned}$$

The 10's complement of 52973 is $10^{10} - 52973 = 9999947027$ or

$$\begin{aligned}
10000000000 &= 10^{10} \\
-0000052973 & \\
\hline
9999947027 &= \text{10's complement of 52973}
\end{aligned}$$

Suppose now it is desired to subtract 325 from 400. The subtraction operation can be changed to one of addition by complementing the subtrahend and adding as follows:

$$
\begin{array}{r}
0000000400 \\
+9999999675 = \text{10's complement of 325} \\
\hline
10000000075 = \text{remainder}
\end{array}
$$

The carry of 1 off-register into the eleventh digit position from the right could not be contained in a 10-digit register; or, as far as a computer having 10-digit registers is concerned, it would be lost, yielding a remainder of 0000000075, or 75. The carry of 1 off-register could, however, be detected by a computer, and it indicates that the remainder is positive and that no recomplementing is necessary. Had there been no carry off-register, it would have indicated that the remainder was negative and should be recomplemented. For example, if 400 is subtracted from 325 by complementing the subtrahend and adding, the remainder would be

$$
\begin{array}{r}
0000000325 \\
+9999999600 = \text{10's complement of 400} \\
\hline
9999999925 = \text{10's complement of the remainder}
\end{array}
$$

The absence of a carry off-register to the left indicates that the remainder thus obtained should be recomplemented and have a negative sign attached to it. If this operation is performed, the remainder will be

$$
\begin{array}{r}
1000000000 = 10^{10} \\
-999999925 = \text{10's complement of the remainder} \\
\hline
000000075 = \text{recomplemented remainder} = 75
\end{array}
$$

Attaching a negative sign to the final remainder makes -75 the correct result.

The above steps may be summarized as follows:

1. Compute the 10's complement of the subtrahend.
2. Add the 10's complement of the subtrahend to the minuend.
3. If there is a carry off-register, the result is positive and no recomplementing is necessary; otherwise, the result is negative and recomplementing is necessary.

Although there are numerous methods of performing both decimal addition and decimal subtraction using the 10's complement, they will not be described here since they would not serve the purpose of this discussion.

With respect to a computer having 10-digit registers, the 9's complement of a number N may be defined as $(10^{10} - 1) - N$, or $9999999999 - N$. That is, the 9's complement may be found by subtracting from 9 each digit of the number whose complement is required. For example, the

9's complement of 325 is $9999999999 - 325 = 9999999674$ or

$$
\begin{array}{l}
9999999999 = 10^{10} - 1 \\
-0000000325 \\
\hline
9999999674 = \text{9's complement of 325}
\end{array}
$$

Suppose now it is desired to subtract 325 from 400, using the 9's complement. If the subtrahend is complemented and addition is performed, the result is

$$
\begin{array}{l}
0000000400 \\
+9999999674 = \text{9's complement of 325} \\
\hline
10000000074 = \text{remainder}
\end{array}
$$

Again, there is a carry of 1 off-register to the left, which again indicates that the remainder is positive; but since the 9's complement of a number is 1 less than the 10's complement, the remainder is 1 less than it should be. Therefore, to correct the remainder, the carry of 1 off-register to the left is added to the LSD of the remainder. This is called the *end-around carry*, and it yields the correct remainder of 0,000,000,075, or 75. Had there been no carry off-register to the left, that, again, would have indicated that the remainder was negative and that recomplementing was necessary. However, since no carry off-register is equivalent to a carry off-register of 0, an end-around carry of 0 might be performed in a computer, as in the case of a carry off-register of 1, to simplify the gating and, hence, the circuitry involved. Adding 0 to the LSD of the remainder would not affect the remainder, and the deficiency of 1 in the remainder would automatically be replaced when the final remainder is recomplemented.

Since end-around carry is normally used in digital computers, it would be well to illustrate the above rules more graphically. In the example below, 6907 is subtracted from 25863, as follows:

$$
\begin{array}{ll}
& 0000025863 \\
& +9999993092 = \text{9's complement of 6907} \\
\text{Result is positive; add} & \overline{10000018955} = \text{uncorrected remainder} \\
& {\longrightarrow}1 = \text{end-around carry} \\
& \overline{0000018956} = \text{final remainder} = 18956
\end{array}
$$

In the example below, 25863 is subtracted from 6907 as follows:

$$
\begin{array}{ll}
& 0000006907 \\
& +9999974136 = \text{9's complement of 25863} \\
\text{Result is negative; add} & \overline{09999981043} = \text{uncorrected remainder} \\
& {\longrightarrow} 0 = \text{end-around carry} \\
& \overline{9999981043} = \text{final remainder} \\
& 0000018956 = \text{final remainder recomplemented} = \\
& \phantom{0000018956 = \text{final}} -18956
\end{array}
$$

The preceding steps may be summarized as follows:

1. Compute the 9's complement of the subtrahend.
2. Add the 9's complement of the subtrahend to the minuend.
3. Perform an end-around carry of 1 or 0.
4. If there is an end-around carry of 0, recomplement the remainder and attach a negative sign; otherwise, omit this step.

The two methods described for subtracting in the decimal system by using the 10's and 9's complements may be applied to other number systems—in particular, the binary system. That is, the so-called "2's complement" and "1's complement" of a binary number are analogous to the 10's and 9's complements, respectively, of a decimal number.

Although subtracting in the decimal system by using the 9's complement instead of the 10's complement requires an extra step, that of an end-around carry, the end-around-carry method is usually used in a computer that utilizes the binary system because of the ease with which the 1's complement of a binary number can be computed, in contrast to computing the 2's complement.

In terms of the arithmetic register under discussion, the 2's complement of a binary number N is $2^{10} - N$. For example, the 2's complement of the binary number 101000101 is $2^{10} - 0101000101$ or

$$
\begin{aligned}
10000000000 &= 2^{10} \\
-0101000101 & \\
\hline
1010111011 &= \text{2's complement of 0101000101}
\end{aligned}
$$

Suppose now it is desired to subtract 101000101 from 110010000. Complementing the subtrahend and adding gives a result of

$$
\begin{aligned}
0110010000 & \\
+1010111011 &= \text{2's complement of 0101000101} \\
\hline
10001001011 &= \text{remainder}
\end{aligned}
$$

As in the case of adding a 10's complement in the decimal system, the carry of 1 off-register to the left indicates that the remainder is positive, and no recomplementing is necessary. The correct remainder is, then, 0001001011, or 1001011. The above example is equivalent to

$$400 - 325 = 75$$

in decimal.

Since the 2's complements of binary numbers have little application in digital computers, no further examples will be given here.

In terms of the computer under discussion, the 1's complement of a binary number is $(2^{10} - 1) - N$, where N is the number whose complement is required. The above expression is equivalent to $1111111111 - N$ or means the 1's complement of a binary number N may be found by subtracting each digit of N from 1, which, in turn, means that the 1's complement of a binary number may be found by changing all the 1s to 0s and all the 0s to 1s. For example, the 1's complement of 101000101 is $1111111111 - 0101000101 = 1010111010$ or

$$
\begin{array}{rl}
1111111111 &= 2^{10} - 1 \\
-0101000101 & \\
\hline
1010111010 &= \text{1's complement of 0101000101}
\end{array}
$$

Note that if in the binary number 0101000101 all the 1s are changed to 0s and all the 0s to 1s, the result is the same as that obtained above, namely, 1010111010. Digital computers are able to compute complements of this type with ease through the use of NOT circuits, or inverters; hence this explains the reason for the almost exclusive use of the 1's complement in digital computer applications.

Since the computation of a 1's complement is such an elementary operation, no further examples will be given here. The next step is to give examples of the end-around-carry method of binary subtraction using the 1's complement.

Three examples of binary subtraction using this method will now be given. In the first example, 16 is subtracted from 25 as follows:

$$
\begin{array}{rl}
11001 &= 25 \\
-10000 &= \text{direct subtraction of 16} \\
\hline
1001 &= 9
\end{array}
$$

$$
\begin{array}{rl}
11001 &= 25 \\
+01111 &= \text{1's complement of 16} \\
\hline
101000 & \\
\rightarrow 1 &= \text{end-around carry} \\
\hline
1001 &= \text{remainder} = 9
\end{array}
$$

In the direct-subtraction method, there is no end-around carry involved; but in adding the complement of the subtrahend, an end-around carry must be performed to obtain the correct result.

In the second example, using larger numbers, 129 is subtracted from 256 as follows:

$$
\begin{array}{rl}
100000000 &= 256 \\
+101111110 &= \text{1's complement of 129} \\
\hline
1001111110 & \\
\rightarrow 1 &= \text{end-around carry} \\
\hline
001111111 &= 127
\end{array}
$$

The examples given thus far have illustrated the subtraction of a smaller number from a larger number. When a larger number is subtracted from a smaller number, the rules governing complementing and end-around carry apply. This is illustrated in the third example, in which 25 is subtracted from 16, yielding a remainder of -9 as follows:

$$10000 = 16$$
$$\underline{+00110} = \text{1's complement of 25}$$
$$10110 = \text{1's complement of remainder}$$

Since there is no carry off-register, the remainder must be recomplemented and have a negative sign attached to it; this makes the final remainder $-01001 = -9$.

Several subtraction problems should be solved by using both the direct method and the 1's complement method until facility that can come only through practice is acquired. The work can always be checked by using decimal equivalents.

In a later chapter, it will be seen that multiplication is reduced to a series of additions and that division is reduced to a series of subtractions.

Octal System

The octal system has a radix of 8, and it employs the symbols 0 through 7. Because 8 is a power of 2, the octal system has special characteristics that make it especially useful in situations involving binary numbers. This will be illustrated after octal-to-decimal and decimal-to-octal conversion have been discussed.

An octal number can be converted to decimal by the same method described for other number systems. For example, the octal number 516 means

$$5 \times 8^2 + 1 \times 8^1 + 6 \times 8^0 = 320 + 8 + 6 = 334$$

Therefore, 516 in octal is equivalent to 334 in decimal.

The most convenient way of converting a decimal integer to octal is to divide the decimal integer successively by 8 and record the remainders, as in the double-dabble method for converting a decimal integer to binary. For example, the decimal integer 492 can be converted to octal as follows:

Successive remainders

$492 \div 8 = 61$	4
$61 \div 8 = 7$	5
$7 \div 8 = 0$	7

Thus, 754 in octal is equivalent to 492 in decimal.

Octal fractions obey the same rules as those for other number systems explained above and are expressed in terms of negative powers of 8. For example, the octal number 0.436 means

$$4 \times 8^{-1} + 3 \times 8^{-2} + 6 \times 8^{-3} = \tfrac{4}{8} + \tfrac{3}{64} + \tfrac{6}{512}$$
$$= 0.5 + 0.04687 + 0.01172 = 0.55859$$

Thus, 0.436 in octal is equivalent to 0.55859 in decimal.

A decimal fraction may be converted to octal by successively multiplying the decimal number by 8 and recording the integer parts of the resulting products in a manner similar to that explained earlier for decimal-to-binary fraction conversion. For example, the decimal fraction 0.597 may be converted to octal as follows:

	Integer parts
$0.597 \times 8 = 4.776$	4
$0.776 \times 8 = 6.208$	6
$0.208 \times 8 = 1.664$	1
$0.664 \times 8 = 5.312$	5
$0.312 \times 8 = 2.496$	2

Thus, the octal number 0.46152+ is equivalent to the decimal number 0.597, although it is an approximation in that the octal fraction is nonterminating. The result may be checked by converting the octal fraction 0.46152 to decimal as follows:

$$4 \times 8^{-1} + 6 \times 8^{-2} + 1 \times 8^{-3} + 5 \times 8^{-4} + 2 \times 8^{-5}$$
$$= \tfrac{4}{8} + \tfrac{6}{64} + \tfrac{1}{512} + \tfrac{5}{4096} + \tfrac{2}{32768}$$
$$= 0.5 + 0.09375 + 0.00195 + 0.00122 + 0.00006$$
$$= 0.59598$$

The above result is equal to 0.596 when rounded off to three decimal places.

The octal number system is of special importance because of its relation to the binary system. That is, octal-to-binary and binary-to-octal conversions may be performed by mere inspection. For example, the decimal number 334 is equivalent to the octal number 516 and the binary number 101001110. If the digits in the binary number 101001110 are separated into groups of three digits each, 101 001 110 is obtained. If each of these digit groups is now considered as a separate number and each digit group is replaced by its octal equivalent, 5 1 6, or 516, is obtained; this is the octal equivalent of the binary number 101001110. Going in the reverse direction, the octal number 1753 is equivalent to the binary number 001 111 101 011, or 1111101011. The same rules apply to octal and binary fractions. For example, the octal number 0.3471 is equivalent to the binary number 0.011 100 111 001, or binary 0.011100111001; and the binary number 0.1101110011, when blocked off in the form 0.110 111 001 100, is equivalent to the octal number 0.6714. Also, the mixed binary number 1111.0011, when blocked off in the form 001 111.001 100, is equivalent to the octal number 17.14.

The detailed rules for binary-to-octal conversion are as follows:

1. To convert a binary integer to octal, begin at the binary point and, going to the left, block off the number into groups of three digits each. If the number of digits in the binary integer is not a multiple of three, fill out the last group at the extreme left with 0s.
2. To convert a binary fraction to octal, begin at the binary point and, going to the right, block off the number into groups of three digits each. If the number of digits in the binary fraction is not a multiple of three, fill out the last group at the extreme right with 0s.
3. Replace each binary digit with the equivalent octal digit.

To convert an octal number to binary, apply the above rules in reverse. It is easy to prove these rules mathematically. This might be tried as an exercise.

The octal number system affords many conveniences. When a binary number is being recorded on paper, it is usually more convenient to write it in octal. For example, computer programmers and programming manuals use the octal system as a convenient notation for binary numbers. Also, when a large decimal number is being converted to binary, it is usually more convenient to convert it to octal first and then to binary since fewer divisions are required in dividing a decimal number by 8 instead of 2.

Excess-3 Code

Another numbering system often used in computers is known as the excess-3 code. This is a special case of a broader group called *binary-coded decimals*. In any binary-coded decimal system, each decimal digit is changed into its binary equivalent. For example, decimal 436 is 0100 0011 0110 in binary-coded decimal. There are certain binary configurations never used in this system, as can be seen from Table 3.8. Four bits are needed in each group to allow for the symbols 8 and 9, which cannot be represented with three binary bits.

Table 3.8 shows an important comparison of several systems. Notice that the excess-3 code is, in each case, three more than the binary-coded decimal, and that in both these codes there are six unused four-bit numbers, such as 1110. In Table 3.8, the column to the left in the binary-coded decimal and excess-3 systems indicates the carry propagated to the next higher order.

To convert from decimal to excess-3 code, remember first that numbers of two or more digits are converted digit by digit to binary-coded decimal, and then 3 is added to each four-bit binary group. For example, decimal

Table 3.8 Comparison of Number Systems

Decimal	Binary	Binary-coded decimal		Excess-3	
0	0000		0000		0011
1	0001		0001		0100
2	0010		0010		0101
3	0011		0011		0110
4	0100		0100		0111
5	0101		0101		1000
6	0110		0110		1001
7	0111		0111		1010
8	1000		1000		1011
9	1001		1001		1100
10	1010	0001	0000	0100	0011
11	1011	0001	0001	0100	0100
12	1100	0001	0010	0100	0101
13	1101	0001	0011	0100	0110
14	1110	0001	0100	0100	0111
15	1111	0001	0101	0100	1000

428 in excess-3 code is expressed as follows:

```
428 = 0100 0010 1000    binary-coded decimal
      0011 0011 0011    adding 3 to each four-bit binary group
      0111 0101 1011    equals 428 in excess-3
```

To reconvert back to binary-coded decimal, 3 must be subtracted from each four-bit binary group. For example, to express the excess-3 configuration 1100 0101 1010 in decimal:

```
1100 0101 1010    excess-3
0011 0011 0011    subtracting 3 from each four-bit binary group
1001 0010 0111    results in binary-coded decimal
  9    2    7      decimal equivalent
```

Hence excess-3 1100 0101 1010 is 927 in decimal, as shown in the preceding example.

It is possible to add numbers in excess-3 code, but when this is tried, complications arise. Notice that in excess-3 code in lower numbers, 0000, 0001, and 0010 are not used; in the higher numbers, 1101, 1110, and 1111 are not used. Consequently, if 9 and 1 are added, a method must be used that gives the following result of 10:

$$+9 = 1100$$
$$+1 = 0100$$
$$\text{Carry } 0100 \qquad 0011$$

Moreover, even the simpler addition of $3 + 4 = 7$ is involved, as illustrated at the top of page 55.

$$+3 = \quad 0110$$
$$+4 = \quad 0111$$

1101	sum with excess of 6
−0011	subtract binary 3
1010	excess-3 equivalent of 7

The above is an illustration of a simple rule. If two excess-3 numbers whose sum is 9 or less are added, regular binary addition is performed; and then 0011 (binary 3) is subtracted from the result.

To return to $9 + 1 = 10$, if regular binary addition of the two numbers in excess-3 code is used, the result obtained is

$$1100$$
$$\underline{0100}$$
$$10000$$

A carry of 1 is generated, and the 0000 obtained with the carry is 3 too small. So the 1 must be put over into the next higher order, and binary 3 must be added to both orders.

Consider the following example of $6 + 7 = 13$ in excess-3 code:

$$6 = 1001$$
$$+7 = \underline{1010}$$

Carry	1	0011
Add		0011
13 =	0100	0110

Two rules for addition in excess-3 code, which have been illustrated in the preceding paragraphs, can now be stated.

Two numbers in excess-3 code, when added together, produce an excess-6 answer. If the sum of the two numbers is less than 10, subtract 3 to get the right sum. If the sum of the two numbers is greater than 10, take the carry that is generated, place it into the next higher order as 0100 (carry of $0001 + 0011$), and then add 0011 to the right-hand binary group to get the correct result.

Gray Code

Another number system similar to binary is the Gray code, or *reflected binary system*. The outstanding feature of the Gray-code system is that successive integers differ from one another by only one digit. This is advantageous in analog-to-digital conversion equipment. The use of Gray code to perform arithmetical operations is quite complex; for this reason it is not in common use for this purpose. Since Gray code is used for input and output information, some method of conversion between Gray code and binary is needed. Table 3.9 shows the relationship between numbers in the decimal and binary systems and the Gray code.

Notice that the change from binary 0111 (7) to 1000 (8) requires a

Table 3.9 Comparison of Decimal, Binary, and Gray-code Systems

Decimal	Binary	Gray code
0	0000	0000
1	0001	0001
2	0010	0011
3	0011	0010
4	0100	0110
5	0101	0111
6	0110	0101
7	0111	0100
8	1000	1100
9	1001	1101
10	1010	1111
11	1011	1110
12	1100	1010
13	1101	1011
14	1110	1001
15	1111	1000
16	10000	11000

change from three 1s to only one. In the Gray-code system, there is a change of only one digit.

To convert a binary number to Gray code, write the MSD of the binary number as the MSD of the Gray-code number. The sum of the MSD and the first digit to its right, disregarding the carry if any, is the next digit of the Gray-code number. This process is continued until the least significant order is reached.

As an example, the conversion from binary 1101 (13) to Gray code is as follows:

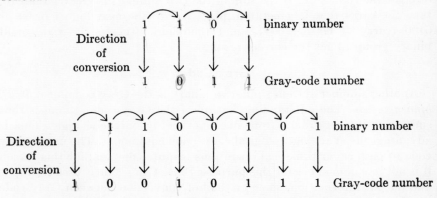

A Gray-code number can be converted to binary by a similar process. The MSD is again the same in both systems. The next binary digit is the sum of the corresponding Gray-code digit and the preceding binary digit, again disregarding a carry if it occurs.

The conversion of Gray-code 1110 (11) to binary is as follows:

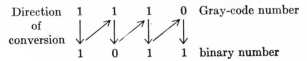

The following example illustrates conversion of Gray-code 10010111-(229) to its binary equivalent:

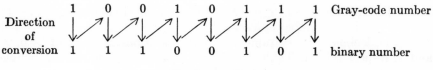

Biquinary Code

The biquinary code was one of the earlier decimal codes used in computers to conserve hardware. It evolved from the decimal ring counter, a device which used 10 bistable devices connected to indicate the 10 decimal digits. The biquinary code can also represent 10 decimal digits, and it uses only seven positions to accomplish this. The term "biquinary"

Table 3.10 Comparison of Biquinary and Decimal Notation

Decimal	Decimal counter	Biquinary counter
	9876543210	5043210
0	0000000001	01-00001
1	0000000010	01-00010
2	0000000100	01-00100
3	0000001000	01-01000
4	0000010000	01-10000
5	0000100000	10-00001
6	0001000000	10-00010
7	0010000000	10-00100
8	0100000000	10-01000
9	1000000000	10-10000

indicates that there are two groups of digits: one group contains two digits and the other group contains five digits. The quinary portion (the two most significant digits) counts in steps of five and indicates whether the five-digit binary portion is counting from 0 to 4 the first or second time. If the two most significant digits indicate 01, the binary portion is counting in the range from 0 to 4; if the indication is 10, the binary portion is counting in the 5 to 9 range.

Table 3.10 illustrates the configurations of a biquinary counter as compared with a conventional ring counter.

Although the use of the biquinary code resulted in fewer units to indicate 10 states or conditions, design engineers were still striving to reduce the amount of units needed, since only two of the seven units were being used at any one time. This led to the utilization of another radix other than base 10.

Ternary Code

The last code to be discussed here is the ternary system. It is based on radix 3 and uses the three symbols -1, 0, and $+1$. These are abbreviated to $-0+$. With these three symbols, a total of 27 decimal digits, from -13 to $+13$ inclusive, can be represented.

In the decimal-ternary table (3.11) the positions are valued as 9, 3, and 1, respectively. If Table 3.11 is not understood, the radix principle

Table 3.11 Decimal-Ternary Notation

Decimal	Ternary	Decimal	Ternary
-13	$- - -$	0	000
-12	$- -0$	$+1$	$00+$
-11	$- -+$	$+2$	$0+-$
-10	$-0-$	$+3$	$0+0$
-9	-00	$+4$	$0++$
-8	$-0+$	$+5$	$+--$
-7	$-+-$	$+6$	$+-0$
-6	$-+0$	$+7$	$+-+$
-5	$-++$	$+8$	$+0-$
-4	$0--$	$+9$	$+00$
-3	$0-0$	$+10$	$+0+$
-2	$0-+$	$+11$	$++-$
-1	$00-$	$+12$	$++0$

should be recalled. In this case, radix 3 is used. For example,

$$+9 = (+1 \times 3^2) + (0 \times 3^1) + (0 \times 3^0)$$

or (abbreviated) $+00 = +9$. Also,

$$-10 = (-1 \times 3^2) + (0 \times 3^1) + (-1 \times 3^0) = (-9,0,-1),$$

or (abbreviated) $-0- = -10$.

Addition may be performed in ternary by the use of the following rules:

1. Adding unlike signs gives 0.
2. Adding two pluses gives a minus with a plus carry.
3. Adding two minuses gives a plus with a minus carry.

The following are three addition examples of these rules:

1.		2.		3.	
$+5 = +--$		$-7 = -+-$		$-8 = -0+$	
$+4 = 0++$		$-2 = 0-+$		$+10 = +0+$	
$+9 = +00$		$-9 = -00$		$+2 = 0+-$	

The reader should try a number of addition problems to gain facility with ternary notation.

Subtraction is done by complementing the subtrahend and adding. To complement a ternary number, leave the 0s unchanged, and change $+$ to $-$ and $-$ to $+$.

The following are two examples of the subtraction rules:

Subtract 7 *from* 12	*Subtract* 10 *from* 8
$+12 = ++0$	$+8 = +0-$
$-7 = -+-$	$-10 = -0-$
$+5 = +--$	$-2 = 0-+$

In this chapter a number of the basic codes used in computers have been considered. These codes are fundamental, and they are subject to modification and development in each new machine. Frequently it has been found possible to incorporate various types of error-spotting devices which stop the machine, ring a bell, or flash a light if an error occurs. For instance, the check-sorting computers used in banks use a certain number, like 344-510-0, for each customer. If that were a customer's number and he wrote a check with a wrong number, perhaps 344-511-0, it would probably be rejected automatically, rather than being charged to someone else. As an example, his bank might check such errors by having all account numbers add up to prime numbers. The error would be detected because $3 + 4 + 4 + 5 + 1 + 0 = 17$, which is a prime number, while the number $3 + 4 + 4 + 5 + 1 + 1 = 18$ is not.

Another bank might set up its customer number to total multiples of 10, like 347-510-0 = 20. At that bank, a check with the number 344-510-0 would be discarded.

Summary

The most common numbering system in use today is the decimal system, employing 10 digits and having a radix of 10. The first electronic computers utilized this system; but because of the large amount of hardware required to represent large numbers, the machines were unwieldy and relatively slow in operation. Since digital computers use signals which have only two levels, the binary numbering system with radix 2 was adopted without much difficulty. This resulted in a substantial saving in the amount of hardware required to represent a given number. For example, the decimal number 9 may now be represented by binary 1001 instead of 0100000000, the notation displayed in a decimal ring counter. The binary system has been modified in a variety of ways to develop the other number codes, such as the binary-coded decimal system, the excess-3 system, and the Gray code.

It is possible to add, subtract, multiply, and divide in the binary system. Machines can perform these operations more rapidly and with greater ease with the binary system than they can with the decimal system. The later machines use a combination of two systems in order to make it easier for the operators to follow the operations within the machine. Most computers receive their instructions in decimal form, convert to binary, perform the required calculations, and reconvert the results back to answers which are printed out by the computer in decimal.

The octal system is based on radix 8 and has special uses in computers. It is fairly simple for the machine to convert from octal to binary-coded decimal and vice versa. Some of the conversions from one radix to another are more difficult, but the steps involved have been fully explained in this chapter.

Fractions, as well as negative numbers, can be represented readily in binary, octal, and binary-coded decimal systems. Some computers place the decimal point at the extreme left and operate only on numbers between +1 and −1. By correct placement of the decimal point, using what is called the *floating point,* all numbers can be adjusted to these machines.

Computers perform calculations at a high rate of speed, sometimes thousands of calculations in 1 sec. If numbering systems are used in which many digits must change simultaneously, it is possible for errors to occur in the operation. For example, in going from 999 to 1,000, it is necessary to change four digits simultaneously. To cope with this problem, cyclic codes such as the Gray code have been developed. In the Gray code, no more than one digit at a time is changed in counting. In this code, 7 is written as 0100 and 8 as 1100. In this case the digit at the extreme left is the only one changed.

Two other numbering systems were briefly discussed in this chapter, namely, the biquinary code and the ternary system. The biquinary code has two parts, somewhat like the abacus, and the ternary code is limited to the use of three symbols, usually −, 0, and +. These codes are not used so frequently in computers as are the other systems considered in this chapter.

QUESTIONS

3.1 Define radix.

3.2 Define order.

3.3 Why is the binary system of numeration preferred in modern high-speed computers?

3.4 What is the binary equivalent of decimal 257?

3.5 Convert binary 0.101101 to decimal notation.

3.6 Convert binary 110001 to decimal notation.

3.7 Describe the double-dabble method for converting binary integers to decimal notation and convert the following numbers by using this method:

$$110101 \qquad 010110 \qquad 1111111.011$$

3.8 Using the arithmetical reverse of the double-dabble method, convert the following decimal numbers to binary:

$$34 \qquad 178 \qquad 3.142$$

3.9 Subtract the following numbers:

1101	1000	11010
111	100	11001

3.10 Describe the 1's complement.

3.11 Using the 1's complement method, subtract the following numbers:

$$\frac{10001}{01010} \qquad \frac{101011}{100110} \qquad \frac{10100010}{11001011}$$

3.12 Multiply the following binary numbers and check results by converting all numbers to decimal:

$$\frac{111}{101} \qquad \frac{10001}{110} \qquad \frac{10010}{01111}$$

3.13 Change the following Gray-code numbers to binary notation:

$$0110 \qquad 1001 \qquad 11111 \qquad 101101$$

3.14 Change the following decimal and binary numbers to octal notation:

$$19 \quad 62 \quad 27 \qquad 101101 \quad 1010 \quad 111111$$

3.15 Change the following binary numbers to Gray code:

$$1101 \qquad 10111 \qquad 10001 \qquad 10101$$

3.16 Change the following decimal numbers to excess-3 code:

$$27 \qquad 637 \qquad 128$$

Chapter **4**

Boolean Algebra

In the previous chapter the various numbering systems which can be used in computers were presented, with emphasis placed on the binary system. It will be recalled that in the binary system there are only two discrete notations: 0 and 1. In this chapter, this system will be utilized to introduce and demonstrate a simplified method of computer-function analysis called *Boolean algebra*. Sometimes referred to as the "algebra of logic," Boolean algebra lends itself well to electrical applications where there are switches that are closed or open and circuits in which an electric current is flowing or is not flowing. Any device that has two states, or conditions, may be represented by a Boolean-algebra notation.

Compare the possibility of describing computer functions by simple equations with the method of analysis and troubleshooting of electronic equipment such as radios, television sets, or radar sets. In the case of the latter group, meters, oscilloscopes, and schematic wiring diagrams are needed to locate troubles in the equipment. Although computers are in a sense more complex, Boolean algebra permits the detailed diagrams to be simplified so that the technician can "see the forest in spite of the trees." Boolean algebra has in recent years developed along with computers and has proved to be a great asset in both design and troubleshooting.

Why study Boolean algebra? A working knowledge of Boolean algebra can be the technician's and engineer's most valuable tool. In fact, logic is becoming widely understood by students in colleges and technical institutes and even by well-informed laymen. If this chapter is studied conscientiously, it will provide a firm foundation for proper interpretation of the more complex logic diagrams in the following chapters. If a career is planned in the telephone or computer fields, mastery of Boolean algebra is imperative.

History of Boolean Algebra

Boolean algebra is named after George Boole, who, about 1847, wrote papers on the mathematical analysis of logic. Boole was a distinguished professor in a great English university and made no claim to be a mathematician. He was a philosopher, especially interested in man's intellect and thought processes.

The importance of George Boole's contribution was not recognized for some 90 years; meanwhile, his unused books gathered dust on library shelves. Then in 1937 a Bell Telephone engineer, interested in problems arising from telephone expansion, became urgently in need of a method of simplifying multiple switching and dialing networks. C. E. Shannon took Boole's original ideas and developed the logic now called Boolean logic, or Boolean algebra. Since that time this treatment of electric circuits has enormously simplified work in both the telephone and the computer fields.

There are many possible manipulations of Boolean algebra that are beyond the scope of this book, but the basic operations are covered in this chapter. Other texts on the subject are listed in Appendix II.

Basic Principles of Boolean Algebra

Boole's logic is based upon the premise that a statement is either *true* or *false*. True statements have a value of 1, while false statements have a value of 0.

The nature of digital computers and data processors, which have "all-or-nothing" signal levels, facilitates the use of Boolean algebra in descriptive analysis of the functions of the electronic circuits employed. To say this another way, designers have found the algebra of logic to be a shortcut method useful in describing the operation of a variety of electronic circuits used in digital equipment.

Boolean algebra, although confusing at first glance, is an extremely simple form of algebra. While it does not necessarily lead to the best circuit (one with the smallest number of components), it provides a convenient method of representing switching circuits. The remainder of this discussion is devoted to the development of the basic rules of Boolean algebra and to the demonstration of its application in switching circuits.

In Boolean algebra, only two values, or numbers, are to be considered: 0 and 1. The 0 signifies "false" or, in the actual circuitry, the absence of a signal. The 1 signifies "true," or the presence of a signal.

Of prime importance are the definitions given to the symbols + and ×. Normally, they mean *add* and *multiply*, respectively. However, in Boolean algebra they are the logical connectives, making valid the combination of two or more logical elements into a proposition. The addition symbol is assigned the meaning "OR" and the multiplication symbol is assigned the meaning "AND." Symbolic logic is used extensively in Boolean algebra, and the logical elements of a proposition are indicated by letters. For example, $A + B = 1$ is written for the statement "A OR B equals 1," and $AB = 1$ for the statement "A AND B equals 1." The results obtained when the OR function is applied to the basic combinations of 0s and 1s are shown as follows:

1. $0 + 0 = 0$ **2.** $0 + 1 = 1$ **3.** $1 + 1 = 1$

The first Boolean equation means that 0 OR 0 is equal to 0. The second equation means that 0 OR 1 is equal to 1, because the OR function dictates that the resulting quantity is equal to 1 when any of the given elements is 1. With this premise, then the third equation means that 1 OR 1 is also equal to 1. (No quantities higher than 1 are used in Boolean algebra.)

The rules for the AND function are now illustrated:

4. $0 \times 0 = 0$ **5.** $0 \times 1 = 0$ **6.** $1 \times 1 = 1$

The AND sign indicates that the resulting quantity is equal to 1 only when *all* of the given elements are 1; otherwise the resulting quantity is equal to 0.

At this point it is now possible to substitute letter symbols for one of the variables used in the basic rules to emphasize important relationships. The concepts of these equations may be grasped more easily by substituting for A each of the following values which it may have (1 or 0)·

7. $A + 0 = A$ **8.** $A + 1 = 1$ **9.** $A + A = A$ OR

10. $A0 = 0$ **11.** $A1 = A$ **12.** $AA = A$ AND

In equation (7) the result will be definitely dependent upon A, for if A is 0, then the result will be 0; if A is 1, then the result will be 1. In equation (8), the result will be 1 regardless of the value of A. Equation (9) indicates redundancy. It may therefore be reduced to the value of A. Equation (10) is similar to multiplication in ordinary algebra; if 0 is a factor, then the product or result is 0. The result of equation (11) is determined solely by A, and (12) is another case of redundancy since AA reduces to A.

Commutative law. There are four important postulates or laws that are extremely important in the manipulation of Boolean equations. The first of these is the commutative law, which states that the results of the AND and OR connectives are unaffected by the sequence of the logical elements that they connect:

$$A + B = B + A$$
$$AB = BA$$

Hence, as long as the same type of logical connective is used between a given group of elements, the positions of the elements on either side of the equals sign may be interchanged.

Associative law. The law of association states that the elements of a proposition may be grouped in any quantity so long as they are connected by the same sign:

$$A + (B + C) = (A + B) + C$$
$$A(BC) = (AB)C$$

Distributive law. The distributive law is contingent on the characteristics of the logical connectives themselves and can be proved by manipulation of the entities.

13. $A(B + C) = AB + AC$

Equation (13) is proved by simple algebraic expansion. Also

14. $A + BC = (A + B)(A + C)$

PROOF:

$$(A + B)(A + C) = AA + AC + AB + BC$$
$$= A(1 + C + B) + BC$$

but $A(1 + C + B)$ is reducible to A [property (11)]; therefore,

$$(A + B)(A + C) = A(1 + C + B) + BC = A + BC$$

The distributive law is most frequently used in the reduction and simplification of Boolean equations.

The law of NOT. A unique concept peculiar to Boolean algebra is the NOT function, indicated by a bar over a symbol or a "prime" sign placed immediately after the symbol. The NOT sign means "the converse of," or the alternate value of, either the symbol or the logical connective. For example, $\bar{1}$ (NOT 1) is equal to 0, for if it is not 1, the only other value it can have is 0. Conversely, $\bar{0}$ (NOT 0) can only be equal to 1. It follows, then, that if a variable A is assigned the value of 1, then $\bar{A}$ (A NOT) is equal to 0, for if A is not 1, the only other value it can have is 0. When the NOT function is applied to a logical connective, the connective assumes the alternate function: for example, $\mp$ (OR NOT), becomes AND, and $\times$ (AND NOT) becomes OR. From the preceding definition, the following rules are obtained:

$A + \bar{A} = 1$ (either A OR A NOT is equal to 1)
$A\bar{A} = 0$ (A AND A NOT can never occur simultaneously)
$\bar{\bar{A}} = A$ (the converse of A NOT is A)

De Morgan's laws. The final laws to be discussed are De Morgan's laws, which apply the principles of the NOT function to an equation containing more than one element:

$$\overline{AB} = \bar{A} + \bar{B}$$
$$\overline{A + B} = \bar{A}\bar{B}$$

A brief example of the benefits of Boolean equation simplification is shown in Fig. 4.1. As shown in equation (14), $(A + B)(A + C)$ reduces to $A + BC$. The original configuration is shown in Fig. 4.1a; it requires two OR gates and one AND gate and utilizes six diodes (two for each gate). The simplified version performs the same function but requires only one AND gate and one OR gate, resulting in a saving of two diodes.

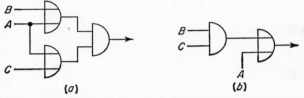

Fig. 4.1 Equivalent logical diagrams $(A + B)(A + C) = A + BC$.

In this case only two diodes were eliminated, but in actual computers, where hundreds of these gates are used, the reduction of components results in a substantial reduction in the cost of the equipments.

The following discussion illustrates a method of developing Boolean equations from logical diagrams. Beginning with first-order logic (single-gate function) and progressing through fourth-order logic (four-step gating sequence), rules will be evolved for writing the equations.

Equations from Logical Diagrams

In the gating sequences used in digital computers, it will be observed that two important conventions are followed: AND gates are normally connected to OR gates, and OR gates are normally connected to AND gates. Seldom will one AND gate connect to another AND gate; it is equally unusual for an OR gate to provide an input to another OR gate, because the diodes of one gate may simply be connected to the diode load resistor of the gate that it supplies, provided that both gates perform the same function. The limiting factor in this practice is the power requirement of the gate.

First-order logic. Figure 4.2 shows logical diagrams of first-order AND and OR circuits. This, of course, presents nothing new but provides a springboard for accepting new concepts.

The equation for Fig. 4.2a may be written $A \times B \times C \times D = E$. The

$\times$ between each letter may be eliminated as in regular algebra, allowing the expression to be stated as $ABCD = E$. If this term is translated verbally, it becomes: "If, and only if, inputs A, B, C, and D are true simultaneously, there will be an output E; further, this output will exist only for the duration of the minimum time signal."

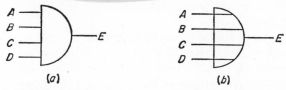

Fig. 4.2 Logical diagrams for first-order logic AND and OR circuits. (a) $ABCD = E$. (b) $A + B + C + D = E$.

For the OR circuit of Fig. 4.2b the equation may be written

$$A + B + C + D = E$$

The sign of addition between each letter may *not* be omitted to simplify the expression. Again, translated verbally, this becomes: "If any one of the inputs A or B or C or D is true, then there will be an output E; further, this output will exist for the entire period of time that any one of these signals is true."

Second-order logic. Working with logical diagrams which are compounded by having an AND circuit supply an OR circuit, or vice versa, gives rise to a problem of grouping within the equation. This indicates the requirement for a universal system which will allow the systematic expansion of the functions within an expression. In Fig. 4.3 examples of this type of expression are given.

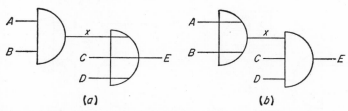

Fig. 4.3 Logical diagrams for second-order logic AND and OR circuits. (a) $AB + C + D = E$. (b) $(A + B)CD = E$.

Figure 4.3a shows an AND circuit supplying an OR circuit. Only four discrete inputs are involved, however, and writing the equation for this diagram goes one step further. Designating the output of the AND circuit in Fig. 4.3a as x simplifies the problem. The equation for the OR circuit becomes $x + C + D = E$. However, this does not indicate the structure of x; but x taken by itself may be stated as $AB = x$. Therefore, the complete equation for output E may be described as $AB + C + D = E$. In the OR circuit, three distinct inputs are recognized. One of these inputs is in the form of an AND circuit. Therefore, the final equation should be an expression of three terms which will indicate that the overall diagram consists of an OR circuit being supplied by an AND circuit. This is called an overall OR gate.

Figure 4.3b shows the converse of Fig. 4.3a. It is an OR circuit supplying an AND circuit. Similarly, there are still only four discrete inputs involved. However, the logic arrangement complicates matters somewhat. Again, designating the output of the circuit $(A + B)$ as x simplifies the problem. The equation then will be $xCD = E$, but the contents of x are not apparent. The output x nevertheless describes the OR gate, $A + B = x$. Combining directly the expression $A + B$ with CD would result in $A + BCD$, which would give a false impression of the circuits. Therefore, an additional step must be taken to ensure that circuits of more than first-order logic will not be misconstrued.

The parentheses and other similar marks of grouping used in ordinary algebra form the separation between terms. Thus, the term $A + B$ would be placed in parentheses $(A + B)$ to indicate a complete quantity to be combined in an AND circuit with CD to make up the output signal E. The equation is written $(A + B)CD = E$. Use of the other symbols for grouping will be discussed as they are required.

Third-order logic. It is now convenient to analyze more complex forms of the same types of logical diagrams, included in Fig. 4.4. These are treated in the same manner as those of Fig. 4.3.

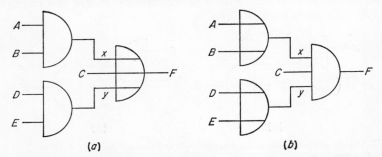

Fig. 4.4 Third-order logical diagrams. (a) $AB + DE + C = F$. (b) $(A + B)C(D + E) = F$.

Figure 4.4a illustrates two AND circuits supplying an OR circuit. While a total of five discrete inputs is involved, the OR circuit receives only three. Therefore, in the same manner as before, the two AND gates may be designated x and y to simplify writing the equations.

The equation for Fig. 4.4a will be $x + C + y = F$. Working with one

AND gate at a time gives $AB = x$, $DE = y$; therefore, the entire equation is $AB + C + DE = F$. Again it should be noted that each AND function is treated as a total quantity.

The technique of designating the outputs of a secondary circuit may appear cumbersome at this point; however, this is a useful tool until proficiency is attained. Also, when the equation for a four-level complex logical diagram is written, this "crutch" will eliminate mistakes.

Figure 4.4b illustrates two OR circuits supplying an AND circuit. Again, five discrete inputs are involved, but the AND circuit receives only three. As before, the input OR gates may be designated x and y for simplification.

The equation for Fig. 4.4b will be $xCy = F$. The equation $A + B = x$ is now developed. This case points up the necessity for tools of separation. For example, if $A + B$ were combined with Cy without parentheses, the final equation would be $A + BCy$, which alters the logic. Therefore, the marks of a complete term or expression must be included to form $(A + B)Cy$. The remaining portion y, which equals $D + E$, is now added. This will round out the equation in its correct form:

$$(A + B)C(D + E) = F$$

This is read "quantity A or B and C and quantity D or E equals F."

Two additional OR circuits will be considered in order to show the treatment of third- and fourth-order logical diagrams.

Fourth-order logic. Figure 4.5 illustrates an overall OR circuit. By using x and y to identify the secondary inputs, the problem of setting up the equation resolves itself to a matter of expanding y and x.

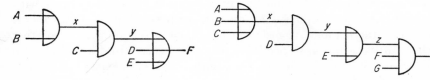

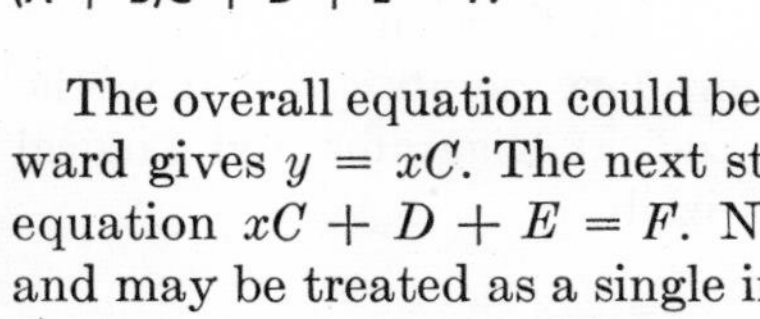

Fig. 4.5 Third-order logical diagram, $(A + B)C + D + E = F$.

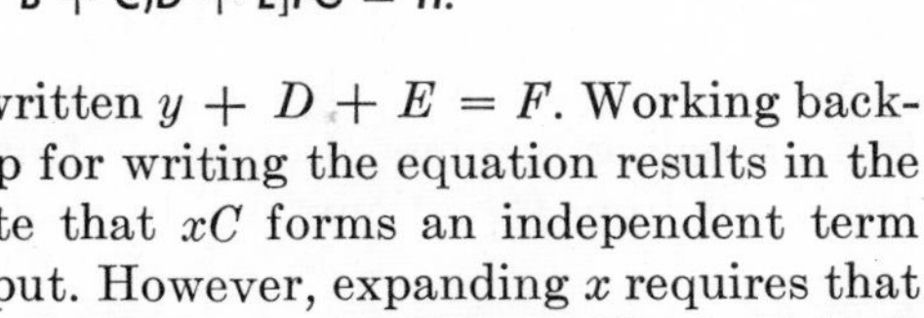

Fig. 4.6 Fourth-order logical diagram, $[(A + B + C)D + E]FG = H$.

The overall equation could be written $y + D + E = F$. Working backward gives $y = xC$. The next step for writing the equation results in the equation $xC + D + E = F$. Note that xC forms an independent term and may be treated as a single input. However, expanding x requires that $A + B$ be enclosed within parentheses before being combined with C. Now the complete expression is $(A + B)C + D + E = F$. The total number of inputs to the final OR circuit remains at three.

The diagram in Fig. 4.6 represents an overall AND circuit with three inputs. Three letters x, y, and z are employed to indicate the undeveloped secondary inputs. Solving in the same manner as before gives the first equation as $zFG = H$. In a step-by-step process, the stages are completed as follows:

1. $zFG = H$
2. $y + E = z$; therefore, substituting for z,
3. $(y + E)FG = H$
4. $xD = y$; therefore, substituting for y,
5. $(xD + E)FG = H$
6. $A + B + C = x$; therefore, substituting for x,
7. $[(A + B + C)D + E]FG = H$

In step 5 an OR circuit was placed in parentheses in order to retain a given quantity, either xD or E. Within this quantity exists another quantity $A + B + C$, which is represented by x. Therefore, to maintain identity and correct separation, the quantity $A + B + C$ must be enclosed in parentheses, and the total expression $(A + B + C)D + E$ must be placed in brackets at step 7.

In addition to the parentheses and brackets, braces, vincula, or other signs of grouping may be employed for these equations. Speed and confidence with the operations required can be gained through practice.

Logical Diagrams from Equations

Simple equations, such as $ABCD = E$ or $A + B + C + D = E$, pose no particular problem in drawing out the correct logical diagram. The equation $(A + B)(C + D) = E$ will also offer little challenge. This second equation should be immediately recognized as an AND circuit with two inputs, each of which is an OR gate with two inputs. If we follow through in the manner suggested in the previous section, by designating each quantity x and y, respectively, the task evolves to drawing an AND circuit with the inputs x and y. Then both x and y are expanded to show their individual structure.

For the purpose of illustration, one difficult problem will be taken step by step from the equation to the finished logical diagram.

At the conclusion of this example the primary points covered in the two preceding sections (Equations from Logical Diagrams and Logical Diagrams from Equations) will be summarized.

Example

The equation: $[(A + B + C)(D + E) + F + G(H + I)]J = K$.

Step 1. Identify the overall circuit type.
  a. Two-input AND circuit.
  b. J and quantity within bracket.

Step 2. Perform simplest operations first.
   a. Draw logic for an AND circuit first.
   b. Show two inputs J and z (Fig. 4.7).

Fig. 4.7 $Jz = K$.

Step 3. Write the equations for z.
   a. $(A + B + C)(D + E) + F + G(H + I) = z$.
   b. Brackets no longer necessary.
   c. Identify remaining circuit.
      (1) OR gate with three inputs.
      (2) z represents OR output.
Step 4. Develop inputs to OR circuit.
   a. Identify the three inputs w, x, and y (Fig. 4.8).

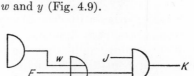

Fig. 4.8 $(w + x + y)J = K$.

   b. Write the equation for each label.
      (1) $(A + B + C)(D + E) = w$
      (2) $F = x$
      (3) $G(H + I) = y$
Step 5. Perform simplest operations.
   a. Substitute F for x.
   b. Show two AND inputs for w and y (Fig. 4.9).

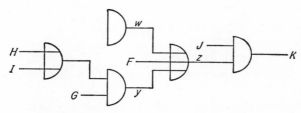

Fig. 4.9 $(w + y + F)J = K$.

Step 6. Expand AND gate y.
   a. Single input G.
   b. OR circuit input $H + I$ (Fig. 4.10).

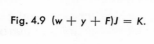

Fig. 4.10 $[w + F + G(H + I)]J = K$.

Step 7. Expand AND gate w.
   a. Two OR circuit inputs.
   b. Identify and expand (Fig. 4.11).
      (1) $A + B + C$.
      (2) $D + E$.

Step 8. Diagram completed.
    a. Check each portion of equation for agreement.
    b. Write equation from diagram as a check for errors.

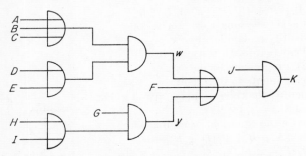

Fig. 4.11 $[(A + B + C)(D + E) + F + G(H + I)]J = K.$

Summary of Principles for Conversion

Translation of either a Boolean algebra equation into a logical diagram or a logical diagram into a Boolean equation is the technician's most useful tool for developing troubleshooting techniques for computers and data-processing equipments. The principles applicable for performing a conversion from equation to diagram and vice versa are summarized as follows:

1. Always perform the simplest operation first.
2. Recognize the type of overall circuit involved.
3. Combine like functions of the same logic order.
    a. AND circuits should not supply AND circuits.
        (1) $(AB)(CD) = x.$
        (2) $ADCB = x.$
    b. OR circuits should not supply OR circuits.
        (1) $(A + B) + (C + D) = x.$
        (2) $A + B + C + D = x.$
    c. Exceptions are sometimes necessitated by driving-power requirements.
4. Designate secondary inputs where possible to avoid mistakes in expanding.
5. Use marks of grouping.
    a. If an OR function is to be used with one or more signals in an AND function, parentheses, brackets, or vincula must be used for separation.
        (1) $(A + B)(C + D) = x.$
        (2) $(A + B + C + D)E = x.$

b. If an OR function is to be used with another OR function in an AND function, each term must be enclosed with marks of grouping.

(1) $(A + C + D)(D + E + F) = x$.

(2) $(A + B + C)(D + E) = x$.

c. If an AND function is to be used with another AND function of the same logic level in an AND function, marks of separation are not required.

Signal Designations

Within any large computer or data processor there are hundreds of different signals, each of which has a special importance and some job to perform. Attempting to memorize the origin of all the signals seems impossible. However, the task is not so towering as it may appear. A general organization of signals according to type and function simplifies the problem. While there are exceptions, a key to most of the situations to be encountered is as follows:

1. To correctly categorize signals, the flip-flop is mentioned again in passing. This is merely a logical element used in computers and processors for storage and counting; it has two outputs, 0 and 1. A capital letter represents a flip-flop output; for example, when a flip-flop is designated A,

   a. ONE-side output is written A.

   b. ZERO-side output is written as either A' or $\bar{A}$ (A NOT).

2. A subscript numeral is added to indicate order within a series, as in a serial counter with five flip-flops.

   a. A_1, A_2, A_3, A_4, and A_5 for ONE-side outputs.

   b. A_1', A_2', A_3', A_4', and A_5' for ZERO-side outputs.

3. Gated signals are given a lowercase letter.

   a. $a_1 a_2 a_3 + b_1 b_2 b_3 = c$.

   b. $abc = d$.

4. The outputs of inverters are given a prime, or NOT, sign (signal A' is read "A NOT").

   a. Signal A into an inverter becomes A'.

   b. To avoid confusion, the lowercase signals are called *little*.

   (1) a' is read "little a NOT."

   (2) a_1' is read "little a one NOT."

The NOT function is also used to derive equations to detect specified counts in a register or counter. Consider the problem of detecting the decimal value of 10 in a four-stage serial counter. The binary configuration will be 1010. This means simply that the flip-flops will have the configuration shown in Fig. 4.12. A_1 will be in the ZERO state, A_2 in the ONE state, A_3 in the ZERO state, and, finally, A_4 in the ONE state. To have an output when this count occurs, an AND circuit could be designed to accept inputs from the flip-flops so that only the combination of 1010 will cause an output. The corresponding AND gate is connected as shown in Fig. 4.13.

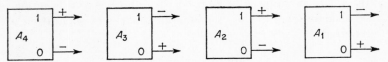

Fig. 4.12 Flip-flops indicating 1010 (decimal 10).

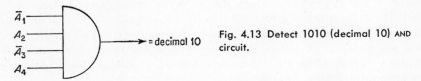

Fig. 4.13 Detect 1010 (decimal 10) AND circuit.

Essentially the principles of applying the NOT function to an equation have been illustrated in the paragraph above. For clarification, the rule for applying the NOT function to an equation may be stated: When an equation or function is to be given the NOT function, make all terms and signs opposite; that portion of the equation to be given the NOT function will be enclosed with marks of grouping. An example of this is as follows:

$$A + (\overline{BC + DE}) = A + (\bar{B} + \bar{C})(\bar{D} + \bar{E})$$

Inverters. Remember that most computer components utilize two selected voltage levels. Suppose these are 0 volt for the "on," or "true," condition and −20 volts for the "off," or "false," condition. Then terms like the following could be used:

$$A = 0 \text{ volt}$$
$$B = 0 \text{ volt}$$
$$A' = -20 \text{ volts}$$
$$B' = -20 \text{ volts}$$

Now if an inverter is used, it would change an input of 0 volt to an output of −20 volts. Also, if −20 volts is applied to the inverter, the output would be 0 volt. In the circuit shown in Fig. 4.14, the output of the AND gate shown is present if A is present and B is not present.

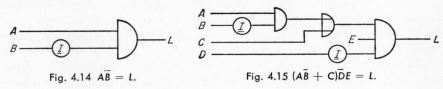

Fig. 4.14 $A\bar{B} = L.$ Fig. 4.15 $(A\bar{B} + C)\bar{D}E = L.$

The diagram in Fig. 4.14 indicates that when A is present and B is not present the gate will be enabled. In this case the circuit must have 0 volt applied at its A input and -20 volts at its B input.

Although the equation for the circuit shown in Fig. 4.15 is

$$[(AB') + C]D'E = L$$

it could also be written $ED'(C + AB') = L$.

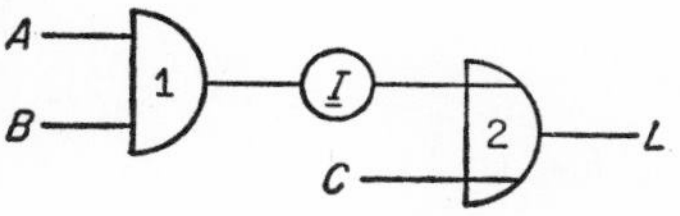

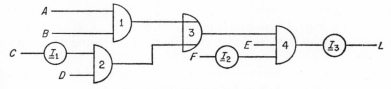

Fig. 4.16 $\overline{AB} + C = L$. 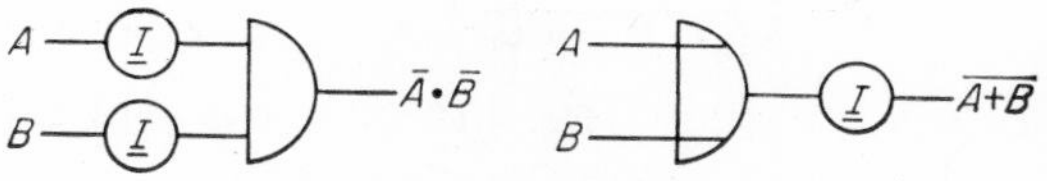   Fig. 4.17 $\overline{A + B} = \bar{A} \cdot \bar{B}$.

Another system involving an inverter is shown in Fig. 4.16. The inverter introduces a very important concept which will be used later in this book. Notice that $GA1$ is an AND gate feeding an inverter; so there will be an input to $GA2$ if there is no output from $GA1$. However, if either A or B is absent, there will be no output from $GA1$; so $AB = A' + B'$. This is an extremely important concept. Then $C + A' + B' = L$ could be written for this. Similarly, $\overline{A + B} = \bar{A} \cdot \bar{B}$ is the same as the logical diagram of Fig. 4.17.

To expand this idea to more complicated equations, the following rule is used: When an equation or function is to be given the NOT function, change all the signs between terms and invert each term as follows:

$$\overline{(AB + C'D)EF'} = L$$
$$(\bar{A} + \bar{B})(C + \bar{D}) + \bar{E} + F = L$$

The original equation was basically an overall AND circuit of three inputs. This is clearly seen from the diagram in Fig. 4.18 by looking at $GA4$.

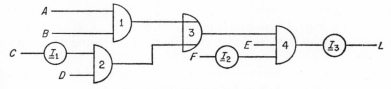

Fig. 4.18 $\overline{(AB + C'D)EF'} = L$.

However, the line over the whole function is represented by I_3; negating, or inverting, the function provides the equivalent circuit shown in Fig. 4.19. Hence, by looking at $GA8$ it can be seen that the result is an overall OR circuit with three inputs with I_3 eliminated.

In the first case, three AND gates, an OR gate, and three inverters were needed. In the second case an equivalent circuit has been constructed out of three OR gates, an AND gate, and four inverters.

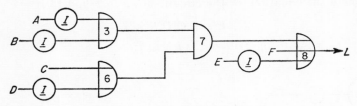

Fig. 4.19 $(\overline{A} + \overline{B})(C + \overline{D}) + \overline{E} + F = L.$

Summary of Conversion Principles

The following steps summarize the principles of conversion from logic diagrams to Boolean algebra and back again. It will be found later that a complete grasp of this subject matter will be a most useful tool in troubleshooting digital computers.

1. Decide on the type of overall circuit represented by the diagram (last gate) or by the given equation. Is it a three-input AND circuit or a four-input OR circuit, etc.?
2. Perform the simplest operation first, then proceed to the more complicated operations.
3. Combine like functions wherever possible.
4. Use brackets and parentheses as in regular algebra.
5. Use signs of grouping before manipulating NOT functions.
6. The innermost expressions in a complex function are farthest from the output in the diagram.

Considerable proficiency should be developed in manipulation of equations, in changing equations around through the use of Boolean algebra, in drawing equivalent circuits from equations, and in deriving equations from logical circuit diagrams. These equations in actual computers are extremely complex but may be simplified by applying the foregoing principles.

Take the complex equation given below, simplify it, and draw a diagram for the original equation and for its simplified form:

$$\overline{AB + D(C + A') + E(F + G)} = L$$

On a sheet of paper, copy this equation. Put down this book and try to simplify the equation and make the two diagrams. After this has been done, check your work against the following solution.

The given equation is a three-part OR circuit assigned the NOT function. So the last gate on the right will be an OR gate and an inverter. The complete diagram is shown in Fig. 4.20.

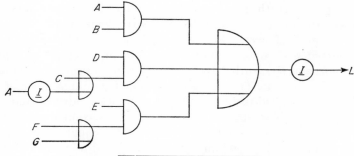

Fig. 4.20 $\overline{AB + D(C + A') + E(F + G)} = L.$

Another way to express the equation is to carry through the NOT function by applying De Morgan's law:

$$\overline{AB + D(C + A') + E(F + G)} = (\overline{AB})[\overline{D(C + A')}]\,[\overline{E(F + G)}]$$
$$= (\bar{A} + \bar{B})(\bar{D} + \bar{C}A)(\bar{E} + \overline{FG})$$

Now the circuit is an overall AND gate with three inputs from three OR gates. The original diagram (Fig. 4.20) is preferred because it used only two inverters, whereas the second drawing (Fig. 4.21) used seven inverters and requires the same number of gates.

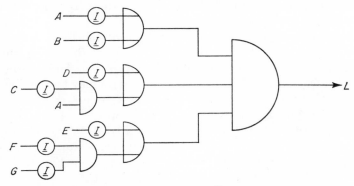

Fig. 4.21 $(\bar{A} + \bar{B})(\bar{D} + \bar{C}A)(\bar{E} + \overline{FG}) = L.$

The reader should work several problems of this type. The practice will promote proficiency and will bring out some point that may not have been fully appreciated.

A Table Method of Simplification

Truth tables, introduced in Chap. 2, were shown as graphic representations of the characteristics of logic circuits. A heretofore unmentioned characteristic of truth tables is their ability to suggest methods of Boolean equation reduction and, consequently, logic simplification. Consider the example shown in Fig. 4.22. The two-variable circuit will produce an output when one, but not both, of the input variables is present.

Three blocks of the truth table are filled in to indicate conditions that will produce an output. To use the truth table for minimization of terms, look for adjacent filled-in blocks. Adjacent blocks indicate that a term may be eliminated because its true form and its complement are used with one or more unchanging variables. The equation of Fig. 4.22 is thereby simplified by combining the terms in adjacent blocks with an OR sign and eliminating the superfluous term.

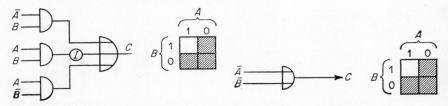

Fig. 4.22 Logical diagram and truth table for $\bar{A}B + A\bar{B} + \overline{AB} = C$.

Fig. 4.23 Logical diagram and truth table for $\bar{A} + \bar{B} = C$.

In a vertical direction the table yields $\bar{A}B + \overline{AB} = \bar{A}(B + \bar{B}) = \bar{A}1 = \bar{A}$; the variable that drops out in this instance is B, since $(B + \bar{B})$ will always be equal to 1.

In a similar fashion, combining the adjacent blocks in a horizontal direction yields $A\bar{B} + \overline{AB} = \bar{B}(A + \bar{A}) = \bar{B}1 = \bar{B}$. Notice that the term $\overline{AB}$ was used twice in this simplifying operation. An important rule to remember when using this method is that a term may be combined with other adjacent terms as many times as is deemed necessary to simplify the entire logical expression. Hence, the entire expression $A\bar{B} + B\bar{A} + \overline{AB}$ has been reduced to $\bar{A} + \bar{B}$ with the use of a truth table. When a truth table is used in this manner it is often referred to as a Karnaugh map. The logical diagram and truth table for $\bar{A} + \bar{B}$ is shown in Fig. 4.23. Notice that the truth table is identical with that of Fig. 4.22.

Simplification chart for three variables. An example showing how a Karnaugh map is used to simplify a logical expression of three variables is given in Fig. 4.24. The three-variable Karnaugh map is drawn so that each variable overlaps with the "true" and "false" conditions of the other two variables. In this form, each conceivable configuration of the three variables may be located on the chart. The blocks are numbered to facilitate location identification, and the shaded blocks represent each of the four terms of the logical equation. The adjacent shaded blocks (1 and 2) are combined to form $ABC + AB\bar{C}$, which reduces to $AB(C + \bar{C})$ or AB. Blocks 2 and 3 are combined and reduced to $AC(B + \bar{B})$ or AC, and

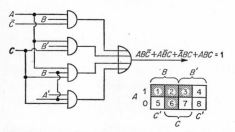

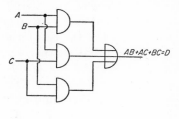

Fig. 4.24 Logical diagram and Karnaugh map for $AB\bar{C} + ABC + \bar{A}BC + ABC = D$.

Fig. 4.25 Logical diagram for $AB + AC + BC = D$.

blocks 2 and 6 are combined and reduced to $BC(A + \bar{A})$ or BC. The resulting expression in its simplest form is $AB + AC + BC$. The simplified logical diagram is shown in Fig. 4.25.

Simplification chart for four variables. The final example of the Karnaugh map or chart method of minimization of terms illustrates how

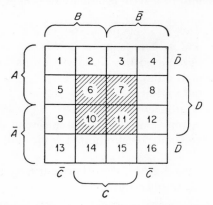

Fig. 4.26 Karnaugh map for $\bar{A}BCD + A\bar{B}CD + \bar{A}BCD + ABCD$.

a four-variable logical expression of four terms can be reduced to its simplest form. In order to accommodate all possible arrangements of a four-variable equation, the chart must contain 16 squares. The equation to be studied for reduction is $ABCD + A\bar{B}CD + \bar{A}BCD + \overline{AB}CD$. Again, each variable is arranged to effect a complete overlap with the remaining three variables as shown in Fig. 4.26. The squares are numbered from 1 to 16 and the blocks that describe the terms of the logical expression are shaded.

Blocks 6 and 7 combine to form $ABCD + A\bar{B}CD$. The changing variable $(B + \bar{B})$ is the superfluous term and is thereby eliminated, and the two terms reduce to ACD. Blocks 10 and 11 combine to form $\bar{A}BCD + \bar{A}\bar{B}CD$. The changing variable is again $B + \bar{B}$, which is dropped, and the two terms reduce to $\bar{A}CD$. Observe that the original four-term expression has reduced to the two-term expression $ACD + \bar{A}CD$. By observation it can be seen that another superfluous variable exists, namely, $A + \bar{A}$. The original expression $(ABCD + A\bar{B}CD + \bar{A}BCD + \bar{A}\bar{B}CD)$ in its simplest form is, therefore, CD. The point emphasized here is that whenever a grouping of four mutually adjacent blocks occurs, the four terms can be reduced to a product of two variables.

A summary of rules for the construction and use of a Karnaugh map follows:

1. The number of blocks required to accommodate n variables is 2^n blocks; hence, a chart for two variables will contain four blocks; a chart for three variables will contain eight blocks, and so forth.
2. The variables are arranged within the chart to provide an overlap, one with the other.
3. Each block that contains a term is indicated by shading or by inserting a 1.
4. All adjacent blocks are subjects for simplification since they contain at least one variable and its complement; in this case it is the superfluous term and may be eliminated to effect the elimination of a term.
5. The blocks considered adjacent are:
   a. Blocks horizontally adjacent
   b. Blocks vertically adjacent
   c. Blocks on the extreme ends of the same row or column
6. A total of three terms may be eliminated from four mutually adjacent blocks.
7. Any block may be combined with other mutually adjacent blocks as often as required to simplify the logical expression.

Summary

During the past 20 years, Boolean algebra has become increasingly important to complex telephone dialing systems and computers. It is an extremely simple form of algebra that describes logical switching functions. Because of its ability to express complicated switching functions in terms of "true" or "false," Boolean algebra is well suited for analysis, troubleshooting, and design of computer circuitry.

The basic rules of Boolean algebra reduce all functions to either AND or OR. The AND function requires that all factors contributing to this function be "high" before a "high," or "true," output may be obtained. In the OR function, any contributing factor that is "high" produces a "true" output.

Boolean algebra represents and analyzes logical switching functions, but it does not always lead to the best or most efficient circuit.

Application of Boolean algebra to logical switching circuits will help evolve numerous approaches to the solution of problems of logic encountered in computers and data processors; and it is directly applicable to the design of diode matrices, adders, subtracters, and other logical functions. Practice and facility in the use of Boolean algebra is a necessity for the computer technician and specialist. Table 4.1 presents a summary of identities of Boolean algebra.

Table 4.1 Summary of the Basic Boolean Algebra Identities

Fundamental operations

OR	AND	NOT
$0 + 0 = 0$	$0 \times 0 = 0$	$\bar{0} = 1$
$0 + 1 = 1$	$0 \times 1 = 0$	$\bar{1} = 0$
$1 + 1 = 1$	$1 \times 1 = 1$	
$A + 0 = A$	$A \times 0 = 0$	
$A + 1 = 1$	$A \times 1 = A$	$A + \bar{A} = 1$
$A + A = A$	$A \times A = A$	$A\bar{A} = 0$
$A + \bar{A} = 1$	$A \times \bar{A} = 0$	$\bar{\bar{A}} = A$

Associative laws

$(A + B) + C = A + (B + C)$
$(AB)C = A(BC)$

Distributive laws

$A(B + C) = AB + AC$
$A + BC = (A + B)(A + C)$

Commutative laws

$A + B = B + A$
$AB = BA$

De Morgan's laws

$\overline{AB} = \bar{A} + \bar{B}$
$\overline{A + B} = \bar{A} \cdot \bar{B}$

QUESTIONS

4.1 Define and give an example of (a) commutative law, (b) distributive law, (c) associative law, and (d) De Morgan's law.

4.2 Explain briefly how Boolean algebra is used in digital computers.

4.3 Write in tabular form the basic rules for AND and OR functions.

4.4 How do the truth tables differ from the table of rules?

4.5 NOT the following equations:

a. $AB + AC = Y$
b. $A + BC = Y$
c. $ABC + AD = Y'$
d. $(AC)'(AB + CD) = Y$

4.6 Draw the logical diagrams for the following equations:

a. $(AB)(C + D) + e = y$
b. $A + AB(C + D) = y$
c. $(A + B'C)(A' + B + C) = x$
d. $A(B + CDE) + F(G + H) = z$

Chapter 5

Fundamentals of Magnetic Devices

When a mathematician works a problem, he may write his computations on paper. He does this to have a step-by-step record of the process used in arriving at the final solution. In a like manner, a computer requires a memory or storage device to record its arithmetical operations, both intermediate and final. In some computers the memory system is also used to store the program, which lists the type and sequence of operations to be performed.

Magnetic drums and magnetic coincident-current core devices are the memory elements most widely used in advanced computers at the present time. For a comprehension of coincident-current devices it is necessary to understand the fundamentals of ferromagnetism, with particular emphasis on the characteristics of the magnetic materials used.

This chapter deals with the basic concepts of ferromagnetism, beginning with an explanation of magnetic flux, field forces, and domain alignment and including an explanation of the hysteresis loops of common ferromagnetic substances and ferrite cores.

Basic Electromagnetism

This chapter covers the artificial creation of magnetic behavior by electric currents. A magnetic field exists concentrically about any current-carrying conductor as shown in Fig. 5.1. This magnetic field is commonly known as magnetic flux. If a paper is placed so that a current-carrying wire runs directly through it, iron filings scattered on the paper align in a manner to describe the magnetic field.

The right-hand rule is used to determine the direction of the lines of magnetic flux about the wire. This rule states that if the thumb of the right hand points along the wire in the direction of conventional current flow (opposite to the direction of electron flow), the direction of flux or magnetic force about the conductor is indicated by the direction of the fingers of the closed hand (see Fig. 5.2).

If a conductor is extended lengthwise and wound in a close spiral or helical form, an even larger magnetic field is formed. The cross section of the magnetic field section is shown in Fig. 5.3. [A dot (·) in the center of the wire designates electrons coming out of the paper, and a plus (+)

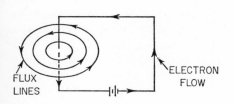

Fig. 5.1 Direction of magnetic flux about a current-carrying conductor.

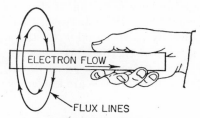

Fig. 5.2 Right-hand rule.

designates electrons going into the paper.] Figure 5.3 shows that, according to the right-hand rule, the magnetic fields of the individual wires combine with neighboring turns of wire to form a large magnetic field.

As either the number of turns of wire or the amount of current passing through the wire is increased, the magnetic field will become proportionately stronger. The magnetizing force, termed magnetomotive force, is directly proportional to the number of turns of wire and to the amount of

Fig. 5.3. The combination effect of single conductor fields (cross section of a coil).

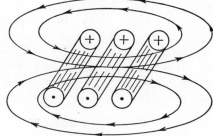

current flowing through it. Therefore, the unit of magnetizing force is called the ampere-turn, represented by NI, where N is the number of turns and I is the current in amperes. Another unit of magnetomotive force is the gilbert. This unit is directly related to ampere-turns by the formula $H = 0.4\pi NI$. In diagrams, graphs, and discussions, the letter H is frequently used to represent magnetomotive force.

Basic units of measurement. There are many magnetic measurements that can be made starting with the definition of a unit magnetic pole.

Each magnet has two poles, north and south. A simple compass needle has a north-seeking pole and a south-seeking pole. One pole never exists without the other; but for the sake of fundamental definition, imagine two identical poles, 1 cm apart, repelling each other with a force of 1 dyne (Fig. 5.4). A dyne is $\frac{1}{980}$ gram and represents the force which will accelerate a 1-gram mass at the rate of 1 cm/sec each second.

These poles are, by definition, unit poles and have one line of force acting between them. If stronger poles of five units each were used, there would be 25 lines between them since the force between two poles varies directly as the product of the strength of the poles and inversely as the square of the distance between them. If these two five-unit poles were moved twice as far apart (2 cm), the field would only be $\frac{25}{4}$ lines. Since these lines of force are known as maxwells, the field between the two poles

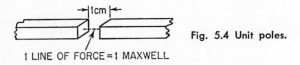

Fig. 5.4 Unit poles.

1 LINE OF FORCE = 1 MAXWELL

in the latter case is 6.25 maxwells. Maxwells, then, are the units of magnetic flux, often represented by the Greek letter ϕ (phi). This relationship can now be written in a general formula, as follows:

$$\phi = \frac{P \times P'}{d^2}$$

where ϕ = flux, maxwells
d = distance between poles
P and P' = strength of magnetic poles in terms of a unit pole

If a piece of glass is inserted between the poles, the strength of the magnetic field might be expected to be reduced; but glass, paper, and many other materials have no effect on the lines of force. A piece of iron or steel, however, does have considerable effect; the lines of force will converge in their attempt to pass through the metal, which offers less resistance than the surrounding air. Brass will have an effect opposite to that of iron, causing the lines of force to diverge around it. Other metals affect the magnetic field to a lesser degree. The ease with which magnetic flux is transmitted by a substance is measured by its reluctance. The unit of reluctance most frequently used is the rel.

It can now be seen that there is, in magnetism, a relationship very similar to Ohm's law in electricity:

$$\text{Resistance} = \frac{\text{electromotive force}}{\text{current}} \qquad \text{Reluctance} = \frac{\text{magnetomotive force}}{\text{magnetic flux}}$$

Just as resistance equals the electromotive force divided by the current, so reluctance equals magnetomotive force divided by magnetic flux.

It is frequently more useful to use the reciprocal of reluctance. This is termed permeability, represented by the Greek letter mu (μ). The permeability of a material is the ratio of the flux in the material to the flux that would exist in the same area if the material were replaced by a vacuum. For all practical purposes, most materials have a permeability value of $\mu = 1$; but there are some exceptions: for iron or steel, μ varies from 50 to 2,000; for Permalloy (nickel-iron), $\mu = 87,000$. Accurate magnetic measurements are much more difficult to make than electrical measurements; these figures will therefore vary widely depending on actual composition of the material and conditions under which the test for permeability is performed.

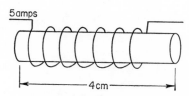

Fig. 5.5 Simple electromagnet.

Referring to Fig. 5.5, suppose 5 amp of current is passed through eight turns of wire wrapped around an iron bar which is 4 cm long. This will produce a magnetomotive force of 40 amp-turns, or 50.4 gilberts. Since the bar is 4 cm long, there are 12.6 gilberts/cm. An oersted is the number of gilberts per centimeter of length; so there are 12.6 oersteds present in the material. Suppose the bar were 2 cm² in cross-sectional area; there would then be a flux density of 6.3 oersteds for each square centimeter. The term gauss is a measure of this flux density, so there now exists 6.3 gauss in this bar. Flux density, with the gauss as the unit, is usually represented by B. This is an important quantity in the field of magnetic measurements.

To grasp what follows, it is of great importance to visualize clearly the meaning of gauss, maxwell, gilbert, and oersted and to remember the meanings of B, H, μ, and ϕ. These definitions should be reviewed thoroughly before continuing.

Magnetization and Hysteresis Curves

In terms of permeability, there are generally three types of magnetic materials: diamagnetic, paramagnetic, and ferromagnetic. Diamagnetic materials have a permeability of less than 1; paramagnetic substances have a permeability slightly greater than 1 and ferromagnetic materials, much greater than 1.

Most ferromagnetic substances consist of domains, which are small subelements which exhibit individual states of magnetic behavior. When most of these domains are aligned in the same direction, the ferromagnetic substance is said to be magnetized. Domains are filamentlike in form, with volumes of approximately 10^{-9} cm^3, and are of lengths varying from less than one up to several centimeters. In the crystal of a substance such as iron, there are many magnetic domains which can be arranged along directions of easy magnetization as shown in Fig. 5.6.

Direction of easy magnetization means that a given field applied along a certain axis provides optimum rearrangement of domains within a crystal. In the case of iron, a smaller field force is required along the 100 direction than along either the 110 or 111 direction. The characteristics of nickel are quite different, with the direction of easy magnetization being along the 110 axis.

Despite the fact that the domain is a small body, its change of state causes significant results. The alignment and reorientation of domains

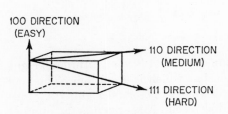

Fig. 5.6 Domain alignment directions in a crystal of iron.

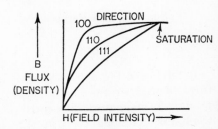

Fig. 5.7 Magnetization curves of an iron crystal.

brings about physical stress to the point that the physical dimensions of the material actually change. This change is called magnetostriction.

If the magnetization curve (Fig. 5.7) is greatly enlarged, it is apparent that the change in field density (B) caused by a change in field intensity (H) does not follow a smooth curve. Rather, the overall curve is a series of small steps, which are caused by the sudden switching of domains within the crystal. This is known as the *Barkhausen effect* and may be detected as audible clicks when a secondary loop is wound on a specimen and its output is amplified and applied to earphones or a loudspeaker.

Upon application of increasingly greater magnetic forces, the domains align in the direction of the applied force more swiftly and in greater numbers. When all domains are aligned in the easy direction of magnetization and this axis coincides with the applied magnetic field, then magnetic saturation has been reached (Fig. 5.7).

Although the equation for permeability is $\mu = B/H$, it can be seen on the magnetization curve that B does not usually follow in direct proportion as field intensity (H) is increased. Thus, it becomes clear that μ is not a fixed value but depends chiefly on the type of material and the magnitude of the magnetizing force.

The change from the demagnetized state to one of magnetic saturation is shown in Fig. 5.7. If the applied field is removed, magnetization falls to a point below saturation (see Fig. 5.8).

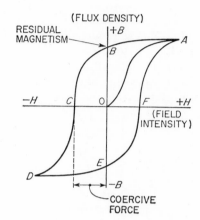

Fig. 5.8 Hysteresis loop for iron.

Hysteresis loops. When a piece of iron is magnetized, considerable energy is expended in lining up the magnetic domains in a definite direction. When these domains are aligned first in one direction and then in the other many times each second, such as, for example, in an a-c circuit, considerable energy is lost in the form of heat. This waste of energy is a hysteresis loss and is evidenced by heat given off by the metallic core or laminations in a-c motors and transformers. Hysteresis loss occurs because the magnetization of the core does not reverse in polarity at the same time that the magnetizing force does.

In order to plot a hysteresis loop, a magnetizing field is applied to a demagnetized piece of iron residing at point O (Fig. 5.8).

The applied field can be increased in intensity by increasing the current in the conductor surrounding the iron. After a considerable increase in the intensity, all the domains are aligned and the easy axis of magnetization coincides with the applied field, and magnetic saturation (point A) is reached. If the field intensity is returned to zero, the field density or magnetic flux state of the iron does not follow but decreases to point B. OB is the amount of residual magnetism in the substance. Residual magnetism is the magnetic flux exhibited by the specimen after an induction field is removed.

If the current in the conductor surrounding the magnetic material is reversed and the field intensity is increased to OC, the residual magnetism is reduced to zero by the coercive force. If the reverse current is increased still further to take the field intensity beyond OC, the direction of magnetic flux through the ferromagnetic material also reverses until the material reaches a state of saturation D, the opposite of point A. If the magnetizing force is once removed there is a return from saturation, point D, to the Y axis at point E. Again the curve does not return to zero flux density. OE indicates the reverse residual flux remaining after a $-H$ magnetizing force is removed. If a substantial $+H$ is once again applied, the residual flux is removed and the $+B$ flux is reinstated with a return to point A.

The cycle of forward and reverse magnetization produces a hysteresis loop. The area within the loop is a measure of power dissipated during the cycle. Reiterating, hysteresis is defined as the lag in changes of mag-

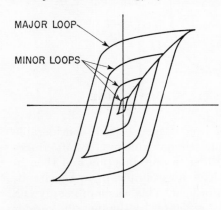

MAJOR LOOP

MINOR LOOPS

Fig. 5.9 Major and minor hysteresis loops.

netization behind the variations in magnetizing force. The greater the lag, the more power is consumed in reducing or reversing the state of magnetization. This lag is not a function of time. It must be emphasized that nowhere in the B-H curves is time considered.

Actually, there are several related hysteresis loops upon which a given piece of ferromagnetic material may operate (see Fig. 5.9). The outermost loop is known as the major loop. The magnetization forces needed to establish it are greater than those used in forming the minor loops contained within it. The ferrite cores used in the main memory of many computers operate on a minor loop.

Ferromagnetism and Information Storage

The choice of two states of residual flux in a ferromagnetic material readily affords application as a storage of intelligence. The binary system, widely used in computers, uses a combination of only 0s and 1s to represent any information, whether numerical or alphabetical. Consequently, for the binary system only a simple bistable device is needed. In Fig. 5.10 point B on the hysteresis loop could represent ONE, and point E could represent ZERO, or vice versa. Thus it is convenient, size and economy permitting, to use a ferromagnetic substance as a computer storage device.

However, the residual flux in either state is relatively small in comparison with the maximum flux experienced when the core is switched by a full-select pulse. Some material with the property of a much larger residual flux, almost as large as the flux present while a magnetizing force is being applied, is thus required for core storage. The ideal core would literally have a rectangular hysteresis loop. Since this ideal material is not practicable, a satisfactory substitute with a hysteresis loop approaching the qualities of a rectangular loop is used, as shown in Fig. 5.10.

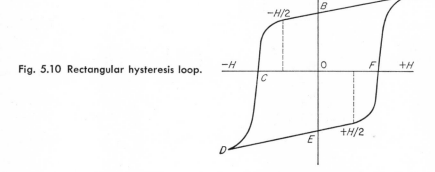

Fig. 5.10 Rectangular hysteresis loop.

In the hysteresis loop in Fig. 5.10, point B represents the residual flux in a typical ferrite core after the magnetizing force which brought saturation to A is removed. This is the ONE state of the core. Point E represents residual flux in the opposite direction when a reverse magnetizing force is applied to saturation point D and then removed. This is the ZERO state. The ferrite loop has a characteristic much more nearly square than that of the iron hysteresis loop, and it is considered a rectangular hysteresis loop.

There are two reasons for the selection of the ferrite core with its rectangular hysteresis loop in a coincident-current memory system. First, the two residual states of the cores contain much more flux than does iron under equal conditions. When information is stored in the cores and read out, a larger-amplitude output signal and, consequently, a higher signal-to-noise ratio result. Second, a rectangular type of hysteresis loop is preferred in that it can, by amplitude selection, discriminate against small switching currents through the conductors threading the core. A small

less susceptible to noise   *☐ hysteresis*

current in a conductor through a ferrite core might generate a magnetizing force $-H/2$, which is known as a half-select current (see Fig. 5.10). If the core is in the ONE state (point B), this is not enough current to switch the core to the ZERO state. Only the full field force $-H$, caused perhaps by the combined time-coincident effects of two such currents in conductors through the core, could switch the core to the ZERO state. It will be noted that at some point $-H/2$ and $-H$, a small additional magnetizing force suddenly switches the core from the ONE state to the ZERO state. However, the core receives only $-H/2$, $-H$, $+H/2$, $+H$, or no force at all.

The ferrite core and the bimag core. There are two types of ferromagnetic cores used currently in computers. The first type discussed is the ferrite core, a small toroid composed of brittle ceramic-type material,

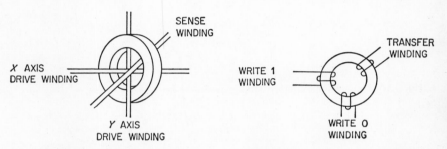

Fig. 5.11 Ferrite memory core.   Fig. 5.12 Bimag core and windings.

As the name implies, the ferrite core is composed of various iron compounds. The basic ingredient used is the iron ore hematite (Fe_2O_3), which may be blended with (1) FeO to form iron ferrite (Fe_3O_4), (2) NiO to form nickel ferrite ($NiFe_2O_4$), or (3) MnO to form manganese ferrite ($MnFe_2O_4$). Some of the materials used do not exhibit any worthwhile magnetic properties by themselves; but when they are mixed, bound, heated in a kiln and cooled, the resulting compound displays strong ferromagnetic characteristics. The percentage of mixture and chemical blending is a carefully controlled process of firing the oxides at a predetermined temperature to produce a material possessing the desired switching characteristics.

Because of the small physical sizes attainable (less than 0.1 in. OD), the ferrite cores find extensive usage in the large main memory of computers. At the present state of the art, it is possible to store thousands of words of information in a few cubic feet of space. The wires used to read or write information are threaded through the center of the core as shown in Fig. 5.11. Simultaneous currents on both the X- and the Y-axis winding will switch the core. The change of core states is detected by the sense winding.

The other type of core to be discussed is more frequently used in temporary storage and shifting applications. This is the metallic-tape type or bimag core, so termed because of its bimagnetic properties. The bimag cores are physically larger than the ferrite cores. To compose the bimag cores, various types of metallic substances are mixed chemically to form an alloy that is usually cast in thin sheets. These sheets are then cut into small strips and wound on a toroidal ceramic bobbin to become the well-known tape-wound core. Typical dimensions of the bimag core vary from $\frac{1}{4}$ to 1 in., depending on the application. Windings that insert and remove binary information are wrapped around the core as shown in Fig. 5.12.

Summary

In magnetism there is a formula parallel to Ohm's law in electricity:

$$\text{Reluctance} = \frac{\text{magnetomotive force}}{\text{magnetic flux}}$$

Permeability, represented by the Greek symbol μ (mu), is the reciprocal of reluctance. Magnetomotive force H is measured in ampere-turns or in gilberts. The gilbert is equal to $0.4\pi NI$, where NI is ampere-turns.

Magnetization curves and hysteresis loops are graphs of field density (B) plotted against field intensity (H). The magnetic characteristics of different materials plotted in graphs demonstrate that the permeability (μ) of all materials varies according to the applied field intensity (H).

Many modern computers use small ferromagnetic cores as bistable switching and storage elements which switch their magnetic state at the application of an electric pulse. These cores are composed of metallic alloys and compounds possessing almost square hysteresis loops that produce sudden switching, noise discrimination, and storage of a large amount of residual flux. The two core types in general use are known as bimag and ferrite. These cores will be discussed in detail in Chap. 15.

QUESTIONS

5.1 Describe the right-hand rule.
5.2 Define reluctance and permeability.
5.3 What are the three classifications of magnetic materials?
5.4 What is the term used to describe the strength of a magnet?
5.5 What is domain alignment? Barkhausen effect? Saturation?
5.6 What is meant by residual magnetism?
5.7 Describe coercive force.
5.8 What is hysteresis? Describe the loop plotted from a highly efficient laminated magnetic material. How does this contrast with solid magnetic material of low efficiency?
5.9 Does a ferrite memory core normally operate on a major or a minor loop? Why?
5.10 Give two reasons why a rectangular hysteresis loop is preferred for magnetic information storage devices.

Chapter 6

Introduction to Semiconductor Devices

Much of the rapid advancement that has been made in the development of digital computers is attributable to the similarly rapid advancements made in the development of semiconductor devices. The two semiconductor devices most widely used in computers are the diode and the transistor. The utilization of these two devices in computers has made it possible to develop compact computers that can perform more operations at a faster rate of speed and yet consume less power than the earlier vacuum-tube computers. Semiconductor devices may be used whenever their advantages (economy of operation, ruggedness, low power requirements, and small size) outweigh their disadvantages (temperature sensitivity, relative cost, and slightly higher noise figure) as compared with vacuum tubes. The increased utilization of diodes and transistors has made it essential that technicians acquire an understanding of their operation.

The oldest semiconductor device which is still in use is probably the point-contact diode. The use of silicon diodes in microwave equipments in World War II led to intensive research into the nature of semiconductor materials in order to improve the diodes. The outgrowth of this research was the development of the transistor. The first type developed was named the *point-contact* transistor. With its advent new theories concerning the action and operation of semiconductors were evolved. The junction transistor and the surface-barrier transistor were outgrowths of these new theories.

Transistor means *transfer resistor* and is a solid material capable of transferring an electric signal voltage from a low-resistance input to a high-resistance output. Hence, the transistor is a device capable of amplification.

The purpose of this chapter is to discuss some of the chemical and the electrical properties of semiconductor materials, to describe the physical and the electrical characteristics of the diode and the transistor, and to show how semiconductor diodes and transistors are used in practical circuits.

The chapter is divided into six parts:

I. Properties of Semiconductor Materials
II. The Junction Diode
III. The Junction Transistor
IV. Transistor-Amplifier Configurations
V. Graphical Method of Circuit Analysis
VI. Bias and Temperature-stabilizing Circuits

Each part is complete, with its own summary, and is presented in the order best suited for the comprehension of the subject matter.

PART I: PROPERTIES OF SEMICONDUCTOR MATERIALS

The striking difference between semiconductor devices and vacuum tubes is the manner in which current through the two devices is controlled. In a vacuum tube, the current flowing through the vacuum is controlled by varying the voltages on the electrodes placed in the vacuum. On the other hand, the semiconductor device is a solid material with no internal electrodes, and the current flowing through this solid material is controlled by impressing voltages at points or areas on the surface of the material. The properties of the semiconductor materials themselves make it possible to control the flow of current through the semiconductor device.

Definition of Semiconductor

Semiconductor materials are those that have resistance values too high to allow good conduction and yet too low to provide good insulation. The resistivity of a material is dependent upon the number of available current carriers in the material. The arrangement of the atoms in the semiconductor material makes it possible to control the quantity of current carriers and hence control the resistivity of the material. The ability to control the quantity of current carriers in the material made possible the development of the transistor. The two semiconductor materials used in the manufacture of diodes and transistors are silicon and germanium.

Atomic Structure

The solid-state physics and quantum mechanics involved in the complete study of semiconductor materials is complex and is of primary

interest only to the physicist and the metallurgist. It is unnecessary for
the engineer or the technician to delve as deeply into these subjects as
the physicist in order to understand the theory of transistors. A basic
qualitative explanation of atomic structure will suffice.

The number of electrons rotating in orbit around the nucleus of an
atom is different for each element. The number of rotating electrons is
called the *atomic number* of the element. There are as many free protons
(positive charge) in the nucleus as there are electrons (negative charge) in
orbit so that the net electric charge of an atom in its stable state is zero.
The rotating electrons are grouped together according to the distances of
their orbits away from the nucleus. A group of electrons whose orbits are
approximately the same distance from the nucleus is called a *shell*. There

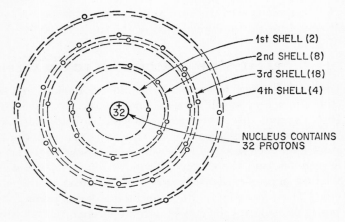

Fig. 6.1 Shell structure of a germanium atom.

is a maximum number of electrons that may be contained in any shell.
The first shell is composed of the group of electrons closest to the nucleus.
This shell contains no more than two electrons (see Fig. 6.1). The second
shell or group of electrons is farther away and contains a maximum of
eight electrons. The maximum number of electrons that can be contained
in any shell is $2n^2$, where n is the shell number. For example, in the third
shell the maximum number of electrons is $2 \times 3^2 = 2 \times 9 = 18$. This
formula holds true for every shell except the outer shell, whose peculiarity
is described in the following paragraph.

A diagram of the shell configuration of the germanium atom is shown
in Fig. 6.1. Note that the first, second, and third shells of this atom are
complete; however, the last shell contains only four electrons. By adding
the number of electrons in all four shells, the atomic number of 32 is
obtained for this atom. One very important fact to remember is that no

atom can have more than eight electrons in its outer shell. This is true even if it means that some of the inner shells do not contain their maximum number of electrons. Additional shells may exist, but the outer shell can never exceed eight electrons. Some of the shell arrangements are given in Table 6.1.

Arrangement of germanium and silicon in solid state. The atoms in most metals are arranged in a definite, orderly manner with respect to each other. This arrangement is the resultant of several types of forces

Table 6.1 Electron Shell Arrangements in Atoms

	Atomic number	Shell					
		1	2	3	4	5	6
Helium	2	2					
Neon	10	2	8				
Argon	18	2	8	8			
Krypton	36	2	8	18	8		
Xenon	54	2	8	18	18	8	
Radon	86	2	8	18	32	18	8
Lithium	3	2	1				
Sodium	11	2	8	1			
Potassium	19	2	8	8	1		
Cesium	55	2	8	18	18	8	1
Copper	29	2	8	18	1		
Silver	47	2	8	18	18	1	
Gold	79	2	8	18	32	18	1
Aluminum	13	2	8	3			
Gallium	31	2	8	18	3		
Arsenic	33	2	8	18	5		
Antimony	51	2	8	18	18	5	
Carbon	6	2	4				
Silicon	14	2	8	4			
Germanium	32	2	8	18	4		

that hold atoms in their respective positions. Here we are interested in the force that holds in place the atoms of crystalline structures, such as silicon or germanium.

The force that holds silicon and germanium atoms in place is termed a *covalent* force. Consider that when two atoms, each containing less than eight electrons in its outer shell, are brought together, each atom tries to complete its valence (outer) shell with eight electrons. The atoms of germanium or silicon, when combined in the natural state of a solid, are packed so closely that the valence-electron orbits of adjacent atoms interlink with each other. Each of the four valence-electron orbits interlinks with an electron orbit of an adjacent atom so that every atom appears to have eight electrons instead of four. As a result of this interlinking, every atom appears to have a complete valence shell. This action is illustrated in Fig. 6.2.

The interlinking of adjacent electrons creates an attracting force between atoms. This force is the covalent force previously mentioned and is sometimes referred to as a covalent bond. A diagram illustrating the position of the atoms of germanium with respect to each other is shown in Fig. 6.3.

Only the nuclei (represented by the +32) and the valence electrons (represented by the dots) of the atoms are shown in the diagram. The broken lines between each pair of atoms represent the covalent bonds which hold the atoms in their fixed positions. Silicon, with an atomic

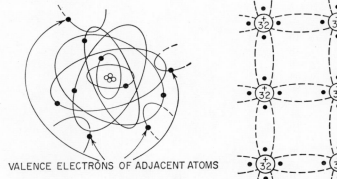

VALENCE ELECTRONS OF ADJACENT ATOMS

Fig. 6.2 Interlinking of valence electrons in solid material.

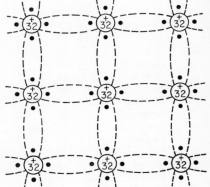

Fig. 6.3 A germanium crystal.

number of 14, has the same type of configuration. The particular crystal structure just described is called a crystal lattice.

Conduction Properties of Semiconductors

The valence electrons of atoms are the electrons that contribute to the conduction of current in a material. To be available as current carriers, the electrons must be broken away from the atom and be free to move through the material. If a sufficient amount of energy is applied to the material, some of the valence electrons will leave their valence shell. The energy used to move the valence electrons may be in the form of an electric field or light. The unit of measurement of this energy is the *electron-volt*. An electron-volt is the amount of energy an electron acquires when accelerated through a difference of potential of 1 volt. Approximately 0.75 ev is required to break a valence electron from an atom of germanium.

Hole carriers in semiconductors. So far, only the electron has been considered as a current carrier. However, some materials that have a crystal lattice structure have positive current carriers called holes. The nature of a hole may be understood by referring to Fig. 6.4.

Basically, a hole represents the absence of a valence electron in a crystal lattice structure. When an electron acquires sufficient energy to leave its parent atom, its orbit no longer interlinks with the orbit of a valence electron from a nearby atom as illustrated in Fig. 6.2. As a result, a "void" area is formed in the region where the two orbital paths interlinked. This void area is termed a hole. The hole is indicated by the circle in the crystal lattice structure shown in Fig. 6.4. The hole concept applies only to materials having a crystal lattice structure.

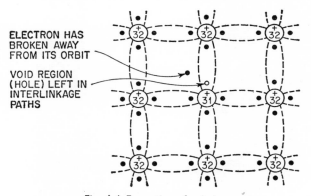

ELECTRON HAS
BROKEN AWAY
FROM ITS ORBIT

VOID REGION
(HOLE) LEFT IN
INTERLINKAGE
PATHS

Fig. 6.4 Formation of a hole.

To be a current carrier, the hole must be able to pass through the crystal material. Since the hole is not a physical object, it cannot physically move; however, a relative motion occurs. The relative motion of the hole results from the electron motion within the crystal material. When a void exists in the lattice structure as shown in Fig. 6.4, an electron from a nearby atom leaves its atom and goes into the orbit around the atom where an electron vacancy existed. However, when the attracted electron leaves its atom, another void is formed. Thus even though the original void has been "filled," another void has been formed. The hole has, in effect, moved from one atom to another; and it is apparent that the hole motion is in a direction opposite to that of the electrons. Hole motion is restricted to jumps from atom to atom, while electrons move more freely through the crystal lattice structure. For the sake of explanation, holes are assumed to be actual particles capable of motion and having a charge equal (but opposite) to that of the electron.

It has been shown that semiconductors have two types of current carriers, the negatively charged electrons and the positively charged holes, and that both carriers contribute to the conductivity of the material. In their pure form, semiconductors do not have enough available current carriers to produce the amount of conductivity required for diode or transistor operation. It is necessary to increase the conductivity of these materials, thereby lowering the resistivity of the material, by inserting additional carriers in the material. Either electrons or holes may be inserted. Both methods will now be discussed.

Insertion of electrons. More electron carriers can be inserted into a semiconductor material if an element which contains five valence electrons is added to the crystalline structure. As discussed previously, germanium atoms have four valence electrons and the path of each electron interlinks with the path of a neighbor atom's valence electron. If an element such as

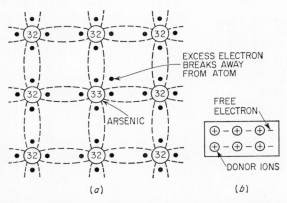

Fig. 6.5 N-type semiconductor. (a) Lattice structure. (b) Conventional diagram.

arsenic, which has five valence electrons, is inserted by chemical means into germanium, four of the arsenic's valence electrons will form bonds with four germanium atoms as shown in Fig. 6.5. However, the fifth electron will not enter into a bond. Heat energy at room temperature is more than sufficient to cause this extra electron to break away from its bond to the arsenic atom. An atom that provides an excess of electrons in a semiconductor material is known as a *donor* atom. A semiconductor material containing donor atoms is called a donor-type (or N-type) semiconductor.

Figure 6.5a illustrates the lattice structure with an arsenic atom added. Note that the excess electron does not enter into the lattice-structure bonds and is therefore relatively free.

The diagram in Fig. 6.5b, which is the conventional method of showing N-type semiconductor material, shows only the free electrons that have broken away from the donor atoms and the resulting *ions* (unneutralized atoms) that are formed. When an excess electron leaves a donor atom, the atom becomes positively charged because the total number of electrons is *one less* than the total number of protons. Hence, the donor atom becomes a positive ion. The electron carriers are indicated by the negative sign and the donor ions are indicated by the encircled positive signs in Fig. 6.5*b*. Even though the material has ions and free electrons, the net charge of the N-type material is zero because it has as many positive ions as it has free electrons.

Insertion of holes. Additional hole carriers may be inserted into a semiconductor material by chemically inserting into the crystal structure atoms of an element with only three valence electrons. Such an atom has only three electrons with which to enter into a covalent bond. Since four

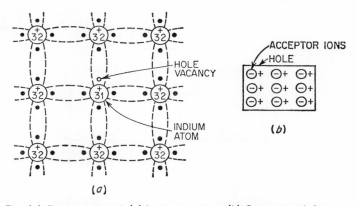

Fig. 6.6 P-type material. (a) Lattice structure. (b) Conventional diagram.

electrons are needed to complete the crystal lattice, the vacancy existing in the fourth bond is called a hole. Figure 6.6*a* illustrates this situation. The indium atom shown in Fig. 6.6*a*, when placed in a germanium crystal lattice structure, is called an *acceptor* atom since it may accept an electron from a nearby atom. The semiconductor material is called acceptor (or P-type) material. When the acceptor atom gains an electron, it becomes a negative ion. The conventional diagram is shown in Fig. 6.6*b*.

Current flow between P-type material and an external circuit. The convenience of treating the hole as a real particle has already been discussed; however, two other points must be made clear. First, the concept of a hole is limited only to semiconductor materials having a crystal lattice structure. Second, holes cannot flow in the external circuits in which semiconductor devices are used, but only within the semiconductor material. The manner in which the holes in a semiconductor may increase the current flow in the external circuit is illustrated in Fig. 6.7, which shows a battery connected to a piece of P-type semiconductor material.

Holes diffuse through a semiconductor toward the negative electrode. As a result, large numbers of acceptor atoms near the positive electrode become charged and form negative ions. The hole vacancies represented in Fig. 6.6a are filled by electrons. When a hole reaches the negative electrode, it attracts an electron from the battery terminal. To compensate for this electron, the positive battery terminal will attract one electron from a negative ion. Thus, for every electron that leaves the negative terminal of the battery one enters the positive terminal and a current flow caused exclusively by electrons flows through the external circuit. The magnitude of this current flow depends upon the number of hole carriers in the P-type semiconductor.

Ratio of donor or acceptor atoms in a semiconductor. In actual practice, the insertion of donor and acceptor atoms into a material (doping) is not so simple as it appears here. Much work and research have been done

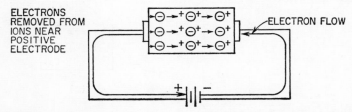

Fig. 6.7 Current flow between a P-type semiconductor and an external circuit.

to control closely the number of impurity atoms (donor or acceptor) inserted in the pure semiconductor material. A typical ratio of impurity atoms to germanium atoms in a semiconductor material is $1:(1 \times 10^7)$, that is, one impurity atom for every 10 million germanium atoms. Adding impurities in this ratio will decrease the resistivity of pure germanium from 60 to 4 ohms/cm^3 in the doped material.

Comparison of Silicon and Germanium

Both silicon and germanium are used in diode and transistor manufacture. Both materials can be made into N-type or P-type semiconductors. Silicon is less sensitive to temperature effects than germanium; consequently more energy is required to break an electron away from a silicon atom than from a germanium atom. The importance of this fact will be seen in the study of junction diodes, covered in Part II.

Summary of Part I

Before proceeding to Part II, The Junction Diode, the following points should be kept in mind:

1. Junction diodes and transistors are made of either germanium or silicon.
2. Germanium and silicon belong to a class of materials termed semiconductors.
3. Semiconductor materials have a value of resistivity too high to provide good conduction yet too low to provide good insulation.
4. The resistivity of semiconductor material may be decreased by increasing the number of available current carriers in the material.
5. Electron carriers may be added to semiconductor material by inserting an element, such as arsenic, with five valence electrons in its crystal lattice structure. One additional electron over and above that required by the covalent bonds is available. This electron is free to move.
6. Holes can be inserted in semiconductor material by inserting a material, such as indium, with three valence electrons in its crystal lattice structure. Only three electrons are available to enter covalent bonds, leaving a void, or hole.
7. Material that has been given electrons as current carriers is termed donor, or N-type, material; material that has been given holes as current carriers is termed acceptor, or P-type, material.
8. The hole concept applies only to materials held by covalent bonds and having a crystal lattice structure.

PART II: THE JUNCTION DIODE

If a section of N-type material is joined to a section of P-type material, the resulting combination is a PN junction diode. The rectifying ability of this type of diode is determined by the electrical action occurring at the junction between the two regions. The junction action will be discussed in the following paragraph.

Junction Voltage

It is known that when two dissimilar metals are joined together, a voltage difference exists at the junction between the two metals. Thermocouples and solar batteries make use of this principle. P-type material and N-type material are dissimilar metals; hence, when the two metals are combined, a voltage exists between them. The following text will show why this voltage exists across a PN junction and will describe the effects of this junction upon the current carriers in the P and N regions.

At this point it is well to review two characteristics of P- and N-type materials. One characteristic is the ionization process and the other is the net charge of the materials.

The donor atoms in the N material become positive ions when electrons break away from these atoms. In the P material, the acceptor atoms become negative ions when electrons from nearby donor atoms combine with the holes of acceptor atoms.

Both materials are electrically neutral before they are joined, as illustrated in Fig. 6.8. In the N material the net negative charge of the free electrons in motion is balanced by the net positive charge of the stationary donor ions. The net positive charge of the holes in motion in the

P material is balanced by the net negative charge of the stationary acceptor ions.

When the two materials are joined, it would appear that all the electrons and holes would cross the junction and a complete recombination would occur. This situation does not occur because as soon as the two materials are joined, electrons nearest the junction cross over and combine with holes in the P region. When this occurs, the two materials are no longer neutral. As electrons from the N region cross over and combine with holes in the P region, the number of holes is reduced. Because of this, there are more negative ions than there are holes in the P region and the net charge of the P region becomes negative. The N region becomes positively charged since there are more positive ions than there are electrons. This action causes an electric field to exist between the two oppositely charged regions. This field is illustrated in Fig. 6.9.

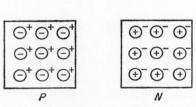

Fig. 6.8 P and N material before combination.

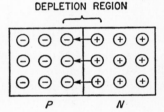

Fig. 6.9 Electric field at PN junction.

The electric field is shown existing between the positive ions nearest the junction in the N region and the negative ions nearest the junction in the P region. The conventionally chosen direction of an electric field is from positive to negative. When the magnitude of the electric field shown in Fig. 6.9 becomes sufficiently large, no more holes are able to cross into the N region and no more electrons are able to cross into the P region. The field repels carriers (holes and electrons) away from the junction so that the ions near the junction cannot be neutralized. The electric field extends a short distance into both regions where these ions exist. Since no carriers are present in the region under the influence of the electric field, the region is termed the *depletion region*.

The voltage existing at the junction is the *potential barrier* since carriers are prevented from crossing the junction. The magnitude of the potential barrier is about 0.03 volt.

If conduction is to occur through the PN junction diode, an external voltage must be applied across the diode to reduce the potential barrier. An external voltage of one polarity will decrease the junction barrier while a voltage of the opposite polarity will increase the junction barrier and prevent the carriers from crossing the junction. The former voltage is *forward bias* and the latter voltage is *reverse bias.*

Forward Bias

Figure 6.10 shows a diode biased in the forward direction. The correct connection for forward bias can be remembered if we consider that the positive terminal repels holes in the P region toward the junction and the negative terminal repels electrons in the N region toward the junction. A more detailed discussion will show how forward bias reduces the potential barrier.

A diode is composed of either germanium or silicon and has a high resistance value. An external voltage is impressed across the diode with

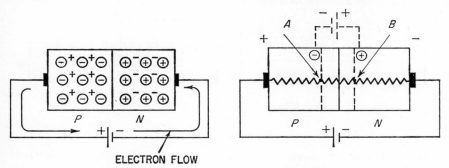

ELECTRON FLOW

Fig. 6.10 Forward bias.   Fig. 6.11 Diode resistance.

the polarities indicated in Fig. 6.11. The important consideration is the resistance at the junction region between the points *A* and *B*. The potential barrier may be indicated by a battery drawn across the junction. Because of the polarity of the applied voltage, point *A* is more positive than point *B*. The voltage drop between these two points opposes the potential barrier; hence the net junction potential is reduced. It would appear that the potential barrier would be completely eliminated, but this is not true. As the barrier is reduced, carriers are able to cross the junction and the current through the diode increases. As the current increases, a greater voltage is dropped across the P region and the N region, while the remaining voltage is dropped across the junction resistance. Actually, as the current increases the junction resistance decreases. The voltage drop across this decreasing resistance is never sufficient to completely overcome the potential barrier.

It should be remembered that holes do not flow through the external circuit. An equilibrium exists where, for every electron-hole recombination, a positive ion from the N region attracts an electron from the negative terminal. For every electron that leaves the negative terminal an electron from a negative ion in the P region is attracted to the positive terminal. Hence, current in the external circuit is due strictly to electron flow.

Reverse Bias

If the external battery is applied to a diode in a direction shown in Fig. 6.12, the potential at *A* is more negative than the potential at *B*. The voltage drop across the junction resistance adds to the barrier voltage. The carriers are repelled even further away from the junction; hence, no forward current flows.

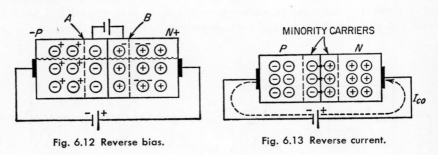

Fig. 6.12 Reverse bias.   Fig. 6.13 Reverse current.

Reverse Current

Even though the diode is reverse-biased, a small amount of current flows in the reverse direction. This current is caused by *minority carriers*. Minority carriers are the small number of electrons that exist in the P region and the small number of holes that exist in the N region. These minority carriers are present because heat energy breaks a few covalent bonds in both regions, thereby freeing some electrons. In the P region, the freed electrons are the minority carriers. In the N region, the holes that are left in the germanium or silicon atoms are the minority carriers.

The direction of the potential barrier is such that the minority carriers may cross the junction. Since reverse bias aids the potential barrier, the minority carriers are pulled across the junction and a reverse current flows as shown in Fig. 6.13.

Minority-carrier current is called leakage current or cutoff current. The notation I_{co} is used to express this current. The current is dependent upon temperature, and its value doubles for every 10°C increase in temperature.

Diode Breakdown

If a large number of covalent bonds are broken, the number of minority carriers may become greater than the majority carriers, so that the diode will conduct equally well in both directions. The energy that breaks these bonds may also be caused by a reverse voltage impressed across the diode. If the reverse voltage is large enough, an almost complete break-down of covalent bonds will occur.

Diode Curve

A characteristic curve of the junction diode is shown in Fig. 6.14. The voltage E_f is the forward bias voltage. As the magnitude of the forward bias increases, the forward current increases until saturation occurs. When the diode is reverse-biased by the voltage E_r, only the reverse current flows. Observe that the reverse current remains fairly constant until

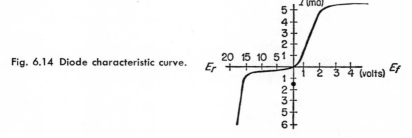

Fig. 6.14 Diode characteristic curve.

the reverse voltage is increased to a point where the current suddenly increases. At this point the reverse voltage breaks practically all the covalent bonds in the diode. The heat generated as a result of the break-down will ruin a normal diode.

Diode Symbol and Rectifying Action

The diode symbol is shown in Fig. 6.15. The direction of the arrow of the diode symbol is in the direction of hole movement through the diode when the diode is biased in the forward direction. The arrow represents the anode and the line represents the cathode.

Fig. 6.15 Rectifying action of a diode.

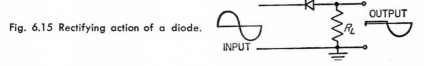

A positive voltage with respect to ground will reverse-bias the diode and only the leakage current will appear at the output. The negative voltage alternation will forward-bias the diode and the negative alternation will appear across the output. A small fraction of the input voltage is dropped across the diode during the negative alternation. For a given current, the voltage drop across a silicon diode is greater than the drop across a germanium diode.

Zener Diodes

The reverse-breakdown characteristics of a diode have been exploited to make a device capable of voltage regulation in much the same manner as a gas regulating tube. The voltage at which breakdown occurs is called the zener voltage. When breakdown occurs, the reverse current increases to a relatively large value and is independent of any further increase in reverse voltage. This means that over a wide range of current, the voltage across a diode will remain constant when operated at the zener point. If the diode does not become damaged by heat dissipation, the reverse current will decrease to its low value when the reverse voltage is decreased from its zener point. It is possible to manufacture diodes whose zener points are fairly sharp and have reference voltages that range from a few to several hundred volts. The diodes are physically constructed so that within the specified range of current operation they will not become damaged by heat. A zener characteristic curve is shown in Fig. 6.16.

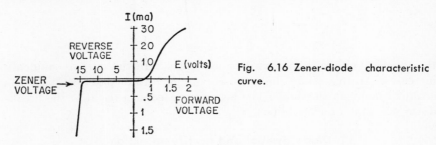

Fig. 6.16 Zener-diode characteristic curve.

Summary of Part II

Before proceeding to Part III, The Junction Transistor, the following points should be kept in mind:

1. A junction diode consists of a section of P-type material combined with a section of N-type material.
   NOTE: Two separate sections of material are not physically joined together. Actually the diode is made of a single crystal in which one section is P material and the other section is N material. The formation of PN junctions will be discussed in the next section.
2. The rectifying action of the junction is due to the potential difference existing between the P and N materials when they are combined.
3. The potential difference, or barrier, prevents the majority carriers of both regions from crossing the junction.
4. An external voltage may be applied to overcome the effect of the potential barrier. This external voltage is the *forward bias*.
5. An external voltage that increases the effect of the potential barrier is termed *reverse bias*.
6. A leakage current I_{co} flows through the diode circuit because of the minority carriers present in the P and N regions (reverse-bias conditions).

7. If the reverse voltage is too large, diode breakdown will occur.
8. The point at which reverse-voltage breakdown occurs is called the zener point.
9. Diodes may be constructed to operate at the zener point without damage and hence be used as voltage reference elements.

PART III: THE JUNCTION TRANSISTOR

The junction transistor is an extension of the junction diode. Its electrical action also depends upon the junction between two regions. Unlike the diode, the transistor is capable of amplification by transferring a signal from a low input impedance to a high output impedance.

Construction

There are two basic types of transistors: NPN and PNP units. The NPN junction transistor is formed by placing a narrow strip of P material between two relatively wide sections of N-type material. The PNP junction is formed by placing a narrow strip of N material between two relatively wide sections of P material. Both units are illustrated in Fig. 6.17.

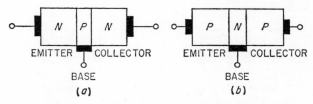

Fig. 6.17 Junction transistors. (a) NPN transistor. (b) PNP transistor.

Each of the three regions has metal contacts which connect the sections to the external circuit. The three sections are known respectively as the emitter, base, and collector. The emitter is analogous to the cathode of a vacuum tube, the base is analogous to the grid, and the collector is analogous to the plate. The emitter-base junction is commonly referred to as the emitter junction and the collector-base junction is commonly referred to as the collector junction. The emitter and the collector cannot be interchanged because the collector resistance is higher than the emitter resistance. The collector resistance is made higher by using a lower ratio of doping in the collector region. The collector area is generally made larger than the emitter area to collect most of the diffusing carriers.

Bias Requirements

In order to amplify the power of an electric signal, the transistor must allow current to flow through it at a controlled rate. The junction regions are still of primary consideration. The junction bias requirements of both types of transistors will now be discussed.

NPN-Transistor Biasing

The diagram of the NPN transistor showing the direction of the potential barriers is given in Fig. 6.18. Note that the potential barriers at the emitter and collector junctions are in opposite directions.

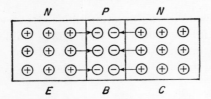

Fig. 6.18 Direction of potential barriers in junction transistors.

Since in an NPN transistor the majority carriers of the emitter are electrons, the problem is to effect an electron flow from the emitter, through the base and collector regions and back, through the external circuit, to the emitter. To accomplish this, the emitter junction must be biased in the *forward* direction and the collector junction must be biased in the *reverse* direction.

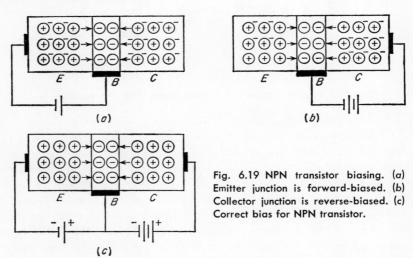

Fig. 6.19 NPN transistor biasing. (a) Emitter junction is forward-biased. (b) Collector junction is reverse-biased. (c) Correct bias for NPN transistor.

Figure 6.19a shows the emitter junction biased in the forward direction. Forward bias overcomes the potential barrier and allows electrons from the emitter to cross over into the base region. The problem now is to draw these electrons from the base region into the collector region and out through the external circuit. After the electrons cross the emitter junction they drift toward the collector junction. The potential barrier at the collector junction is in a direction that will allow electrons to cross the junction (electrons flow against the arrow). The collector junction is *reverse-biased* so that it *aids* the potential barrier at the junction (Fig. 6.19*b*).

When the electrons cross from the emitter into the base region, some electron-hole recombinations occur. However, the base is made narrow with respect to the emitter and collector so that more electrons enter the base region than there are holes in the base region. About 95 per cent of the electrons from the emitter diffuse through the base region into the collector region.

Current Relationship

When the total emitter and collector current are considered, two more currents must be taken into account. These are the *base recombination current* and the *collector cutoff current*. The base recombination current is caused by electron-hole recombinations in the base region. The reader may recall from diode theory that an electron from the battery compensates for every electron-hole recombination. This recombination current flows between the emitter and base and is designated I_r in Fig. 6.20.

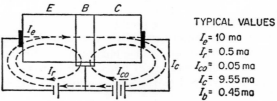

Fig. 6.20 Transistor static currents (electron flow).

TYPICAL VALUES
I_e = 10 ma
I_r = 0.5 ma
I_{co} = 0.05 ma
I_c = 9.55 ma
I_b = 0.45 ma

Aside from the emitter current, a cutoff current I_{co} flows between the collector and base circuit since the collector junction is biased in the reverse direction. Note that the cutoff current will add to the current in the collector circuit and subtract from the recombination current in the base circuit. The collector current I_c may be expressed as

1. $I_c = I_e - I_r + I_{co}$

The base current is

2. $I_b = I_r - I_{co}$

From equation (1), the emitter current is

3. $I_e = I_c + I_r - I_{co}$

Magnitude of Bias Voltages

The forward-bias voltage applied to the emitter junction is usually a few tenths of a volt and seldom exceeds 1 volt. The reverse collector voltage ranges from 1 to 40 volts or more. A value between 5 and 10 volts, however, can be considered average. There is a limit to the magnitude of the reverse collector voltage that may be applied to the transistor. Since the collector junction is reverse-biased, the depletion area at the junction is increased. If the reverse voltage is too large consequently, the depletion will extend the width of the base region; the emitter and collector will become ohmically connected and transistor action will be lost. This action is termed *punch-through*. Reverse voltage may also break covalent bonds and cause thermal runaway.

Control of Transistor Current

The amount of current that flows through a transistor is more dependent upon the bias between the emitter and base than upon the collector supply voltage. The amount of emitter current, and consequently the collector current, is controlled by varying the forward-bias voltage. The action is similar to the control of plate current in a vacuum tube by the control of the grid voltage.

PNP Transistor Bias Requirements

Since the emitter's majority carriers are holes, the holes must traverse the emitter junction, diffuse through the base region, traverse the collector junction, and cause current flow through the collector and emitter batteries that will inject holes back in the emitter. (Remember that hole flow is restricted to the semiconductor material.)

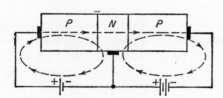

Fig. 6.21 Biasing arrangements for PNP transistor.

To accomplish this, the emitter junction must be biased in the forward direction and the collector junction must be biased in the reverse direction as shown in Fig. 6.21.

The arrows in Fig. 6.21 point in the direction of *conventional current flow*. This is a convenient method of describing the circuit operation of the PNP transistor. To avoid confusion, conventional current will be used hereafter to describe both NPN and PNP units. The current relationship in the PNP transistor is the same as in the NPN transistor. Note that the polarities of the bias batteries are exactly the opposite of the NPN unit. However, in both cases the emitter junction is forward-biased and the collector junction is reverse-biased.

Transistor Symbols

The transistor may be illustrated symbolically by three leads, appropriately arranged, to depict the emitter, base, and collector regions. An arrow is placed on the emitter head to indicate the direction of hole flow when the emitter junction is biased in the forward direction. No arrow is placed on the collector terminal.

In Fig. 6.22a the arrow is shown pointing into the base. This is the direction in which holes will flow in a PNP transistor when the emitter junction is biased in the forward direction. Therefore, Fig. 6.22a represents a PNP transistor. Figure 6.22b shows that holes flow away from the base region when forward emitter bias is applied. This describes the

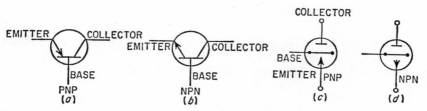

Fig. 6.22 Transistor symbols.

NPN-type transistor. The symbols in Fig. 6.22c and d are used to represent junction transistors. The symbols in Fig. 6.22a and b represent either junction or point-contact types.

Formation of PN Junctions

The physical construction of the junction diode and transistor are not so simple as the diagrams indicate. The process of obtaining chemically pure germanium or silicon, doping the material to form P or N regions, and combining the two regions to form a junction is very involved. Books have been written discussing this subject in great detail. A very elementary description of junction formation will be given here in order to acquaint the reader with some of the processes involved.

Diffusion process. PNP transistors are usually made by a diffusion or alloy process. A piece of P-forming material such as indium is placed approximately in the center of a piece of lightly doped N-type germanium about 0.05 in. square and 0.01 in. thick. The entire assembly is heated to a temperature below the melting point of germanium but above the melting point of indium. The melted indium diffuses into the slab of N-type germanium. The process is then repeated on the other side of the N germanium slab.

The region where the indium atoms diffuse into the N-type germanium becomes P-type germanium. The number of indium atoms that diffuse into the lightly doped N region greatly outnumber the relatively small number of donor atoms. The N germanium is now sandwiched by two sections of P germanium. Figure 6.23a illustrates the three sections that result from this diffusion process and Fig. 6.23b illustrates the completed transistor.

The temperature and the purity of the material can be carefully controlled; however, the junctions of the PN regions are neither even nor parallel. This unevenness results in a variable depletion width along the junction and a variable base width. Electrons leaving the emitter take unequal lengths of time getting across the junctions. There are also regions at the junction where irregular arrangements of donor and acceptor ions form undesired potential hills that impede the flow of holes

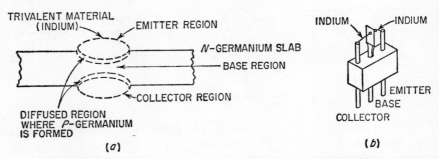

Fig. 6.23 Transistor assembly. (a) Formation of PNP junctions. (b) Completed transistor.

and electrons through the materials. These irregularities, or trapping centers, contribute much of the noise found in transistors. NPN transistors are also made by this process.

Grown-junction method of construction. The grown-junction method is also widely used in forming PN junctions. The following steps, along with the diagram of Fig. 6.24, describe the formation of an NPN junction transistor by this process:

1. Pure germanium is melted in a vat as shown in Fig. 6.24.
2. A small bit of N-forming material is poured into the melted germanium.
3. The N-forming material diffuses throughout the melted germanium, forming N-type germanium.
4. A single germanium crystal (termed the seed) is attached to the end of a rod and dipped into the melted germanium. When the rod is withdrawn, the melted N-type germanium that adheres to the seed crystallizes; the result is an N germanium crystal.

5. After a closely controlled period of time, a P-forming material such as indium is added to the melted germanium. The melted N-type germanium will change to P germanium. The crystal form being pulled from the vat changes from N to P germanium.
6. After another controlled interval, an N-type material is added to the melted germanium, changing the P germanium back to N germanium. The pulled crystal now becomes N-type germanium.
7. After the crystal has been pulled from the melted germanium, it is cut into slabs at right angles to its long axis. Each slab is an NPN unit about the size of a half-dollar and about one-fourth as thick. The slab is then diced into sizes suitable for a transistor. Since the P base region is relatively narrow, a considerable amount of skill is required to locate this region and attach a lead wire to the base.

During the conversion from N to P material and from P to N material the meld goes through a zero hole–electron-pair stage where, at one

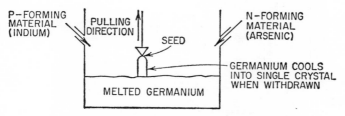

Fig. 6.24 Grown-junction process.

instant, the net number of current carriers is zero. This is due to the cancellation effect between donor and acceptor ions.

Both NPN and PNP units have been made by this process. The characteristics of transistors developed by this method are similar to those of the diffused-junction type.

Surface-barrier transistor. The surface-barrier transistor is constructed somewhat differently from the normal junction-type transistor. However, its electrical action is the same as that of the junction-type transistor.

The operation of the surface-barrier transistor is based upon the physical properties that exist at the surface of germanium or silicon material. At the extreme surface, there are "leftover" covalent bonds. These leftover bonds cause the electrical properties that exist at the surface of the material to be different from the properties exhibited in the interior of the material. If it is N-type material, free electrons from the interior will drift to the surface of the material. The accumulation of electrons at the surface will create a negative charge that will repel any further movement of electrons to the surface. An electric field will exist between the surface and the interior of the material. The area in which this field exists is the surface-barrier region. If electrodes are attached to the N material and a positive voltage is applied, electrons will be attracted from the interior and the width of the barrier region will be reduced.

For transistor action, three distinct regions must be formed: the emitter, base, and collector. Directly under the surfaces of the material a large number of holes are formed as a result of electrons leaving their parent atoms and drifting toward the surface. The breaking of these bonds is due primarily to heat energy. If electrodes are attached to the material as shown in Fig. 6.25a and forward and reverse biases are impressed, holes will leave the area under the emitter electrode, drift through the N material, and be collected by the collector electrode. The

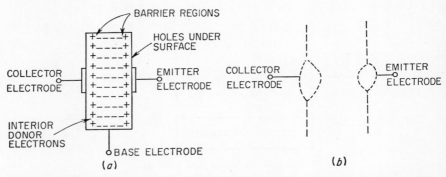

Fig. 6.25 Surface-barrier transistor. (a) Electrical properties. (b) Base narrowed by etching process.

emitter and collector regions are the regions just under the surface and are where holes are formed.

The base region is reduced to the desired width by an etching process as illustrated in Fig. 6.25b. Both sides of the N material are sprayed with a steady stream of electrolyte (an acid solution containing indium and capable of conducting electricity). The electrolyte acts as an etch and reduces the width of the N region. When the desired width is obtained, the polarity of the current through the electrolyte is reversed and a metal indium electrode is formed. By using the etching process the width of the base region can be closely controlled and made very narrow. The frequency response of a transistor is dependent, to a large extent, upon the width of the base region since a transient time is involved. Oscillators that operate beyond 70 Mc have been constructed using surface-barrier transistors. Surface-barrier transistors are also used in high-speed switching circuits.

Summary of Part III

Before proceeding to Part IV, Transistor-Amplifier Configurations, the following points should be reviewed:

1. There are two basic types of junction transistors: the NPN type and the PNP type. The three regions of the transistor are the emitter, the base, and the collector.
2. The base region is made narrower than the emitter and collector regions so that most of the emitter's carriers will diffuse through the base region without recombining.
3. The emitter and collector cannot be interchanged unless the transistor is specifically designed for this purpose.
4. For correct transistor action the emitter junction must be forward-biased and the collector junction must be reverse-biased.
5. The magnitude of the collector voltage is larger than the emitter-base voltage. However, the relatively small forward-bias voltage controls the amount of current flow through the device.
6. A base recombination current occurs because of recombination of some of the emitter's carriers with carriers in the base region.
7. A leakage current flows through the base and collector regions. This current adds to that in the collector circuit and subtracts from the recombination current in the base-emitter circuit.

PART IV: TRANSISTOR-AMPLIFIER CONFIGURATIONS

The transistor is capable of amplifying the power of an electric signal. It is, therefore, an active circuit element. By causing a small current variation in the input circuit, a greater variation will be effected in the output circuit.

There are three basic types of amplifier configurations: the common-base, the common-emitter, and the common-collector. These three types will be discussed separately.

Common-base Configuration

The common-base configuration has the base lead common to both the input and the output circuit. The input is applied between the emitter and base and the output is taken between the collector and base, as illustrated in Fig. 6.26.

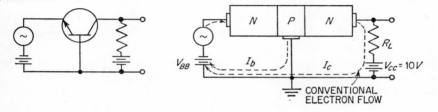

Fig. 6.26 NPN common-base amplifier.

Without application of an input signal to the NPN unit, conventional current flow is in the direction of the arrow. The quiescent collector voltage is then $V_{cc} - E_{R_L}$. Upon application of a positive signal voltage to the input, the emitter forward bias decreases and the emitter current decreases, causing a corresponding decrease in collector current. The voltage drop across R_L decreases and consequently the output voltage increases. The negative alternation of the input signal increases the emitter forward bias, causing the emitter current and consequently the collector current to increase. The increasing collector current causes the voltage drop across R_L to increase; hence the output voltage decreases. The output voltage of the common-base configuration is in phase with the input. The circuit is analogous to a vacuum-tube grounded-grid amplifier.

Current amplification factor.   As mentioned previously, not all of the emitter current reaches the collector since a portion of the emitter current enters the base as recombination current. In the common base configuration, the ratio of the amount of emitter current that reaches the collector to the total emitter current is the *current amplification factor*, expressed by the Greek letter alpha (α). Under static conditions with no input signal applied, $\alpha_o = I_c/I_{co} + I_e$. The quantity I_{co} must be eliminated since it is not a part of the emitter current. Under dynamic conditions, $\alpha = \Delta I_c/\Delta I_e$.

Although most of the total emitter current reaches the collector, the value of α never exceeds 1. Typical values of α range from 0.94 to 0.98. It should be noted that α is a parameter of the transistor and is independent of any associated circuitry. It must also be remembered that the expression α is valid for the common-base configuration only. I_c is the output current and I_e is the input current to the common-base configuration.

Resistance gain.   The common-base configuration has a very high resistance gain. Since the emitter junction is biased in the forward direction, the input resistance is low, usually on the order of 100 ohms. The collector resistance is high, possibly on the order of 1 megohm. The high resistance in the collector circuit is not due to the collector junction resistance or the resistivity of the N material. Initially the collector resistance is very low since electrons are easily drawn across the collector junction. However, in order for this resistance to keep a constant low value, the collector current must increase with a corresponding increase in collector voltage. As the collector voltage is increased, there is an insufficient number of electrons as majority carriers to cause a sufficient increase in collector current. The collector current will remain at a fairly constant low value as the collector voltage increases. The collector resistance will assume a high value.

The slope of the V_{cc}–I_c curve is the output resistance. The sharp increase at A in Fig. 6.27 indicates that there is no appreciable increase in collector current as the collector voltage continues to rise. The resistance gain, R_{out}/R_{in} in the common-base configuration is very high.

Voltage and power gain. Although the common base has a current gain of less than unity, the resistance gain is very high; thus, the common-base circuit has a high voltage gain. This gain can be as high as 1,000.

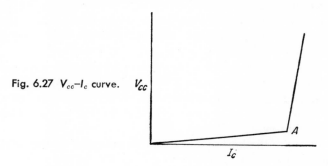

Fig. 6.27 V_{cc}–I_c curve.

The main use of the common-base configuration is as a voltage amplifier. The common-base circuit has a power gain of about the same magnitude as the voltage gain. However, the power gain is not so high as that of the common-emitter circuit. Therefore, the common-base configuration is rarely used as a power amplifier.

Common-emitter Configuration

When the transistor is connected in the common-emitter configuration, the emitter is common to the input and output circuits as shown in Fig. 6.28.

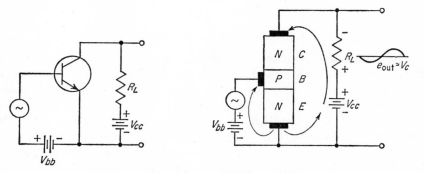

Fig. 6.28 NPN common-emitter amplifier.

The arrows show the direction of conventional current flow through the circuit. The output voltage equals $V_{cc} - E_{RL}$. When a positive-going signal is applied to the base, the input forward bias is increased and the emitter current is increased. The emitter current causes a corresponding increase in collector current which consequently increases the voltage drop across R_L, thereby decreasing the output voltage. The output voltage is then out of phase with the input voltage. The circuit is analogous to a vacuum-tube grounded-cathode circuit.

Current amplification factor. The Greek letter beta (β) expresses the current amplification factor of the transistor when the transistor is placed in the common-emitter configuration. Under static conditions, $\beta_o = I_c/I_b$. Under dynamic conditions, $\beta = \Delta I_c/\Delta I_b$.

Since the collector current is much larger than the base current, the value of β is always greater than 1. Typical values range between 15 and 50 although some transistors have a value of β as high as 100.

β is also a transistor parameter that is measured independently of any associated circuitry.

Means of obtaining both β and α will be discussed in the section covering characteristic curves.

Resistance gain. The common-emitter circuit has a low input resistance compared with its output resistance. Its input resistance averages about 500 ohms and its output resistance averages about 50,000 ohms.

Voltage and power gain. The common-emitter circuit has a current gain greater than 1, but the resistance gain is less than that of the common-base circuit. The voltage gain is high but somewhat less than that of the common-base circuit.

Since the common-emitter circuit has a current and voltage gain, it has the highest power gain of the three amplifier configurations. The common-emitter is the most widely used amplifier configuration because of its power-amplifying capabilities.

Common-collector Configuration

The common-collector amplifier circuit uses the collector terminal as the common terminal for an a-c signal. Even though the proper biases are still present at the emitter and collector junctions, the a-c input is applied between the base and collector terminals and the output is taken from between the emitter and collector terminals as illustrated in Fig. 6.29. The output voltage is $I_e R_L$.

During the positive alternation of the input signal, the emitter forward bias increases, the emitter current increases, and the voltage across R_L increases. Thus, the output voltage is in phase with the input.

The common-collector circuit is analogous to the vacuum-tube cathode-follower circuit. The circuit is an emitter-follower circuit. Like its vacuum-tube counterpart, the common collector circuit has a high input impedance and a low output impedance. The voltage gain is less than 1.

Current gain. The current gain in the common-collector circuit is the ratio of emitter current to base current. This is expressed as $\Delta I_e / \Delta I_b$. Since

1. $\beta = \dfrac{\Delta I_c}{\Delta I_b}$

and $\Delta I_e = \Delta I_c + \Delta I_b$, we can write this ratio as

2. $\dfrac{\Delta I_e}{\Delta I_b} = \dfrac{\Delta I_c + \Delta I_b}{\Delta I_b} = \dfrac{\Delta I_c}{\Delta I_b} + \dfrac{\Delta I_b}{\Delta I_b}$

Since $\Delta I_c / \Delta I_b$ is β, the current gain for the common-collector circuit can be expressed from (2) as $\beta + 1$. The common-collector circuit then has the highest current gain.

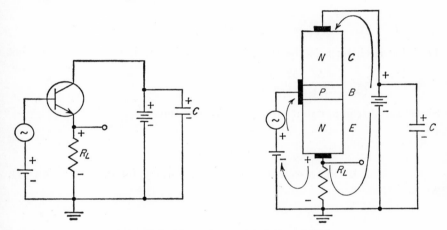

Fig. 6.29 NPN common-collector amplifier.

Comparison of Amplifier Configurations

Table 6.2 gives typical values of input and output resistance and current, voltage, and power gains for the three configurations.

Note that for all three configurations the emitter junction is biased in the forward direction and the collector junction is biased in the reverse direction.

Relation between α and β

It is often convenient to express α in terms of β and vice versa. Let us first express α in terms of β.

The current gain α has been expressed as

1. $\alpha = \dfrac{\Delta I_c}{\Delta I_e}$

Table 6.2 Comparison of Amplifier Configurations

Quantity	Common base	Common emitter	Common collector
Input resistance (ohms)	100	600	40,000
Output resistance (ohms)	500,000	50,000	600
Voltage gain	800	400	0.94
Current gain	0.97	32	33
Power gain	776	12,800	31

Since $I_e = I_b + I_c$,

2. $\dfrac{\Delta I_c}{\Delta I_e} = \dfrac{\Delta I_c}{\Delta I_c + \Delta I_b}$

Dividing each term of the right hand side of equation (2) by ΔI_b, we get

3. $\dfrac{\Delta I_c}{\Delta I_e} = \dfrac{\Delta I_c/\Delta I_b}{(\Delta I_c/\Delta I_b) + (\Delta I_b/\Delta I_b)}$

Since $\Delta I_c/\Delta I_b$ is β, equation (3) can be written as

4. $\alpha = \dfrac{\beta}{\beta + 1}$

β can also be expressed in terms of α. Solving for β in equation (4), we find that

$$\alpha = \frac{\beta}{\beta + 1}$$
$$\beta = \alpha(\beta + 1)$$
$$\beta = \alpha\beta + \alpha$$
$$\beta - \alpha\beta = \alpha$$
$$\beta(1 - \alpha) = \alpha$$

5. $\beta = \dfrac{\alpha}{1 - \alpha}$

Frequency Response

An important characteristic of the transistor is its frequency response. This frequency response is expressed as the α cutoff frequency ($f\alpha_{co}$). With a reference frequency (such as 1,000 cps) the frequency is increased until the value of α drops to 0.707 of its value at the reference frequency. This frequency is then $f\alpha_{co}$. The two commonly used reference frequencies are 270 and 1,000 cps. Figure 6.30 shows a typical frequency curve and the α cutoff point.

The frequency response of a transistor in the common-emitter configuration is poor compared with the frequency response of a transistor in the common-base configuration. This can be shown by observing the corresponding decrease in β as α decreases. Suppose, for example, that α at the reference frequency is 0.95; then, from equation (5),

$$\beta = \frac{\alpha}{1 - \alpha} = \frac{0.95}{1 - 0.95} = 19$$

If α were to decrease by 10 per cent, α would be 0.86; then

$$\beta = \frac{0.86}{1 - 0.86} = 6$$

Thus when α decreased by 10 per cent β decreased by almost 70 per cent.

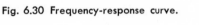
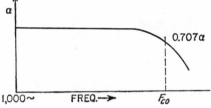

Fig. 6.30 Frequency-response curve.

PNP Amplifier Configurations

Thus far only the NPN-type transistors have been considered as amplifiers. We shall now consider the PNP amplifier configurations. The respective phase relationships for the three configurations are the same for the PNP transistor as for the NPN. The gain and frequency relationships are also the same. The only differences are the bias polarities and the effects of the input signal upon the bias.

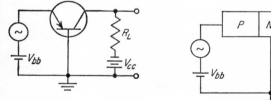
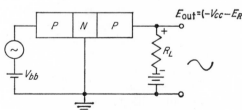

Fig. 6.31 PNP common-base amplifier.

PNP common-base amplifier. Conventional current flow is in the direction of the arrows as shown in Fig. 6.31. The output voltage is $-V_{cc} - E_{RL}$. Application of a positive-going input signal increases the forward bias of the emitter junction. The current increases, the voltage across R_L

increases, and the output voltage increases (becomes less negative). The output signal is in phase with the input signal.

PNP common-emitter amplifier. In the common-emitter PNP amplifier, a positive-going input signal opposes the forward bias as shown in Fig. 6.32. The emitter current decreases, the voltage across R_L decreases, and the output signal goes more negative. The output signal is 180° out of phase with the input signal.

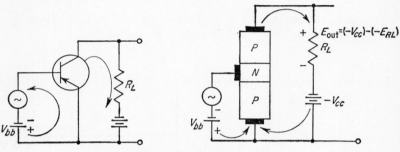

Fig. 6.32 PNP common-emitter amplifier.

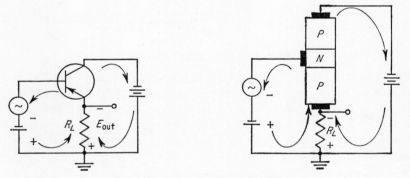

Fig. 6.33 Common-collector amplifier.

PNP common-collector amplifier. In the common-collector configuration illustrated in Fig. 6.33 a positive-going signal will oppose the emitter forward bias. The emitter current will decrease and the voltage across R_L will increase in a positive direction. The output voltage is in phase with the input voltage.

Summary of Part IV

Before proceeding to Part V, Graphical Method of Circuit Analysis, the following points are emphasized:

1. The three amplifier configurations are the common-base, the common-emitter, and the common-collector.

2. The common-base configuration has no signal inversion, has the highest voltage gain of the three configurations, and has current gain less than unity. Impedance matching is a problem because of its high output impedance and low input impedance. The configuration is used primarily for voltage amplification.
3. The common-emitter configuration inverts the phase of an input signal. The circuit has both current and voltage gain and is the most commonly used connection. The circuit has a relatively high power gain. The configuration has a higher input impedance and a lower output impedance than the common-base stage. Impedance matching is not so great a problem.
4. The common-collector configuration has no phase inversion. Its characteristics are similar to those of the vacuum-tube cathode follower. The circuit is used primarily as a buffer stage and for impedance matching.

PART V: GRAPHICAL METHOD OF CIRCUIT ANALYSIS

The relationship between input and output currents and voltages can be determined graphically in a manner similar to that for vacuum-tube graphical analysis. The methods of constructing characteristic curves and the ways in which the curves are used to analyze an amplifier circuit are discussed.

General considerations. It will be recalled that the most widely used vacuum-tube characteristic curves are the family of E_p–I_p static curves as shown in Fig. 6.34.

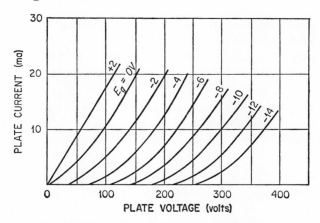

Fig. 6.34 Vacuum-tube plate characteristic curves.

To plot this family of curves, the grid voltage is held constant, the plate voltage is varied, and the resultant plate current is observed. The process is repeated for several values of grid voltage.

One outstanding difference between vacuum tubes and transistors is that vacuum tubes are voltage-operated devices and transistors are current-operated devices. The vacuum tube is considered a voltage-operated device because the plate current varies at a relatively linear rate with respect to the grid voltage, as indicated in Fig. 6.35.

Unlike that of the vacuum tube, the transistor collector current does not vary at a linear rate with respect to an input voltage applied to the emitter-base junction. However, the collector current will vary at a linear

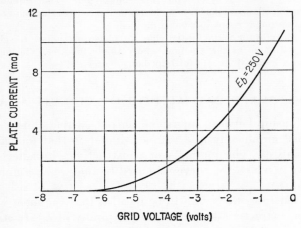

Fig. 6.35 Vacuum-tube E_g–I_p curve.

rate with respect to an input current. The emitter and base sections of a transistor essentially constitute a diode biased in the forward direction. The diode current I_d may be expressed by the following equation:

$$I_d = I_{co}e^{(QV/KT)-1}$$

The quantity e in the equation is the base of the natural logarithms. Its presence here indicates that the associated curve is exponential rather than linear. A diode curve is shown in Fig. 6.36.

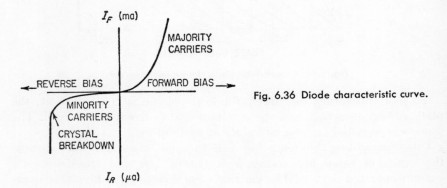

Fig. 6.36 Diode characteristic curve.

A plot of the emitter-base junction voltage versus current would be very similar to the junction-diode curve. The collector current is controlled by the emitter current. The emitter current varies linearly with an input base current rather than an input base voltage. Hence, the collector current varies linearly with an input base current.

Another consideration is that the input impedance to a vacuum tube is high, causing the input source to appear as a constant-voltage source. On the other hand, the input impedance of a transistor is low so that the input source appears to be a constant-current source.

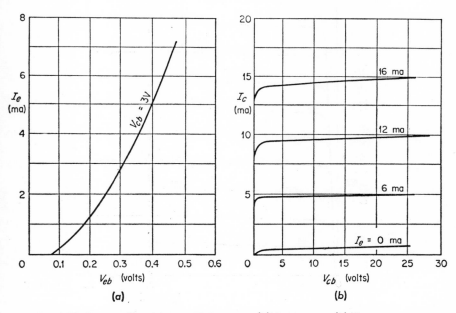

Fig. 6.37 Common-base characteristic curves. (a) Input curve. (b) Output curve.

In a transistor, then, bias currents are constant and are thus comparable to the bias voltage in vacuum tubes, which is also constant.

Characteristic curves can be constructed for all three amplifier configurations. The most commonly used are the common-base configuration and the common-emitter configuration. The curves for both configurations will be discussed in the following paragraphs.

Common-base characteristics. Two sets of curves are used to illustrate the relationship between the input and output currents and voltages. These curves are shown in Fig. 6.37.

Figure 6.37a is an input characteristic curve for the common-base configuration. This curve is a plot of input current versus input voltage with a constant value of collector voltage. The curves are almost identical for all values of collector voltage above 1 volt. Observe that $V_{cb} = 0$, I_e is in a negative quadrant. This is due to a minority-carrier flow I_{co} between the emitter and the base.

Figure 6.37b is a family of collector characteristic curves using constant values of emitter current. These curves are the output static characteristics. The curves are almost parallel to the collector-voltage axis. This situation points out the fact that with a constant emitter current, the

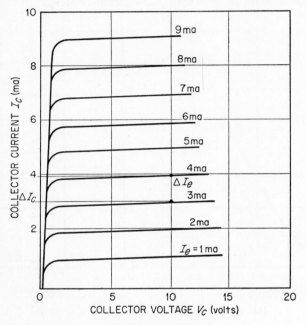

Fig. 6.38 Determination of α.

collector current does not change appreciably with any large change in collector voltage. The slope of the curve is the output resistance.

The common-base current amplification factor α can be determined from the output curves shown in Fig. 6.38 by taking the ratio $\Delta I_c / \Delta I_e$. This value is found to be $(3.95 - 3)$ ma$/(4.00 - 3)$ ma $= 0.95$.

Common-emitter characteristics. The input and output characteristic curves of the common-emitter configuration are shown in Fig. 6.39.

In the common-emitter configuration, the input current is the base current; hence the base current is the controlling parameter. Note that the slopes of the output curves of the common-emitter curves are steeper than the slopes of the common-base output curves. This indicates that the output impedance is low in the common-emitter configuration.

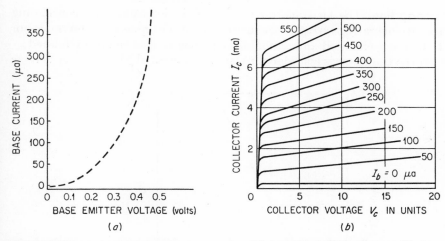

Fig. 6.39 Common-emitter characteristics curves. (a) Input characteristic curve. (b) Output characteristic curve.

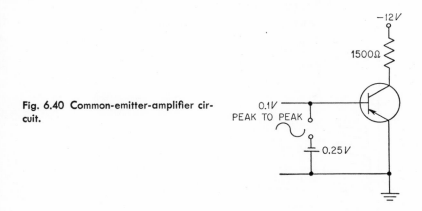

Fig. 6.40 Common-emitter-amplifier circuit.

Graphical analysis. With the circuit of Fig. 6.40, the input and output current and voltage relationships under static and dynamic conditions can now be determined. The curves of Fig. 6.41 will be used to analyze the circuit shown in Fig. 6.40. To do this, the following steps are necessary:

1. Draw the load line for the circuit.
2. Determine the bias current.
3. Determine the operating point.
4. Plot the change in output current and voltage as a result of an input signal.
5. Finally, determine the voltage gain, current gain, and power gain.

Load line. The load line for the circuit is determined by considering the two operating extremes for the transistor, i.e., assuming the transistor to be short-circuited and assuming the transistor to be open-circuited.

If the transistor is considered to be short-circuited, the collector voltage

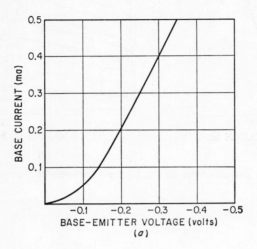

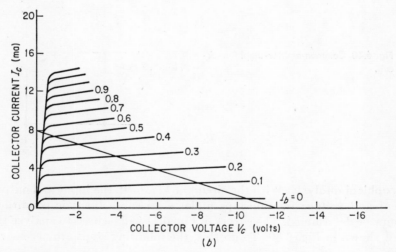

Fig. 6.41 Input and output characteristics curves. (a) Input characteristics. (b) Output characteristics.

is zero and the collector current is limited only by the collector supply voltage and the collector load resistance. The collector current I_c is $V_{cc}/R_L = 12$ volts$/1{,}500$ ohms $= 8$ ma. The $(V_c = 0, I_c = 8$ ma$)$ point is point A on the output curves in Fig. 6.41b.

If the transistor is considered to be open-circuited, the collector current is zero and the collector voltage equals the collector supply voltage; ($V_c = 12$, $I_c = 0$) is point B on the output curves. The load line for the circuit is formed by drawing a straight line connecting the two points as shown in Fig. 6.41b.

Determination of bias current and operating point. It has been pointed out that an input current rather than an input voltage is considered in transistor circuit analysis. The base current rather than the base voltage is the constant shown on the output curve.

Since only a bias voltage and an input voltage signal are shown in the circuit (Fig. 6.40), we must determine what value of input current will flow for a given value of input voltage.

The bias voltage V_{be} is 0.25 volt. Using the input characteristic curve (Fig. 6.41a) and extending the point where 0.25 volt intersects the input curve over to the current axis, we find the corresponding current to be 0.3 ma. The bias current is then 0.3 ma. The point where the 0.3-ma-current curve intersects the load line is the operating point. Projecting from the operating point to the current axis and the voltage axis, we find the static collector current to be 5.5 ma and the static collector voltage to be 4 volts. Any variation in collector current and voltage will vary around these static values of current and voltage.

Relationship between input and output signals. The input signal to the amplifier circuit shown in Fig. 6.40 is a 0.1-volt peak-to-peak symmetrical alternating voltage. This signal will vary 0.05 volt on either side of the input bias voltage. The resultant change in input current is plotted on the input curve. When the input signal rises to 0.05 volt positive, the -0.25 base-to-emitter bias voltage decreases to -0.20 volt. This decrease in voltage causes the bias current to decrease from 0.3 to 0.2 ma. On the negative alternation the magnitude of the forward bias increases from -0.25 to -0.30 volt. This causes an increase in current from 0.3 to 0.4 ma. A 0.1-volt peak-to-peak input-voltage variation has caused a 0.2-ma variation in input current.

The effect of the change in input current on the output circuit may be determined from the output characteristic curves. The change in base current will cause a change in the collector current and voltage. The points of intersection of the 0.2- and the 0.4-ma base currents and the load line are extended to the current and voltage axis. Extending the 0.2-ma intersection point to the voltage axis, we find the corresponding collector voltage to be 6.2 volts. Extending the 0.4-ma intersection point to the voltage axis, we find the corresponding collector voltage to be 2.1 volts. The total output voltage swing, E_{out}, is $6.2 - 2.1 = 4.1$ volts.

The magnitude of the collector-current swing may be determined in the same manner. If we extend the 0.2-ma intersection point to the collector-current axis, the corresponding collector current is 3.6 ma. If we extend the 0.4-ma intersection point to the collector-current axis, the corresponding collector current is 5.4 ma. The total output-current swing, I_c, is 5.4 − 3.6 = 1.8 ma.

Voltage gain. The voltage gain of the amplifier is the ratio of the output voltage to the input voltage. E_{out} is 4.1 volts and E_{in} is 0.1 volt. The voltage gain is $A_e = E_{out}/E_{in}$ = 4.1 volts/0.1 volt = 41.

Current gain. The current gain of the stage is

$$I_c/I_b = 1.8 \text{ ma}/0.2 \text{ ma} = 9$$

Power gain. The power gain is the product of the voltage gain times the current gain: 41 × 9 = 369.

Power-dissipation curve. Transistor manufacturers specify the maximum allowable collector power dissipation. When transistors are used in class A amplifiers, this rating should never be exceeded. A constant power-dissipation curve is constructed on the output curve; then the operating point is placed to the left of the curve.

The collector power is V_cI_c. If the maximum collector dissipation is known, then corresponding values of current and voltage can be calculated by holding the power dissipation constant, varying the collector voltage, and calculating the corresponding value of current. The equation to calculate the collector current I_{cc} is $I_c = P_d/E_c$, where P_d is the power dissipation.

For example, assume that a transistor has a maximum allowable collector dissipation of 30 mw at 25°C. If we assume an initial value of V_c of 16 volts, the collector current I_c = 30 mw/16 volts = 1.8 ma. If we choose another value of collector voltage, 14 volts, the collector current is 2.14 ma. The curve is plotted by using several values of collector voltage. The collector dissipation curve is shown in Fig. 6.42.

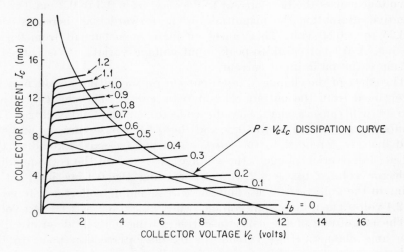

Fig. 6.42 Collector dissipation curve.

Summary of Part V

Before proceeding to Part VI, Bias and Temperature-stabilizing Circuits, the following points are emphasized:

1. Transistor circuits may be analyzed graphically in much the same manner as vacuum-tube circuits.
2. An input current rather than an input voltage is chosen as the controlling parameter.
3. Curves for the common-base and the common-emitter configuration are the two most commonly used curves.
4. By constructing appropriate load lines, values of input resistance, output resistance, current, voltage, and power gain for a stage may be determined.
5. Transistor operation must be kept within the maximum permissible power-dissipation rating. Maximum dissipation occurs at the center of the load line. The load line should be kept to the left of the power-dissipation curve.

PART VI: BIAS AND TEMPERATURE-STABILIZING CIRCUITS

One of the important problems in transistor-amplifier circuits is that of obtaining the proper biases and maintaining these biases despite wide variations of the ambient temperature and variations of transistor characteristics between transistors of the same type.

For the sake of simplicity, the practice of having separate batteries for the input and the output supply has been used. In the common-emitter configuration it is possible to provide bias for both the input and the output circuits with a single battery. The two basic forms of bias arrangements used are fixed bias and self-bias. Both forms of bias and additional methods of temperature-stabilizing the bias will now be discussed.

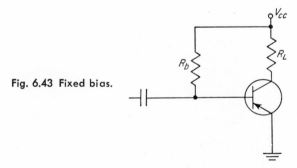

Fig. 6.43 Fixed bias.

Fixed bias. A circuit illustrating fixed bias is shown in Fig. 6.43. A portion of the collector supply voltage is used to provide base voltage through the dropping resistor R_b. The polarity of the base voltage is correct for forward bias. The position of the operating point on the load line for the circuit is dependent upon the amount of current flow caused by the amount of base voltage. The value of the resistance R_b is

$$R_b = \frac{V_{cc} - V_b}{I_b}$$

where V_{cc} = collector supply voltage
 V_b = voltage appearing between base and emitter at operating
   point
 I_b = desired current bias

The main disadvantage of the fixed-bias method is that the operating point will vary if the transistor in the circuit is replaced and when the transistor ages. A more suitable method of bias is discussed below.

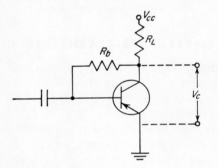

Fig. 6.44 Self-bias.

Self-bias. A circuit using self-bias is shown in Fig. 6.44. The actual collector voltage rather than the collector supply voltage is used to obtain base bias. The value of R_b is

$$R_b = \frac{V_c - V_b}{I_b}$$

where V_c is the collector voltage.

A certain amount of degeneration is introduced in the circuit to stabilize the operating point. If the transistor in the circuit is replaced with a

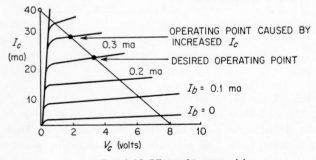

Fig. 6.45 Effect of increased I_c.

transistor that has a higher value of collector current, the magnitude of the collector voltage will decrease. The operating point will attempt to move up on the load line as shown in Fig. 6.45. However, as the collector voltage decreases, the forward bias is reduced, thereby reducing the bias current and moving the operating point back down the load line.

If the collector current is smaller than that desired at the operating point, the magnitude of the collector voltage will increase and the operating point will attempt to move down as shown in Fig. 6.46. However, the forward bias will increase and the operating point will move back up to the desired position.

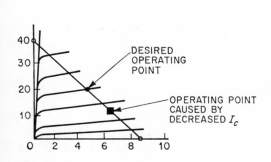

Fig. 6.46 Effect of decreased I_c.

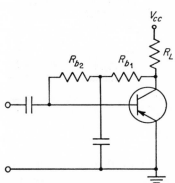

Fig. 6.47 Circuit to prevent degeneration of signal.

It is desirable to use only d-c negative feedback to stabilize the bias and to prevent degeneration of the signal itself. Signal degeneration may be prevented by splitting R_b into two series resistors and shunting the signal to ground through a capacitor as shown in Fig. 6.47.

Effect of temperature upon circuit stability. Transistors are temperature-sensitive devices because the leakage current I_{co} will increase as the temperature increases. In germanium, I_{co} doubles for every 10°C increase in temperature. Another effect is that the I_{co} in the collector circuit may be amplified by a factor β. This increased collector current raises the temperature of the transistor, which in turn will increase I_{co}. The action is regenerative and the transistor will become damaged.

Amplification of I_{co} will occur if the resistivity of the base is very high or if a large resistor is placed in the base lead. We shall consider an open-circuited condition between base and emitter. The way in which I_{co} becomes amplified may be seen in Fig. 6.48.

A leakage current I_{ceo} flows between the collector and emitter when the base is open-circuited. I_{ceo} is the sum of the "normal" I_{co} and the amplified I_{co}.

In Fig. 6.48 the minority electrons from the collector move into the base region. Since there is no path for the minority carriers to leave the base region, they begin to accumulate. This accumulation of current carriers in the base region will attract holes from the emitter. Some of these holes will recombine with the accumulated electrons and the remaining holes will go to the collector.

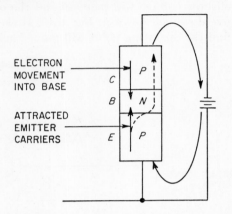

ELECTRON
MOVEMENT
INTO BASE

ATTRACTED
EMITTER
CARRIERS

Fig. 6.48 Generation of I_{ceo}.

The total collector current is $I_{co} + \beta I_{co}$. The I_{co} component flows in the collector circuit because of the recombination of the minority carriers from the base (holes) in the collector region.

Means of temperature stabilization. The obvious method of reducing the effect of temperature is to avoid using a large-value resistor in the base circuit and/or provide a low-resistance path for the minority carriers

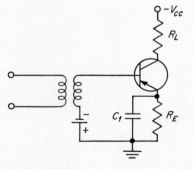

Fig. 6.49 Low d-c resistance path for I_{co}.

out of the base region. The leakage current cannot be reduced below the value of I_{co}, but the amplification effect may be reduced. A low-resistance path is shown in Fig. 6.49. The transformer secondary winding provides a low d-c resistance path. If transformer coupling is not used, a low-value resistor may be placed in the circuit.

The emitter swamping resistor R_e also provides temperature stabilization. If the emitter current should increase, the voltage drop across R_e will increase and reduce the forward bias. Capacitor C_1 bypasses the a-c signal around R_e.

Thermistor stabilization circuit. Another means of temperature stabilization is to use a thermistor in the amplifier circuit.

A thermistor is a temperature-sensitive element whose resistance varies as the temperature varies. The thermistor resistance used in the circuit shown in Fig. 6.50 will decrease as the temperature increases.

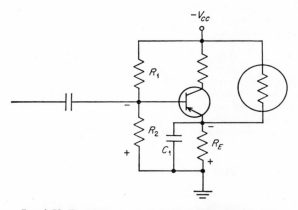

Fig. 6.50 Thermistor temperature-stabilization circuit.

There are two voltage-divider networks shown in Fig. 6.50. R_1 and R_2 form one divider network, and R_e and the thermistor form the second network. The voltage drop across R_2 is in a forward-bias direction and the voltage drop across R_e is in a reverse-bias direction. However, the magnitude of the voltage drop across R_2 is greater than the voltage across R_e; thus, the transistor is forward-biased.

If the temperature should increase, the resistance of the thermistor will decrease and the current through R_e and the thermistor will increase. As a result, the forward bias at the emitter junction will decrease and the emitter current will not increase, owing to the I_{co}.

The circuit is stabilized for both an increase or a decrease in temperature within the range of the thermistor.

Summary

In this chapter the physical and electrical characteristics of semiconductor diodes and transistors and their applications as circuit elements have been discussed. The devices are used extensively in radio communications, control, and computer circuits. The use of the two devices in computer pulse circuits is of primary interest here. The next two chapters will discuss the switching characteristics of transistors, i.e., their response to an input pulse, and will illustrate practical transistorized pulse circuits.

QUESTIONS

Part I: Properties of Semiconductor Materials

6.1 Define the following terms: atomic number, semiconductor, shell, covalent force, hole.

6.2 What is the maximum number of electrons that can be contained in the third shell of an atom?

6.3 What elements can be used as semiconductors?

6.4 What is a donor atom?   An acceptor atom?

6.5 What is a positive ion?   A negative ion?

Part II: The Junction Diode

6.6 How is a potential barrier established?

6.7 Draw a PN junction diode and battery circuit showing forward bias. Show the battery connection for reverse bias.

6.8 Which method of biasing increases the potential barrier?

6.9 What are majority carriers?   Minority carriers?

6.10 What is the zener point on the diode characteristic curve?   Illustrate.

Part III: The Junction Transistor

6.11 Draw the block representation of a PNP transistor, connect load resistor and batteries for normal transistor operation, and designate all internal and external currents.

6.12 Define the following terms: I_c, I_{co}, I_r, I_b, I_e.

6.13 How is I_e related to I_c, I_r, and I_{co}?

6.14 What is the average forward-bias voltage in transistor circuits?   What is the average reverse collector voltage? What will the result be if either of the voltages is exceeded?

6.15 Draw the NPN and PNP transistor symbols.

Part IV: Transistor-Amplifier Configurations

6.16 Illustrate the common-emitter, common-base, and common-collector configurations using a PNP transistor. Show proper battery polarities, input-signal source, and output-signal origin. Which configuration of the three has the highest input resistance? Which produces the highest current amplification? Which configuration has the highest frequency response?

6.17 What are the input-output phase relationships of the three basic configurations?

6.18 What is the formula for α? β?

6.19 What is the relationship between α and β?

6.20 If a transistor with an α of 0.95 is used, what would the total collector current be when $I_b = 40$ μa and $I_{co} = 10$ μa?

Part V: Graphical Method of Circuit Analysis

6.21 Using the circuit shown in Fig. 6.51 and the output characteristic curves of Fig. 6.52, plot the load line for the circuit.

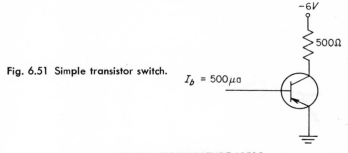

Fig. 6.51 Simple transistor switch. $I_b = 500\mu a$

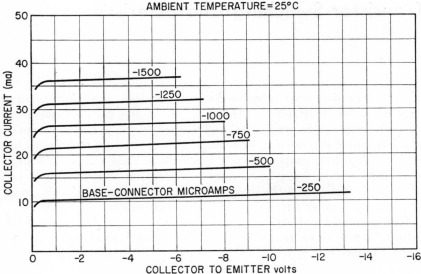

Fig. 6.52 Average collector characteristics.

6.22 What is the maximum power dissipated in the collector along the load line?

6.23 Where does maximum power dissipation occur?

6.24 If the load resistance in Question 6.21 were decreased to a value of 250 ohms, what would be the maximum power dissipated in the collector?

6.25 With the load line plotted for Question 6.24 and a static base current $I_b = 500$ μa, what would be the value of a-c β? (Assume an input signal of ± 250 μa.)

Part VI: Bias and Temperature-stabilizing Circuits

6.26 What are the formula and the procedure for calculating the value of the base-bias resistor R_b when the desired base current I_b is known and the collector supply voltage is known? .

6.27 What is the effect of temperature on circuit stability?

6.28 Illustrate the various transistor biasing methods.

6.29 What are the advantages and disadvantages of connecting the base resistor R_b between the collector and base to obtain bias?

6.30 Describe the process by which a resistor connected between the emitter and ground of a grounded-emitter configuration provides temperature stabilization.

Chapter **7**

Transistor Switching Characteristics

Transistors are being used more extensively in modern computer circuits as switching devices. However, transistors have characteristics such as temperature sensitivity and carrier storage that were not encountered in vacuum-tube switching circuits. Circuit techniques have been developed to compensate for the effects of these characteristics and to improve the response of a transistor to an input pulse. These techniques are employed in the design of many of the gating circuits, multivibrators, and other pulse circuits used in computers.

This chapter will describe the output-pulse characteristics of the transistor with respect to an input pulse and will show how switching response may be improved.

Characteristic-curve Analysis

Transistor switching functions are referred to as *large-signal operation*. The transistor is either switched on to act as an overdriven amplifier or biased completely off. The region of operation on a load line is shown in Fig. 7.1.

The output characteristic curves of a transistor may be divided into three regions: the cutoff region, the active region, and the saturation region. The cutoff region (I) is the region under the $I_b = 0$ curve. The active region (II) is the normal operating region. The saturation region (III) is the region beyond the bend of the characteristic curves. The saturation region is generally defined as the region where the collector voltage becomes smaller than the base voltage (usually a few tenths of a volt). When the collector voltage drops below the base voltage, it causes the collector-base junction to become forward-biased, and the collector begins to inject its carriers into the base.

138

In switching circuits, the transistor is switched between cutoff and saturation or to a point close to saturation. The load line may be to the right of the power-dissipation curve (Fig. 7.1) since the dissipation rating is exceeded for a short period of time. It is still desirable, however, to switch through the active region as quickly as possible.

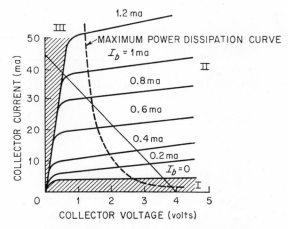

Fig. 7.1 Regions of transistor operation.

Transient Response

In order to analyze the response of a transistor, an ideal current pulse is applied to the base of an amplifier stage and the change in output voltage is observed, as shown in Fig. 7.2. The indicated pulse terminology will also be explained.

Delay time. Delay time (t_d) is the time in which the pulse rises from its minimum value to 10 per cent of its maximum value. The delay is incurred because carriers must initially reach the collector region from the emitter before turn-on begins. The junction capacitance between the base and emitter must also be discharged. Delay time is less than 0.1 μsec and is usually considered a part of rise time.

Rise time. Rise time (t_r) is the time in which the pulse rises from 10 to 90 per cent of its maximum value. Rise time is dependent upon frequency response of the transistor, the circuit capacitance, and the magnitude of the applied base current.

Pulse time. The pulse time (t_p), or width, is the time between the 90 per cent values at the leading and trailing edges.

Storage time. Storage time (t_s) is the time in which the output pulse remains near its maximum value after the input pulse has been removed. This time is often referred to as *saturation delay time*. If the transistor is driven into saturation, the collector-base junction becomes forward-biased so that the collector injects carriers into the base. At turn-off time the excess carriers (holes in a PNP transistor) must be pulled across the base junction into the collector region before the output pulse begins to fall.

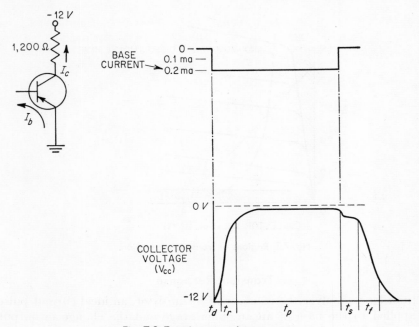

Fig. 7.2 Transistor transient response.

Fall time. Fall time (t_f) is the time in which the output pulse falls from 90 to 10 per cent of its maximum value. The factors governing rise time also apply to fall time.

Methods of Improving Transient Response

In order to achieve high switching rates, it is desirable to make the turn-on and turn-off times of the transistor as short as possible. Turn-on time is the sum of the delay time and the rise time. Turn-off time is the sum of the storage time and the fall time.

Some special-type high-frequency transistors having turn-on and turn-off times in the nanosecond range may even be driven into saturation and still produce little storage time. These special types are used in high-frequency switching applications.

There are circuit techniques that will increase the switching speed of ordinary junction transistors to make them useful as switching devices.

There are two techniques used to improve turn-on and turn-off time: one is to *overdrive* the transistor during turn-on and turn-off time, and the other is to design a circuit to prevent saturation, thereby preventing storage effects.

Overdriving to increase switching speed. The turn-on and turn-off times of the transistor may be reduced by overdriving the transistor. Overdriving means to apply more than the required amount of base current to turn the transistor on or off. The effect of overdrive is illustrated in Figs. 7.3 and 7.4.

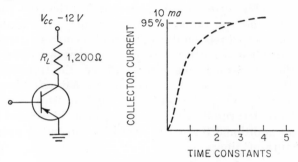

Fig. 7.3 Collector rise time.

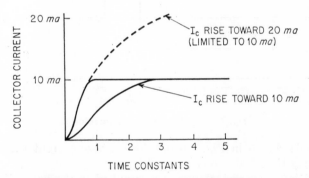

Fig. 7.4 Effect of overdriving during turn-on.

In Fig. 7.3, the maximum collector current is

$$\frac{V_{cc}}{R_L} = \frac{12}{1,200} = 10 \text{ ma}$$

If the transistor has a β of 50, the required amount of base current to keep the collector current at 10 ma is $I_c/\beta = {}^{10}\!/_{50} = 0.2$ ma.

When 0.2 ma of base current is applied, the collector current will increase toward 10 ma at an exponential rate because of the rise-time factors mentioned previously. Since turn-on is considered to be 90 per cent of the maximum collector current, the collector will reach maximum current in approximately three time constants.

Now suppose that 0.4 ma of base current is applied. The collector current attempts to increase to $\beta \times I_b = 50 \times 0.4 = 20$ ma. However, the collector current is limited to 10 ma by the values of V_{cc} and R_L. The latter current curve, upon attempting to rise toward 20 ma, is more linear than the former curve rising to 10 ma. A comparison of the two curves is shown in Fig. 7.4.

In Fig. 7.4 it can be seen that by overdriving the transistor during turn-on, the collector current reaches 10 ma in less than one time constant instead of three time constants. In a like manner, overdriving the transistor in the opposite direction during turn-off decreases turn-off time.

Ideal base-current waveform. An ideal current waveform applied to the base of the transistor is one that overdrives the transistor to obtain rapid turn-on, reduces to a value necessary to maintain the desired collector conduction level, and overdrives the transistor in the opposite direction for rapid turn-off. The ideal waveform illustrated in Fig. 7.5 shows that an additional 0.2 ma of overdrive current is applied during turn-on and turn-off time.

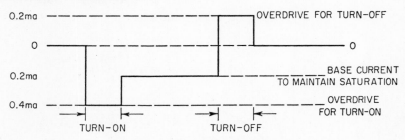

Fig. 7.5 Ideal base-current waveform.

The circuit shown in Fig. 7.6 provides a base-current waveform that approximates the ideal waveform of Fig. 7.5.

The additional overdrive current is supplied to the base by the charge and discharge of capacitor C_1 through the base and emitter of the transistor. The normal base current flows through resistor R_1.

The circuit operation may be more clearly explained by calculating the theoretical values of C_1 and R_1.

If the collector current at saturation is 10 ma and the β of the transistor is 50, then the base current required to saturate the transistor must be 0.2 ma. This value of base current will flow through R_1. Assume that the turn-on time desired is 0.5 μsec. If 0.4 ma of base current will provide the desired turn-on time, then C_1 must provide a charging current of 0.2 ma so that the total base current during turn-on will be 0.4 ma.

The first step is to determine what value of base voltage produces 0.2 ma of base current. This can be done by referring to the input curve for the transistor.

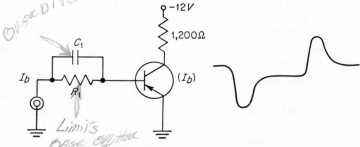

Fig. 7.6 Circuit to provide overdrive.

In Fig. 7.7, 0.2 volt must be applied to the base to allow 0.2 ma to flow through the transistor. If the input voltage varies between 0 and -3 volts, the value of R_1 is

$$\frac{(3 - 0.2) \text{ volts}}{0.2 \text{ ma}} = \frac{2.8}{0.2} = 14,000 \text{ ohms}$$

Fig. 7.7 Input curve.

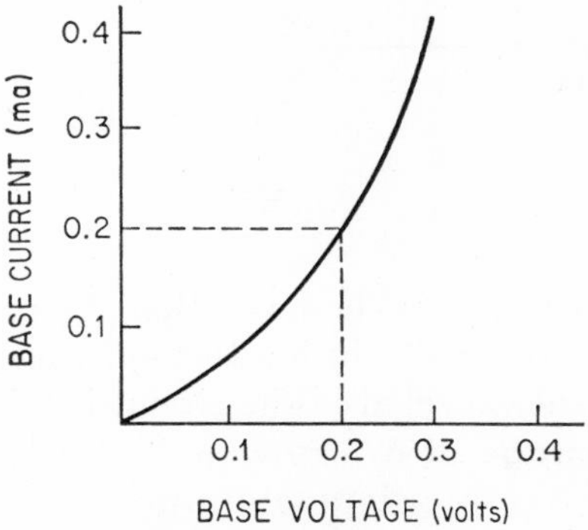

The 0.2-ma overdrive current must be supplied by C_1. The current through a capacitor is found by the following equation:

$$I = \frac{C \, \Delta V}{\Delta t}$$

Therefore

$$C = \frac{I \, \Delta t}{\Delta V}$$

The voltage change ΔV across C_1 is $3 - 0.2 = 2.8$ volts; the required current is 0.2 ma and the turn-on time Δt is 0.5 μsec. Then

$$C_1 = (0.2 \times 10^{-3}) \frac{0.5 \times 10^{-6}}{2.8} = 35 \ \mu\mu\text{f}$$

The capacitor, on charging, inserts additional electrons into the base. At turn-off time the input goes to 0 volt and the capacitor discharges. On discharging, the capacitor attracts electrons from the base region as the transistor is turning off. Electrons flowing out of the base into the base lead tend to turn the transistor off.

Temperature stabilization. The circuit shown in Fig. 7.6 has a high-resistance path for collector leakage current. It was brought out in the discussion on temperature stability (Chap. 6) that if the leakage current is amplified, the magnitude of the collector current flowing during turn-off may produce the same effect as that created by the transistor being turned on; a path must, therefore, be provided for the leakage current to flow out of the base. A low-resistance path may be provided by inserting a resistor between the base and emitter or by inserting a current sink for I_{co} as shown in Fig. 7.8.

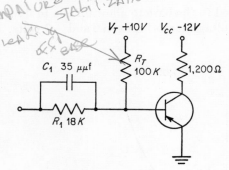

Fig. 7.8 Switching circuit with temperature stabilization.

The ratio V_T/R_T is chosen so that the maximum expected value of I_{co} will flow through R_T during turn-off time. For example, the maximum cutoff current expected in the circuit in Fig. 7.8 is 100 μa.

Disadvantage of overdriving. A disadvantage of overdriving is that driving the transistor into saturation will increase the storage time. When fast turn-on and turn-off is required, special techniques are employed to prevent the circuit from going into saturation. Several of these techniques will now be discussed.

Nonsaturating Techniques

In Fig. 7.1 the saturation region was shown as the region where the collector voltage becomes smaller than the base voltage and the collector junction is forward-biased. Consequently, the collector injects its majority carriers into the base, and turn-off time is increased. The purpose of the nonsaturating techniques discussed here is to prevent the collector voltage from becoming smaller than the base voltage even if the transistor is conducting saturating current, or to prevent the transistor from actually conducting at saturation.

Collector clamp. The simplest method to prevent saturation is the collector clamping method shown in Fig. 7.9. Here the collector voltage is prevented from becoming more positive than the base voltage by diode CR_1. When the collector voltage attempts to become more positive than -1 volt, CR_1 conducts and the collector voltage is clamped at a negative level. If the current flow through CR_1 causes a voltage drop of 0.2 volt across the diode, the collector is clamped at -0.8 volt. Thus, the collector-base junction remains reverse-biased, and the collector does not emit carriers into the base.

A disadvantage of the collector clamp method is that the recovery time of diode CR_1 becomes part of the total turn-off time. The transistor still

Diode adds to storage time

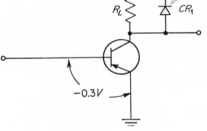

will conduct when Vc drop below 1 volt

Fig. 7.9 Collector clamp to prevent saturation.

conducts maximum current, and the current divides between the load and CR_1.

Single-diode collector clamp. A better nonsaturating technique is to reduce the collector current by controlling the base current. This technique is called *back-clamping.* The circuit is shown in Fig. 7.10.

Assume the collector saturation current is 12 ma. If the current gain is 30, the amount of base current required to saturate the transistor is 0.4 ma. To decrease turn-on time, the 0.4-ma saturation current and the additional overdrive current supplied by C_1 are applied to the base to produce the desired turn-on time. Assume an input pulse forward-biases the base-emitter junction and drives the transistor toward saturation. If the collector current were allowed to reach saturation, then the collector voltage would be approximately -0.1 volt. However, when the collector voltage attempts to become more positive than the negative voltage at the junction of R_1 and R_2 (-1 volt), CR_1 conducts and a portion of the base current is diverted to the collector; hence the collector current cannot increase beyond its value at this point. The total collector current, then, consists of the amplified base current ($\beta \times I_b$) and the excess base current; the current flowing through the load remains constant since it is only the amplified base current. If the voltage drop across CR_1 is 0.2 volt, then the falling collector voltage stops at -0.8 volt; hence CR_1 prevents the collector-base junction from becoming forward-biased by shunting

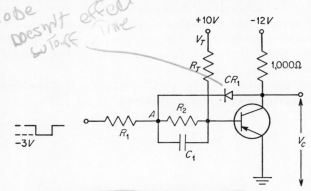

Fig. 7.10 Single-diode back-clamping circuit.

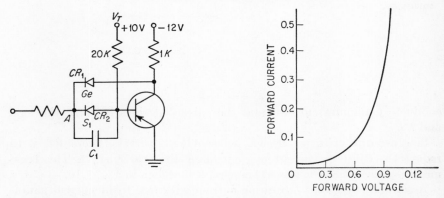

Fig. 7.11 Double-diode clamp circuit and silicon-diode forward-bias characteristics.

the excess input current into the collector. Since only a fraction of the base current flows through CR_1, diode recovery time contributes little to the widening of the output pulse.

Double-diode collector clamp. Resistor R_2 in Fig. 7.10 can be replaced with a silicon diode CR_2, as shown in Fig. 7.11. The resulting circuit operates reliably and is fairly insensitive to minor changes in supply voltages.

A silicon diode is selected for CR_2 because of its inherently higher forward voltage drop than that of the germanium diode CR_1 and its constant forward voltage drop over the relatively wide range of current values normally applied to the base of the switching transistor. The biasing diode CR_2 is forward-biased throughout the functioning of the circuit and has a forward voltage drop of 0.7 volt. The clamping diode CR_1 is reverse-biased when the transistor is cut off. Capacitor C_1 provides the overdrive current the same as in the single-diode clamping circuit (Fig. 7.10). CR_1 will conduct when the transistor is turned on and the collector voltage attempts to go slightly more positive than the negative voltage established at the junction of the two diodes (point A, -1 volt). When CR_1 conducts, it exhibits a forward voltage drop of 0.2 volt; the collector is therefore clamped at -0.8 volt when CR_1 conducts and diverts the excess base current to the collector. The voltage drop of CR_2 establishes the base voltage at -0.3 volt. Because of their different voltage drops,

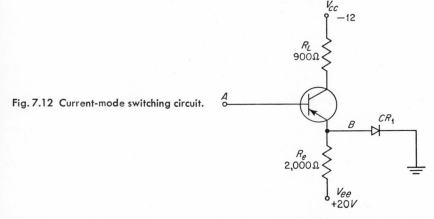

Fig. 7.12 Current-mode switching circuit.

the two diodes will maintain a fixed voltage relationship between the base and collector, keeping the base-collector junction reverse-biased when the transistor is switched on. There are variations of the double-diode clamp circuit, one of which eliminates resistor R_T. This results in a saving of a power supply since V_T is no longer required. Circuit operation is essentially the same.

Current-mode switching. Another method of preventing saturation is to limit the amount of collector current by using a resistor and a voltage supply in the emitter circuit, as shown in Fig. 7.12. The values shown for R_E, R_L, and the supply voltages are chosen so that the collector voltage does not become smaller than the base voltage.

The current supplied by V_{ee} and R_e is switched in and out of the transistor, depending upon the voltage applied to the base. If the base voltage is sufficiently negative, the 10 ma (minus the required base current) flows to the collector circuit.

Assume that the voltage applied to point A is $+0.6$ volt and that the transistor is off. The 10-ma current must flow through CR_1. If 10 ma of current drops 0.3 volt across CR_1, the voltage at point B is 0.3 volt. The base is then 0.3 volt positive with respect to the emitter. If the input drops to -0.6 volt, the emitter junction becomes forward-biased and the 10-ma current flows through the transistor. If the gain of the stage is 50, the base current will be 0.2 ma for a 10-ma current. Assume that the base input characteristics show that the base voltage is 0.2 volt at 0.2-ma base current. When the transistor conducts, the voltage at B is -0.4 volt and diode CR_1 is reverse-biased.

The load resistor R_L may be selected so that the collector voltage is out of the saturation region. The collector voltage V_c may be found by the equation $V_c = V_{cc} - I_E R_L$. Therefore $R_L = (V_{cc} - V_c)/I_E$. If V_c is to be -1 volt and the collector supply voltage is -10 volts,

$$R_L = \frac{10 - 1 \text{ (volts)}}{10 \text{ ma}} = 900 \text{ ohms}$$

High switching speeds are possible using current-mode switches. The circuit may be operated as far out of saturation as desired. A high current may be switched in and out of the transistor by using a relatively small voltage applied to the base.

Nonsaturation by circuit design. It is possible to design switching circuits that will not saturate merely by the correct choice of components. However, these circuits cannot tolerate so much variation in the load as circuits employing nonsaturating techniques.

Summary

The switching speeds of a transistor can be increased by overdriving and by employing nonsaturating techniques. Short turn-on and turn-off times are desirable for faster circuit operation; also the time that the transistor exceeds its power-dissipation rating is decreased. If the pulse terms and circuit techniques discussed here have become familiar, little trouble will be met in analyzing the operation of the transistorized pulse circuits that will be discussed in subsequent sections.

QUESTIONS

7.1 What factors should be taken into consideration when selecting a transistor for switching applications?

7.2 Describe saturation and its effect on switching operations.

7.3 What does the positive peak on the leading edge and the negative peak on the trailing edge of the ideal base-current waveform indicate?

7.4 Refer to Fig. 7.7 and determine the value of base input resistor for Fig. 7.6 when β is 40 and saturation current is 12 ma.

7.5 Why does the diode CR_1 shown in Fig. 7.10 contribute less to the widening of the output pulse than the diode CR_1 shown in Fig. 7.9? Explain.

Chapter **8**

Transistor Gate Logic

Transistor gating circuits are used extensively in modern computers. Gating circuits are switching circuits that provide Yes or No information. The transistors may be connected in series, in parallel, or in series-parallel to provide a variety of logical functions such as the AND, OR, NOT, NOR, and other functions peculiar to the logical design of the computer. Transistor gates have an advantage over diode gates: the transistor is capable of amplifying the input signal, so that the amplitude of a signal is not lost as it passes through several gates.

There are several types of transistor logic configurations which can be used to construct logical gates and systems. The system of logic employed will depend upon the desired switching speed, power requirements, and relative cost of the components used. The basic transistor logical systems are as follows:

1. Direct-coupled transistor logic (DCTL)
2. Resistor transistor logic (RTL)
3. Resistor-capacitor transistor logic (RCTL)
4. Hybrid logic (diodes and transistors)
5. Current-mode logic (CML)

This chapter discusses the five transistor logical systems, including the logical functions obtained and the advantages and disadvantages of each.

Direct-coupled Transistor Logic

DCTL indicates that the output of one amplifier stage is coupled directly to the input of a following stage. A two-stage amplifier circuit is shown in Fig. 8.1.

The amplitude of the voltage swing is small, usually about 0.2 volt.

149

No external circuitry is required to establish the lower-level clamp because the emitter-base junction of Q_2 acts as a diode clamp on the collector of Q_1. Assume that the input voltage varies between -0.1 and -0.3 volt. The -0.1-volt level is considered positive, and the -0.3-volt level is considered negative. The -0.1-volt level is used to turn the transistor off; the load resistor and collector supply voltages are selected so that the transistors saturate when the -0.3-volt level is applied.

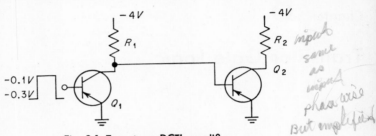

Fig. 8.1 Two-stage DCTL amplifier.

If -0.3 volt is applied to the base of Q_1, Q_1 turns on and its collector voltage drops to -0.1 volt. This voltage is applied to the base of Q_2; hence, Q_2 turns off. When the input to the base of Q_1 rises to -0.1 volt, Q_1 turns off and its collector voltage begins to fall toward -4 volts. However, when the collector voltage reaches -0.3 volt, Q_2 turns on. The base current of Q_2 flows through R_1 and the collector voltage supply. This base current keeps the collector of Q_1 clamped to -0.3 volt when Q_1 is turned off.

The collector voltage of Q_1 varies between -0.1 and -0.3 volt. If another stage is coupled to Q_2, the output of Q_2 will vary by the same amount.

Parallel logical gate. In Fig. 8.2, three transistors are placed in parallel, with the collectors tied to a common point D. If the input at A,

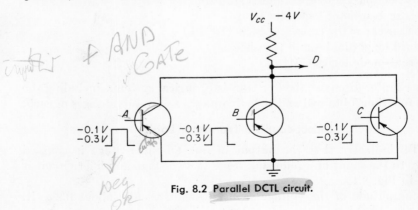

Fig. 8.2 Parallel DCTL circuit.

B, or C is -0.3 volt, the output at D will be -0.1 volt. If all inputs are -0.1 volt simultaneously, the output at D will fall to -4 volts provided it is not coupled to another stage.

The phase of the output signal is inverted since a common-emitter configuration is used. When all three inputs are "positive" (-0.1 volt), the output is negative. When either input is negative, the output is positive. The gate is either a positive-input AND gate with polarity reversal or a negative-input OR gate with polarity reversal.

Series gate. The series gate shown in Fig. 8.3 can perform both AND and OR operations. All three transistors must conduct if current is to flow into the load. If -0.3 volt is applied to all three inputs, the collector

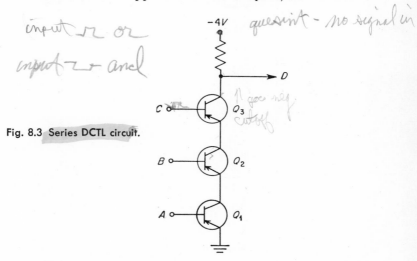

Fig. 8.3 Series DCTL circuit.

of Q_1 supplies the emitter current of Q_2 and the collector of Q_2 supplies the emitter current of Q_3. The circuit is a negative-input AND gate with polarity reversal or a positive-input OR gate with polarity reversal.

Logical gate symbols and notations. Logical schematic diagrams are used as an aid to tracing signals through gates that perform the logical operations of a computer. These schematic diagrams indicate whether a gate is a series or parallel gate and whether the gate is performing an AND or an OR function. The logical symbols for the gates are shown in Fig. 8.4.

In each of the gates shown, a polarity reversal exists. The polarity symbols are necessary to maintain a correct polarity throughout a sequence of gates. This problem is eliminated when two basic assumptions are made in the design of a logical network. These assumptions are:

1. It is unnecessary to select one pulse level to represent a 1 or "true" condition and to maintain this notation throughout the system.

2. An inversion of polarity does not necessarily mean an inversion in logic.

With these two basic assumptions made, the task of arranging gates to perform logical operations becomes easier and more flexible. Most systems use one basic gate to perform both AND and OR operations. For example, a two-input parallel DCTL gate may be chosen as the basic building

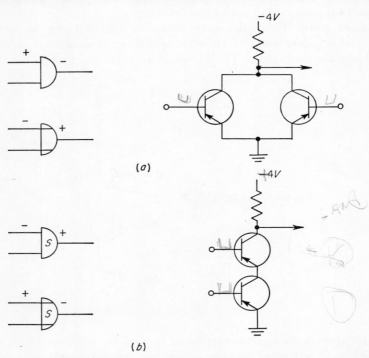

Fig. 8.4 Gate symbols. (a) Parallel gates. (b) Series gates.

block to perform all logical operations. For AND-gate operations, the "true" inputs are positive and the "true" output is negative. For OR-gate operations, the "true" inputs are negative and the "true" output is positive. The equation for the AND gate shown in Fig. 8.5 is $AB = C$, and the equation for the OR gate is $A + B = C$.

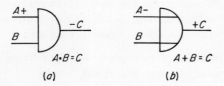

$A \cdot B = C$

(a)

$A + B = C$

(b)

Fig. 8.5 Basic parallel gate used as a building block. (a) AND gate. (b) OR gate.

Most logical sequences have AND gates driving OR gates and OR gates driving AND gates. When such an arrangement exists, the "true" output of an AND gate is of the correct polarity to drive an OR gate, and vice versa. The circuit arrangement shown in Fig. 8.6 can perform two logical functions: $AB + CD = E$ or $(A + B)(C + D) = E$. These logical functions are shown in the logical schematic diagrams of Fig. 8.6a and b. If function a is desired, positive input signals must be used; if b is the desired function, negative input signals must be used.

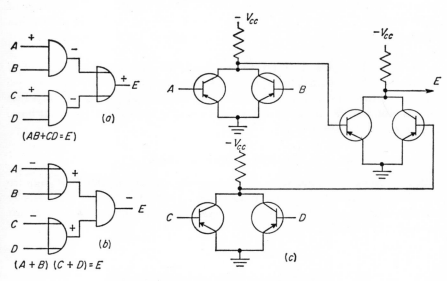

Fig. 8.6 Combinations of AND and OR gates.

DCTL circuit characteristics. Since direct coupling is employed, the characteristics of the circuit are dependent largely upon the transistor itself. The characteristics of the transistors used in this system must be closely controlled. The transistors must have a low saturation voltage from collector to emitter, and they must be driven well into saturation to ensure a stable "on" condition. The surface-barrier type of transistor is the only type that has suitable characteristics for DCTL applications. Diodes are not used with DCTL because of the low voltage levels employed.

DCTL is relatively expensive because of the large number of transistors required. Each logical input requires a separate transistor. There are practical limits to the number of transistors that may be used in parallel or in series. The leakage current I_{co} determines the number of transistors that may be placed in parallel. The sum of the I_{co} current of each transistor flows through the common load resistor. If the total I_{co}

is too large, the collector will not maintain its lower-level voltage (in the example, -0.3 volt) when all transistors are off, but rises toward -0.1 volt. The large I_{co} current produces a false "on" condition. To ensure correct operation, no more than 10 transistors should be placed in parallel.

When series gates are used, the transistor saturation voltage is the limiting factor. The desired saturation voltage is -0.1 volt. This means that the collector voltage of the top transistor is -0.1 volt with respect to ground. If two transistors are placed in series, the saturation voltage of each transistor is 0.05 volt; if three transistors are used, the saturation voltage of each transistor is 0.03 volt. Usually a DCTL logical gate has three transistors.

The switching speed of DCTL is rapid because of the high α cutoff frequency of the transistors. This speed is hampered, however, because the transistor is driven into saturation. The main advantage of DCTL is circuit simplicity. There are other less expensive logical systems that have faster switching speed.

Resistor Transistor Logic

RTL offers a straightforward circuit design which does not require stringent control of transistor parameters. The gate consists of a resistor current-summing network followed by an inverting amplifier. The circuit is shown in Fig. 8.7.

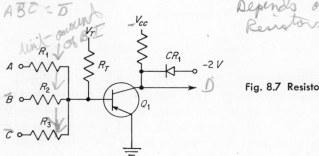

Fig. 8.7 Resistor transistor logic.

The inputs are pulses whose magnitudes are usually at least 1 volt. The resistors R_1, R_2, and R_3 are equal in value. Assume that the input varies between -0.1 and -2 volts. If all three inputs are at the upper level (-0.1 volt), transistor Q_1 will be off. However, the resistor values are chosen so that if one input is at its lower level (-2 volts), Q_1 is driven into the saturation region. If more than one input is at its lower level, the transistor is driven deeper into saturation. The resistors provide a current-summing network, and the total current is drawn through the base of Q_1.

When the transistor is turned off, the collector voltage is clamped to −2 volts by CR_1.

The circuit is a positive-input AND gate or a negative-input OR gate. For ease of logic design, the same assumptions made in the DCTL logic apply to RTL gates. The gates may be considered as straightforward AND or OR gates with polarity reversal. A complex arrangement of gates to perform a logical operation is shown in Fig. 8.8. This arrangement may perform the functions $ABC + DEF = G$ or $(A + B + C)(D + E + F) = G$.

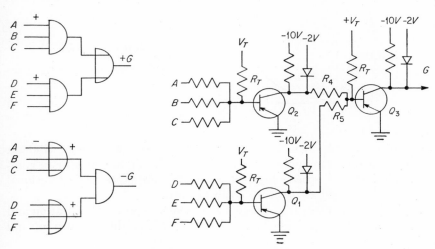

Fig. 8.8 RTL gate combination.

Component calculations. Without considering worst-case aspects, the method of determining base input resistor values will be shown. If the collector current desired is 5 ma and the transistor has a β of 20, the required base current is 0.25 ma. The input characteristic curve gives the amount of base voltage required to provide a 0.25-ma base current.

Figure 8.9 shows that 0.5 volt provides a 0.25-ma base current. Assume that only one input—A, for example—is at its low value. The current through R_1 is the sum of the V_T/R_T current and the base current (Fig. 8.7). If the V_T current is 0.16 ma, the value of the input resistor R_1 is

$$\frac{(2 - 0.5) \text{ volts}}{(0.25 + 0.16) \text{ ma}} = 3{,}670 \text{ ohms}$$

Each input gating resistor will have this value.

When a transistor is off, its base voltage should be close to ground potential. The inputs are usually from the collectors of other transistor stages. For example, the inputs to Q_3 in Fig. 8.8 are from the collectors of Q_1 and Q_2.

To ensure that Q_3 remains off, the temperature-stabilizing network (V_T and R_T) provides a small current through R_4 and R_5 to aid in reverse-biasing the base-emitter junction. The V_T/R_T current is the sum of the expected cutoff current and the current necessary to maintain a base voltage of 0 during turn-off.

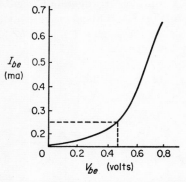

Fig. 8.9 Base input curve.

Circuit characteristics. RTL is applicable to low-frequency switching circuits. However, at higher frequencies the circuit becomes more complex. To increase speed, higher-frequency transistors and additional circuits to provide base overdrive can be used.

Figure 8.10 shows an RTL stage using diodes to prevent saturation and an RL network to provide base-current overdrive during turn-on and turn-off.

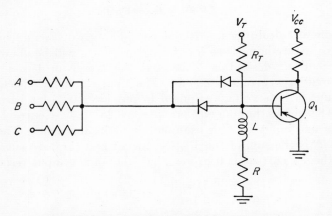

Fig. 8.10 Methods of improving RTL frequency response.

Resistor-Capacitor Transistor Logic

The standard method of providing base overdrive is to use speedup capacitors across the gating resistors as shown in Fig. 8.11.

The use of speedup capacitors may cause malfunctions in circuit operation. Without the coupling capacitors, the gating resistors serve to isolate the low input impedance of transistor Q_1 from the outputs of the collectors at A, B, and C. The coupling capacitors reduce this isolation. If A, B, and C are all at their lower level, the transistor is in saturation. Without the capacitors, if two of the inputs were to go to their upper level the transistor would decrease its conduction slightly but still remain in the saturation region. With the capacitors, the amount of charge current drawn out of the base as the inputs go to their upper level may be sufficient to turn the transistor off. At high frequencies the capacitors increase the amount of interaction between adjacent collectors. These disadvantages limit the number of inputs that may be applied.

Put capacitor in parallel to overdrive it.

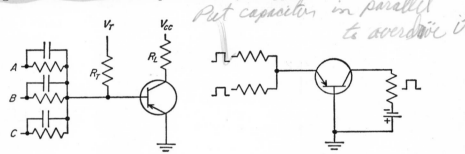

Fig. 8.11 RCTL circuit.   Fig. 8.12 Common-base logic.

Common-base configurations. A common-base configuration such as the one shown in Fig. 8.12 provides logical functions without phase inversions. The circuit does not provide current gain and thereby creates a heavy drain on the input. Coupling between stages presents a greater problem than does the common-emitter configuration since the common-base configuration has a higher output impedance and a lower input impedance.

Hybrid Logic

Hybrid logic is a combination of diode gates and transistor amplifiers. Since diode gates provide no amplification, amplifier stages must be placed between the gates at various intervals to prevent excessive attenuation of the signals.

It is not a task to determine exactly where in a logical sequence to place the amplifier stages. A good approach is to construct a basic building block composed of diode gates combined with an amplifier output. The basic building block will have a known input drive requirement and a known output drive capability. All required logical operations may be accomplished by combining the basic building blocks.

There are two basic switching techniques used in hybrid logic. These techniques differ in the way the transistor-amplifier stage is switched. One technique is voltage switching, in which a voltage is applied to the base of the transistor. The other technique is current switching, in which a constant current is switched in and out of the base of the transistor. Both techniques are now discussed.

Voltage-switching hybrid logic. A basic diode-gate–amplifier configuration is shown in Fig. 8.13. Diodes CR_1 and CR_2 and resistor R_1 constitute an AND gate for positive logic. The voltage at point 1 follows the lowest inputs applied to the gates. The input voltage levels used are -3 volts and 0 volt. The voltage at point 1 is 0 volt only if A and B are 0 volt simultaneously. If one of the inputs—B, for example—falls to -3 volts, CR_2 conducts harder and the entire voltage, disregarding the drop across the diode, is dropped across R_1. The voltage at point 1 falls

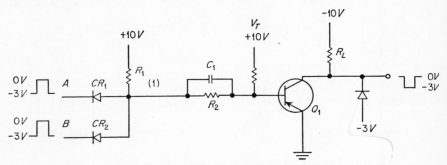

Fig. 8.13 Voltage-switching hybrid gate.

to -3 volts, and CR_1 is reverse-biased. Resistor R_2 limits the voltage applied to the base of Q_1.

The basic block in Fig. 8.13 can be expanded to include more gates. The most widely used sequence is a series of AND gates driving an OR gate. A logical diagram, together with its associated circuit, is shown in Fig. 8.14.

Diode gate G_3 is an OR gate for positive "true" signals. If, for example, point 1 is 0 volt and point 2 is -3 volts, CR_1 conducts harder than CR_2. Point 3 is 0 volt and CR_2 is reverse-biased. Q_1 conducts only when point 3 is -3 volts. The two-stage amplifier provides sufficient power to drive several stages. If required, the NOT function is available at the output of Q_1, and the "true" output is present at Q_2. A logical block usually has four AND gates driving an OR gate.

Current-switching hybrid logic. Current-switching techniques may be preferred to voltage-switching techniques because lower-amplitude pulses may be used and faster switching speed is obtained.

PREFERRED

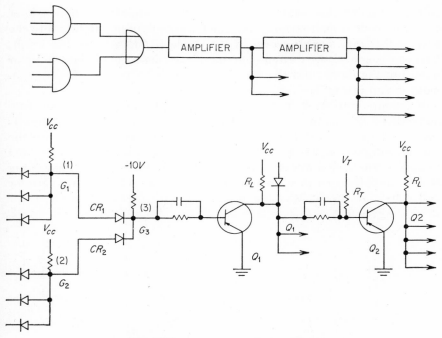

Fig. 8.14 AND-OR gate with inverters.

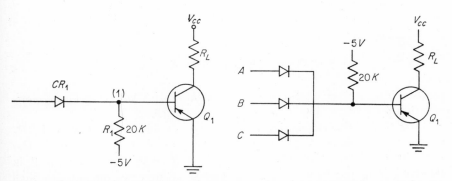

Fig. 8.15 Principle of current switching.   Fig. 8.16 Current-switching logical arrangement.

The principle of current switching is that a constant current is switched into either a transistor base or a diode. In Fig. 8.15 the 20,000-ohm resistor and the −5-volt supply provide the 0.25 ma of current to be switched.

If the input characteristics of the transistor indicate that a 0.25-ma base current requires a base-to-emitter voltage of −0.4 volt, then the voltage at point 1 is -0.4 volt. If -0.4 volt is applied to the anode of CR_1, the diode cannot conduct and the 0.25-ma current will flow into the base of the transistor. However, if the anode of CR_1 rises to $+0.4$ volt, CR_1 can conduct, the 0.25-ma current is switched out of the transistor base into the diode, and the transistor turns off. Consider the arrangement shown in Fig. 8.16.

If the inputs to A, B, and C are -0.4 volt, the diodes cannot conduct and current flows into the base of Q_1, turning Q_1 on. If one of the inputs rises to $+0.4$ volt, the current is diverted away from the base into the conducting diode and the transistor turns off. The voltage swing required to operate the gate is less than 1 volt as compared with the voltage swing of several volts used in voltage switching. The circuit is an OR gate for

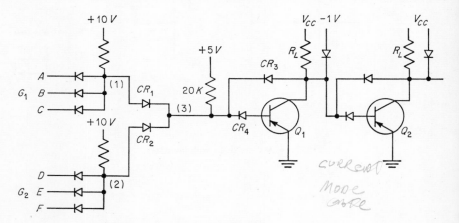

Fig. 8.17 Current-switching circuit with AND-OR input.

positive inputs or an AND gate for negative inputs. An AND-OR gate combination for positive inputs is shown in Fig. 8.17.

Gates G_1 and G_2 are positive AND-gate inputs. The diodes CR_1 and CR_2 provide the OR function for current steering. If the output of one of the AND gates goes positive, G_1 for example, CR_1 conducts and current is removed from the base of Q_1. The two-stage inverter output provides both the NOT function, when required, and current to drive several other inputs.

The inputs to the AND gates are from the collector outputs of other logical stages. A level-shift problem must be overcome to ensure that when all inputs are at their upper levels the voltages at the anodes of CR_1 and CR_2 are sufficiently positive to allow CR_1 and CR_2 to conduct. The problem can be overcome by using silicon diodes in the AND gates and germanium diodes in the OR gates. The silicon diodes have a higher voltage drop than germanium diodes. Assume that the collector potential at input A goes no lower than -0.2 volt. If, for the amount of current drawn, the silicon diode has a voltage drop of 0.6 the voltage at point 1 will be $+0.4$ volt. This voltage is sufficient to allow CR_1 to conduct. When the voltage at A rises to -1 volt, the voltage at point 1 is -0.4 volt and the OR-gate diode CR_1 cannot conduct.

A diode back-clamping circuit may be used to prevent saturation. The back-clamping circuit may also provide a base overdrive current to decrease turn-on time. The constant-current source supplies more than the required amount of base current to saturate the transistor. When the collector potential falls so that CR_3 can conduct, the additional base current flows through CR_3 and is not amplified in the base. CR_4 is a silicon diode used to maintain a constant base voltage.

Circuit characteristics. If the current-steering technique is used, the collector voltage varies by only a few tenths of a volt. This voltage swing is small compared with the collector supply voltage; hence, very little power is consumed. The system is often referred to as *low-level logic*. The base current comes from a constant-current source; therefore, the number of diode inputs does not affect the base current. Since only a small portion of the collector swing is used, the switching speed is increased.

Current-mode Logic

CML utilizes another form of current switching. The input transistor current is provided by a constant-current source. This current is switched from one transistor to the other, as shown in Fig. 8.18. In this illustration the total current is 10 ma. This current flows through the transistor which has the more negative base potential. Assume that the base of Q_1 (point A) is -0.4 volt and the base of Q_2 is grounded. Transistor Q_1 conducts and the 10 ma, less the base current, flows to the collector of Q_1. If we assume a 0.2-volt drop across the base-emitter junction of Q_1, point C is -0.2 volt and the base-emitter junction of Q_2 is reverse-biased. Assume that the voltage at

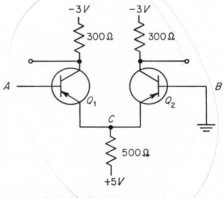

Fig. 8.18 Current-mode switch.

point A rises to $+0.4$ volt. Q_1 turns off and Q_2 conducts. Point C becomes slightly positive because of the base-emitter voltage drop at Q_2.

Figure 8.19 shows a current-mode logical gate. The three inputs to the gate are A, B, and C. If a negative voltage is applied to any input, the collector rises to its upper level. If all inputs are positive simultaneously, the current is switched into Q_4, and the collector of Q_4 rises to its upper level. The circuit is a negative-input OR gate or a positive-input AND gate.

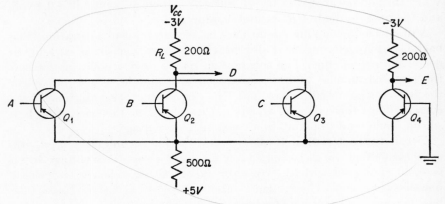

Fig. 8.19 Current-mode logical gate.

The voltages at outputs D and E are the logical inverse of each other; hence, the circuit can provide both an inverted and a noninverted output. If the noninverted output of Q_4 is not required, the transistor may be replaced by a diode.

The circuit can be designed so that the transistor may be operated as far out of saturation as desired. The collector voltage V_c is determined by the following equation:

$$V_c = V_{cc} - I_e R_L$$

If the collector voltage at the upper level shown in Fig. 8.21 is to be -1 volt, the load resistor R_L may be found by the following equation:

$$R_L = \frac{V_{cc} - V_c}{I_e}$$

If V_{cc} is -3 volts and I_e is 10 ma, R_L is determined by the following equation:

$$\frac{(3 - 1) \text{ volts}}{10 \text{ ma}} = 200 \text{ ohms}$$

Coupling PNP and NPN gates. When PNP-transistor gates are used, a sufficiently positive voltage must be applied to the bases to ensure that the gates are off. In this example, the collectors go no more positive than -1 volt. A level shift must be provided between the output from one gate and the input to the following stage. Circuits may be placed between stages to provide this level shift. The level-shift problem may be eliminated if PNP and NPN gates are used alternately. The output of the PNP gate has the correct polarity to switch an NPN gate, and the output of an NPN gate has the correct polarity to switch a PNP gate. A system is shown in Fig. 8.20.

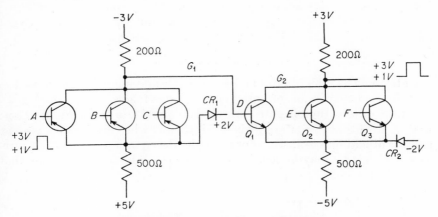

Fig. 8.20 PNP gate driving an NPN gate.

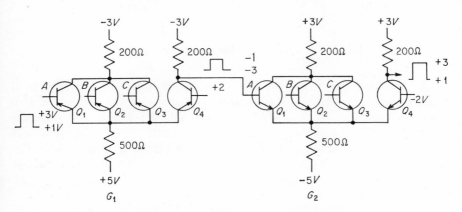

Fig. 8.21 Use of alternate-side collectors to avoid signal inversion.

The collector output of the PNP gate is applied to one of the NPN-gate inputs. Transistor Q_4, shown in Fig. 8.19, has been replaced by diode CR_1. Assume that inputs E and F of G2 are -3 volts so that Q_2 and Q_3 are off. If the input D of G2 is -1 volt, Q_1 conducts. If we assume a 0.4-volt drop across the base and emitter of Q_1, the emitter voltage is -0.6 volt. This voltage disconnects diode CR_2. When the input at D falls to -3 volts, Q_1 cuts off and CR_2 conducts. The collector output of G2 is positive with reference to ground and can be coupled to the input of a PNP gate.

The inversion problem may be avoided by utilizing the output of Q_4 as shown in Fig. 8.21.

Current-mode switching circuits are applicable for high-speed switching. Saturation delay is not a problem since the circuits can be operated as far out of saturation as desired. The transistors used with this type of switching may operate at frequencies in the megacycle range.

Special Gates

Gates such as inhibit gates and gated pulse amplifiers are often used in computers. Descriptions of both types of gates follow.

Inhibit gates. Inhibit gates are used to provide a BUT-NOT function; that is, an output from the gate is obtained only when one input is present and the other input is absent. For example, the equation $A\bar{B} = C$ (A BUT-NOT B equals C) may be achieved by using an inhibit gate such as that shown in Fig. 8.22.

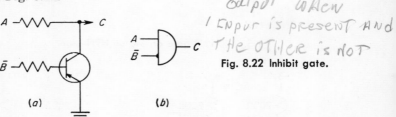

output when 1 input is present and the other is not

Fig. 8.22 Inhibit gate.

(a)   (b)

Assume that the "true" level is −6 volts. If −6 volts is applied to A and B simultaneously, the transistor conducts and the output at C is close to 0 volt. If −6 volts is applied to A, and B is 0 volt, the transistor does not conduct and the voltage at C is −6 volts. C can only be at −6 volts when the condition $A\bar{B}$ exists. The dot on the B input line in Fig. 8.22 indicates that B must not be present if an output C is to be obtained.

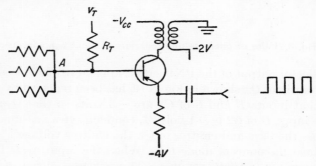

Fig. 8.23 Gated pulse amplifier.

Gated pulse amplifier. A gated pulse amplifier is shown in Fig. 8.23. The pulses applied to the emitter are gated by the voltage applied to the base. The emitter supply is -4 volts, and the input pulses vary between -2 and 0 volt. The duration of the pulses applied to the resistor gates is long compared with the pulses applied to the emitter. If point A is 0 volt, the emitter-base junction remains reverse-biased and the transistor does not conduct. If point A is -4 volts, the base voltage is sufficiently negative to allow conduction when the emitter pulses are applied.

Summary

Transistor logic may be used in preference to diode logic because of amplification and higher switching frequencies attainable.

There are basically five logical systems. The choice of a logical system depends upon the switching speeds desired, the relative cost, the power requirements, and the environment in which the system is used (amount of noise voltage present, etc.).

DCTL is simple and easy to design. Since low voltages are used, noise voltages are a problem. The circuit characteristics depend largely upon the characteristics of the transistor. This system is expensive because a transistor is required for each input.

RTL is economical when high switching speeds are not required. The circuits are easy to design, and the transistor requirements are not so stringent as for DCTL.

RCTL is faster than RTL; however, additional components are required. The coupling capacitors limit the number of inputs applied to a gate.

HTL utilizes the features of diode logic. Considering the amplifier as a part of the logic block provides a basic building block having a known input requirement and a known output drive capability. The transistor is not affected by the number of input gates. Low voltage levels may be used in the current-mode operation, thus reducing the effect of stray capacitance and allowing a faster switching speed.

CML provides high switching speeds. The components may be chosen to keep the transistor well out of saturation. High-speed switching transistors are used in this system.

The common-emitter configuration is that most frequently used in logical circuits. This configuration provides current and voltage gains, but signal inversion is a problem. Inverters may be inserted when required to provide the correct polarity. These are considered as electric inverters rather than logical inverters.

QUESTIONS

8.1 List the five basic transistor gate configurations and give a brief description of each.

8.2 What factors should be considered in the selection of a system of transistor logic?

8.3 Which types of transistor gates are suitable for high switching speeds? Why?

8.4 Which type of transistor gate is the least expensive of the five described?

8.5 Why is the grounded-emitter configuration most commonly used?

8.6 In the DCTL system, what limits the collector voltage of an OFF transistor to less than -1 volt?

8.7 What is the difference between a positive-input AND gate and a negative-input OR gate?

Chapter 9

Multivibrators

A workhorse since the early development of radar, the multivibrator in its various configurations has become the backbone of digital computers. A modification of the multivibrator, known by such names as *flip-flop*, *toggle*, *binary*, or *switch*, is found throughout modern automatic high-speed digital computers. Multivibrators have many applications, from storing binary information to generating, shaping, and delaying pulses. While the subject of multivibrators encompasses a wide range of circuitry, this chapter treats only the most frequently encountered stable and monostable types.

The multivibrator is a two-stage regenerative amplifier characterized by a large excess of positive feedback. Conduction in one amplifier causes rapid cutoff in the other. Such an amplifier may exist in either of two *end states* or *states of conduction*. One state exists when one tube, conducting heavily, holds the other at cutoff. The alternative state exists when the opposite is true.

The states of a multivibrator may be either stable or quasi-stable. A circuit in the stable state remains in one of its end states indefinitely or until externally disturbed. A circuit in the quasi-stable state remains in that state only momentarily and then, after a period determined by circuit time constants, makes an abrupt transition to the opposite state. Multivibrators are classified as astable, monostable, or bistable according to the number of stable end states.

This chapter is divided into two major parts. Part I covers vacuum-tube multivibrators in order to include the basic principles of operation. Part II describes the theory of operation of transistorized multivibrators. The bistable multivibrator is covered in Chap. 10.

166

PART I: MULTIVIBRATOR CIRCUITS EMPLOYING ELECTRON TUBES

Astable (Free-running) Multivibrator

The astable multivibrator, as its name implies, has no stable state. Rather, it oscillates between two states that are semistable (quasi-stable). The circuit is often classified as a free-running relaxation oscillator. The output waveform (Fig. 9.1a) is rectangular and may be symmetrical (square) or nonsymmetrical, depending on the choice of circuit components. The output waveform is the same regardless of the shape or amplitude of the triggering pulse.

Because of its rectangular waveform the astable multivibrator is often used as a pulse generator for testing digital circuitry. It may also be used as a means of frequency division. The circuit most commonly used in these applications is called the *plate-coupled astable multivibrator* and is illustrated in Fig. 9.1.

This circuit is essentially a two-stage RC-coupled voltage amplifier with the output of each stage connected to the input of the other. The circuit arrangement provides the amplification and regenerative feedback required to start and sustain oscillations. A brief description of circuit action will aid in the detailed discussion to follow.

When power is first applied, one tube is driven abruptly into saturation because of regenerative feedback. The other tube, driven by the first, is rapidly cut off. The circuit rests in this semistable state for a period of time determined by coupling time constants. Thereafter, an abrupt transition to the opposite state occurs. The circuit oscillates continuously between these two states until power is removed. The output waveforms (Fig. 9.1) clearly show the on-off action of each tube.

The details of circuit action are more easily understood if the explanation is divided into three parts as follows:

1. The transition to the initial end state
2. The circuit action during the semistable state or rest period
3. The transition to the opposite state

Transition to the initial end state. When power is applied to the circuit shown in Fig. 9.1, the grids (G_1 and G_2) of both tubes are at zero potential. During this interval, surge currents charge capacitors C_1 and C_2 through grid resistors to bias G_1 and G_2 positive with respect to ground (see Fig. 9.2). Both tubes (V_1 and V_2) conduct heavily. Because of variations in the tolerances of circuit components, one tube will conduct more heavily than the other. Assume V_1 conducts more heavily. The increase in current through V_1 increases the voltage drop across R_{L_1} and causes the plate-to-

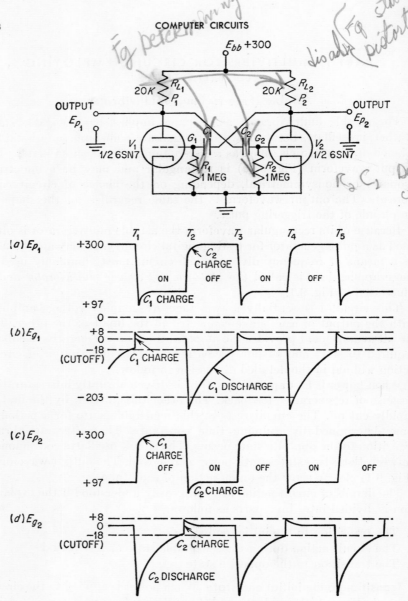

Fig. 9.1 Astable multivibrator and waveforms.

ground potential (E_{p_1}) to decrease. C_2, previously charged by surge currents, now discharges to this lower potential. The discharge current of C_2 flows in the direction shown in Fig. 9.2b and biases G_2 negatively with respect to ground. The current through V_2 decreases. Since a small change in grid voltage results in a large change in plate current, the potential

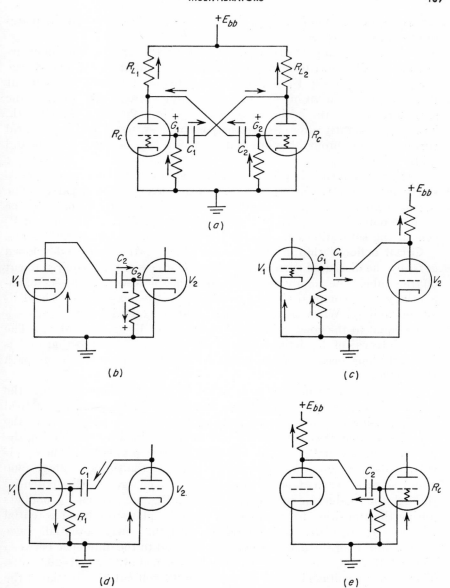

Fig. 9.2 Charge and discharge paths of coupling capacitors. (a) C_1 and C_2 charge paths when power is applied. (b) C_2 discharge path (long time constant). (c) C_1 charge path (short time constant). (d) C_1 discharge path. (e) C_2 charge path.

across R_{L_2} drops considerably and results in a large increase in the plate-to-ground potential of V_2.

Capacitor C_1, previously charged by surge currents, continues its charge, rapidly now, toward the increasing potential at P_2. The charge current of C_1 biases V_1 positively and further increases the current through V_1. As shown in Fig. 9.2c, the charge current of C_1 flows in the same direction as the initial surge current (Fig. 9.2a). The charge path, however, is slightly altered since the positively swinging grid causes grid current to flow through the internal resistance (R_c) between cathode and grid.

The cycle of events described above repeats itself, G_1 becoming progressively more positive as G_2 becomes progressively more negative. The process continues until the negative potential at G_2 cuts V_2 off, and the positive potential at G_1 drives V_1 into grid clamp. With V_2 cut off and V_1 conducting saturation current, the circuit rests in its quasi-stable state.

Circuit action during the rest period. The negative voltage developed at G_2 by the discharge current of C_2 is far in excess of that required to cut off the tube. The highly negative potential, however, decreases exponentially as C_2 completes its discharge and for this reason cannot hold V_2 off indefinitely. When the decreasing negative potential at G_2 reaches a value equal to the conduction level of the tube, V_2 again conducts. The cutoff interval of V_2 determines the duration of the rest period and is relatively long because of the long time constant of the discharge path (Fig. 9.2b).

Circuit action during the rest period is better understood when the magnitude of the coupling voltages is considered. Consider a practical example using the component values of Fig. 9.1. The magnitude of the negative voltage that cuts off V_2 may be determined by considering the potential change at P_1 as V_1 swings from saturation to cutoff. When V_1 is cut off, its plate-to-ground potential is equal to the supply voltage (300 volts) since no current flows through R_{L_1}. C_2 charges to this potential through the conducting tube V_2, as shown in Fig. 9.2e. When V_1 conducts during the transition to the opposite state, its plate-to-ground potential decreases to 97 volts. C_2 discharges toward this lower potential. Since the magnitude of the discharge voltage is equal to the difference between 300 and 97 volts, the negative potential developed at G_2 equals 203 volts. This negative voltage is far in excess of the 18-volt cutoff potential of the tube used in the example. The negative swing of G_2 during this interval and the exponential discharge toward the conduction level of the tube are shown in Fig. 9.1d.

Transition to the opposite state. Transition to the opposite state occurs when V_2 conducts after the rest period. Conduction of V_2 cuts off V_1 because of the regenerative action described previously. V_1 is held at cutoff by the discharge current of C_1 in a manner similar to that described for V_2 cutoff. The charge and discharge paths for C_1 are identical with those of C_2 and are shown in Fig. 9.2c and d.

One complete cycle of the oscillating mode is indicated in the waveform drawing in Fig. 9.1a. Time 1 (t_1) represents the transition to the initial end state; time 2 (t_2), the V_2 rest period; time 3 (t_3), the transition to the opposite state; and time 4 (t_4), the rest period of V_2.

The circuit oscillates continuously in this fashion until power is removed. Since the switching time $(t_1$ and $t_3)$ is small compared with the duration of the rest periods, the frequency of the astable multivibrator depends chiefly on the discharge time of C_1 and C_2 during the rest periods $(t_2$ and $t_4)$. This time is determined by the cutoff potential of the tube, the supply voltage, and the time constant of the discharge paths. The following equation gives the time for one rest period:

$$T = R_1 C_1 \log_e \left(\frac{E_{bb} - E_m}{E_{co}} \right)$$

where E_{bb} = plate supply voltage
E_m = minimum voltage on plate
E_{co} = cutoff voltage corresponding to E_{bb}
T = time for one rest period

The value of the logarithm in the above formula varies only slightly for large changes in $E_{bb} - E_m$. In most practical circuits, this value is approximately equal to 2. Hence, in practical units the following simplified formula may be used with little error:

$$T = 2 R_1 C_1$$

The time for one complete cycle is equal to the sum of the two rest intervals; and in the symmetrical case where $R_1 C_1 = R_2 C_2$, the following formulas apply:

$$T_T = 4RC \qquad F = \frac{1}{4RC}$$

where F = frequency of oscillation

A rectangular pulse waveform, as opposed to a square wave, may be obtained in the output by making the time constants of the two rest periods unequal. Frequency stability suffers, however, when the duration of the two rest periods differs by a factor of more than 10.

Output waveforms. Although the output waveshape is essentially rectangular, small distortions are present because of capacitor charge currents (Fig. 9.1). For example, the positive overshoot in the grid waveform E_{g_2} is due to the voltage dropped across the grid-to-cathode resistance of V_2 during the charge of C_2. An amplified version of this overshoot appears as a negative spike (undershoot) on the plate waveform of V_2 (E_{p_2}); and, since E_{p_2} is coupled to the grid of V_1, the amplified negative spike appears also in the waveform E_{g_1}. This same charge current of C_2 results in the roll-off in the plate waveform of V_1 (E_{p_1}) in the following way: When V_1 cuts off, C_2 charge current flowing through R_{L_1} produces a voltage drop and prevents P_1 from rising immediately to the supply voltage. Overshoot and roll-off in the output waveform may be removed by clipping in succeeding stages or by making slight changes to the basic circuit shown in Fig. 9.1.

Circuit variations. Since all distortion in the output waveshape is due to the flow of grid current during the charge time of C_1 and C_2, it may be eliminated through the use of grid-limiting resistors (RGL) as shown by the circuit and associated waveforms in Fig. 9.3a. Because the grid-limiting resistor is much greater than R_c, most of the voltage developed at point A during the charge interval is dropped across RGL rather than from grid to ground. This effectively reduces the grid voltage to 0. An alternative method for improving the output waveshape is shown in Fig. 9.3b. The output is taken across a series cathode resistor and hence takes the shape of the current in the output tube, an improvement over the plate waveform. In the circuit shown in Fig. 9.3c, the grid resistors are returned to the supply voltage rather than to ground. This arrangement does not affect the output waveshape, but results in considerable improvement in the frequency stability of the basic circuit.

In the basic circuit shown in Fig. 9.1, the slope of the discharge curve during the rest period approaches the conduction level of the tube gradually rather than abruptly because 90 per cent of the discharge curve is used. This is shown by the dotted line in Fig. 9.3c. For this reason, small variations in the conduction level, due to changes in temperature, supply voltage, etc., cause large changes in duration of the rest period. When the grid resistors are returned to the supply voltage, C_1 and C_2 discharge to a higher potential, and only the initial linear portion of the discharge curve is used. Compare the waveforms in Fig. 9.1b with those in Fig. 9.3c. Note that in Fig. 9.3c the discharge curve strikes the conduction level of the tube more abruptly. Changes in the conduction level now result in smaller changes in the time the tube is cut off. This results in improved frequency stability.

The oscillating frequency of the circuit shown in Fig. 9.3c is higher than that of the basic circuit. C_1 and C_2 now discharge to the positive potential of the source rather than to ground; hence, the conduction level is reached sooner. For practical work the duration of one cycle may be determined by the following simplified formulas:

$$T_T = \frac{R_1 C_1 + R_2 C_2}{2}$$

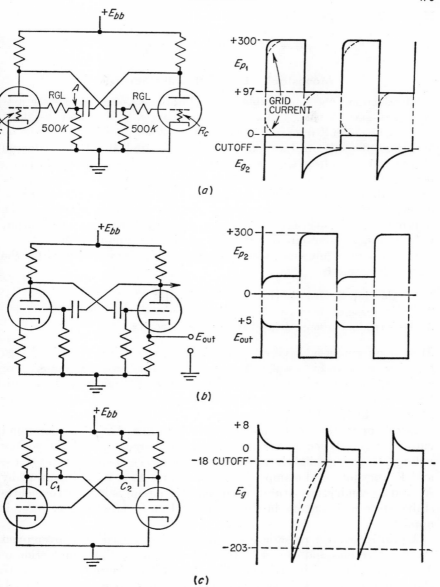

Fig. 9.3 Astable-multivibrator waveforms and circuit variations.

Now if $R_1C_1 = R_2C_2$, then

$$T = RC \quad \text{and} \quad F = \frac{1}{RC}$$

Monostable (One-shot) Multivibrator

Introduction. The monostable multivibrator has one stable state and one quasi-stable state. Unlike the astable type, it does not oscillate. Instead, the circuit rests in a permanently stable condition (one tube on and the other off) until an external trigger is applied. At that time an abrupt transition from the stable to the quasi-stable state occurs. After a period of rest determined by circuit time constants, the multivibrator returns abruptly to the initial permanent state. Each applied trigger produces one complete rectangular pulse. For this reason the circuit is often referred to as the *one-shot multivibrator*. Figure 9.4c compares the output pulse of the one-shot circuit with that of the free-running type.

In computer equipment, the monostable multivibrator is used for the following purposes:

1. To develop accurately timed gating signals
2. To increase or decrease the width of a pulse
3. To introduce a time delay between two circuits

Most free-running multivibrator circuits may be converted to the driven one-shot version by simply biasing one of the tubes to cutoff. For example, if V_1 in Fig. 9.1 is biased to cutoff through R_{g_1}, the circuit becomes identical with the basic plate-coupled monostable multivibrator illustrated in Fig. 9.4.

Circuit operation. Referring to Fig. 9.4, assume V_1 is biased beyond cutoff by E_{cc}. When power is applied, C_2 charges toward the supply voltage. G_2 swings slightly positive because of the charge current of C_2, and V_2 goes into grid clamp (time 1, waveform E_{g_2}). With V_1 cut off by E_{cc} and V_2 conducting saturation current, the circuit is in its permanently stable state and remains in this state until an external trigger pulse is applied.

A positive trigger pulse in excess of 50 volts applied to G_1 overcomes the negative bias and causes V_1 to conduct (time 2, E_{g_1}). Conduction of V_1, due to the positive trigger pulse, initiates an abrupt transition to the opposite state. This switching action is due to regenerative feedback and is identical with the process described for the free-running multivibrator.

During this quasi-stable period, the discharge current of C_2 biases V_2 negatively far beyond the cutoff level of the tube. V_2 remains cut off until the negative potential at G_2 decreases to the conduction level (time 3,

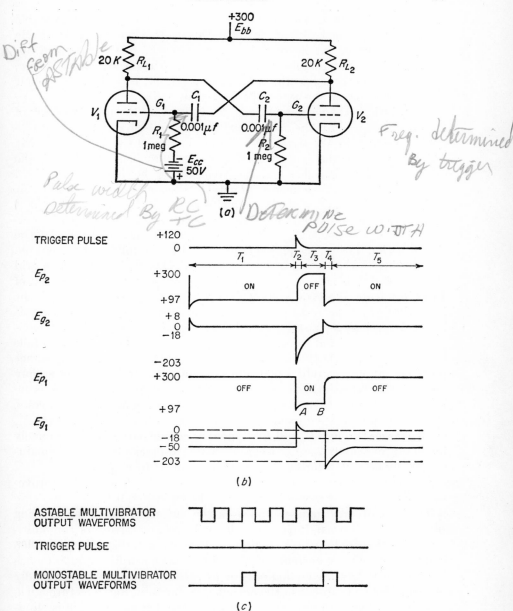

Handwritten annotations: *Dift from ASTABLE*, *Pulse width determined By RC + C*, *Freq. determined By trigger*, *Determine PULSE WIDTH*

(a)

TRIGGER PULSE

E_{p_2}

E_{g_2}

E_{p_1}

E_{g_1}

(b)

ASTABLE MULTIVIBRATOR OUTPUT WAVEFORMS

TRIGGER PULSE

MONOSTABLE MULTIVIBRATOR OUTPUT WAVEFORMS

(c)

Fig. 9.4 (a) Basic plate-coupled monostable-multivibrator circuit. (b) Monostable-multivibrator waveforms. (c) Comparison of free-running and monostable-multivibrator waveforms.

E_{g_2}). When V_2 conducts, switching again occurs and the normal stable state is reestablished (V_1 off, V_2 on). During this return to the stable state, G_1 is driven far beyond the cutoff potential of the tube and approaches the conduction level as C_1 discharges (time 5, E_{g_1}). In this case, however, G_1 never reaches the conduction level, but is held at a -50-volt potential because of the external bias supply $-E_{cc}$.

The width of the output pulse is determined by the time constant of C_2–R_2 as was true for the astable circuit. The roll-off and overshoot distortion present in the waveforms shown in Fig. 9.4 is similar to that which appears in the astable output. As was previously explained, the distortion is due to the flow of grid current during the charge of C_1 and C_2.

It may not be immediately apparent when considering the circuit arrangement in Fig. 9.4 why E_{g_1} remains at 0 volt during the interval A to B. It may seem likely that V_2 would be cut off by E_{cc} after C_1 is completely charged (point A, E_{g_1}). For this reason, an explanation of the circuit action during this period is presented in the following paragraph.

Referring to the circuit in Fig. 9.4, we see that G_1 is driven into grid clamp when V_2 is cut off. At this time, the plate-to-ground potential of V_2 swings from 97 to 300 volts. C_2 charges to this potential through the low grid-to-cathode resistance of V_1. Grid current flowing during this interval develops the positive overshoot at G_1 (Fig. 9.4b). When C_1 is completely charged to 300 volts, grid current ceases and the G_1 potential falls to 0 (point A, E_{g_1}). During the overshoot interval, the low-impedance path (R_c approximately 1,000 ohms) shunts R_1 and the bias supply voltage E_{cc}. When grid current ceases, however, the bias supply is no longer shunted by R_c, and C_1 continues to charge an additional 50 volts. Point G_1 tends to swing from 0 volt toward the negative bias voltage E_{cc} as C_1 charges through R_1 and R_{L_2}. Since the charge path of C_1 is extremely long (approximately 2 sec), C_1 cannot charge appreciably, and G_1 remains effectively at 0 volt during the entire interval (C to B, E_{g_1}).

Circuit variations. The circuit illustrated in Fig. 9.5a is an improvement over the basic monostable circuit shown in Fig. 9.4.

This circuit arrangement improves the output pulse by eliminating some of the roll-off and overshoot distortion characteristic of the multivibrators discussed thus far. As previously explained, this pulse distortion is due to the charge currents of C_1 and C_2. As shown in Fig. 9.5, C_2 has been replaced by the coupling resistor RC. Hence, the distortion normally produced by C_1 is absent in the output waveforms in Fig. 9.5b through d. The dashed lines in these waveforms show the distortion which is eliminated. The overshoot and roll-off distortion still present in the waveforms in Fig. 9.5 is due to the presence of C_2. This coupling element cannot be replaced by a resistor as in the case of C_1 since C_2 also serves as the timing capacitor that determines the pulse duration.

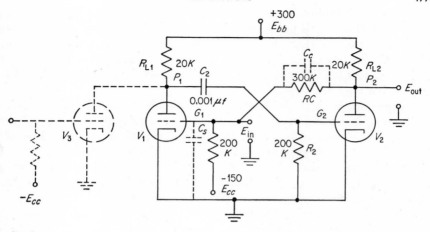

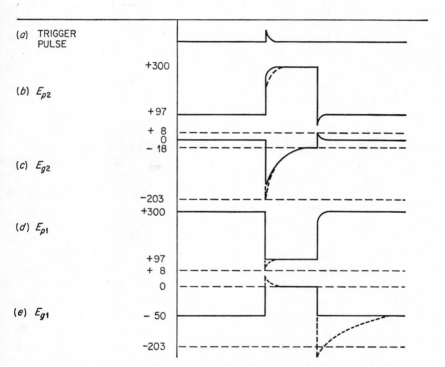

Fig. 9.5 Monostable multivibrator and waveforms.

Commutating cap — to insure reliable triggering

In practical applications, the output is usually taken at the grid of V_1 since the pulse at this point contains no distortion and has steep leading and trailing edges (Fig. 9.5b). If the larger amplitude available at the plates of V_1 and V_2 is desired, the output at P_2 (Fig. 9.5b) is used because of its superior trailing edge. The negative undershoot is then clipped in succeeding stages.

Triggering. Both the basic monostable circuit (Fig. 9.4) and the variation shown in Fig. 9.5 may be triggered by a positive pulse at G_1 or P_2 or by a negative pulse at G_2 or P_1. Reliable triggering will occur only if the impedance of the trigger source is sufficiently high to prevent loading of the multivibrator circuit. In practical work, diode or triode triggering is employed. Triode triggering is generally preferred because this method provides voltage amplification of the trigger pulse.

When triode triggering is employed, the trigger circuit (V_3) is connected as shown in Fig. 9.5. The trigger tube (V_3) is biased to cutoff during the interval between trigger pulses and, hence, presents a high impedance to P_1. A positive trigger pulse at the grid of V_3 drives the tube into grid clamp. The resulting saturation current flowing through R_L causes the potential at P_1 to go sharply negative. The negative pulse at P_1 is coupled to G_2 through C_2 and decreases the conduction in tube V_2. If the resulting increase in the plate-to-ground potential of V_2 is great enough to bring V_1 to the conduction level, regenerative feedback will then complete the switching process.

The commutating capacitor. When pulses of short duration are used to trigger the multivibrator, it is possible for the trigger pulse to have passed before the circuit has time to respond. A small commutating capacitor (approximately 50 $\mu\mu f$) placed across RC, the coupling resistor, will increase the response time of the circuit and ensure reliable triggering. For example, assume the trigger tube has been activated, the negative pulse at P_1 has decreased current in V_2, and the resultant increase in the potential at P_2 is being coupled through RC to G_1. The appearance of the voltage fed to G_1 from P_2 will be delayed by the time required for the distributed capacitance C_s to charge to this more positive voltage. Since C_s must charge through the large coupling resistor RC, it is possible for the trigger pulse to pass before switching has been completed. The commutating capacitor C_c shunts RC and permits C_s to charge rapidly.

Typical application. The monostable multivibrator is frequently used in computer equipment to introduce a time delay between two circuits. Figure 9.6 illustrates how this is accomplished.

Accurately timed pulses termed *clock pulses* (signal A) are applied at the input of a monostable multivibrator. One pulse is produced for each input trigger at the output of the multivibrator (signal B). These pulses are differentiated by an RC network (signal C). The positive peak is clipped (signal *D*), then inverted in the pulse amplifier (signal *E*), and appears at the output as a positive spike. A comparison of the input and output pulses (signals *A* and *E*) shows that the output pulse is delayed

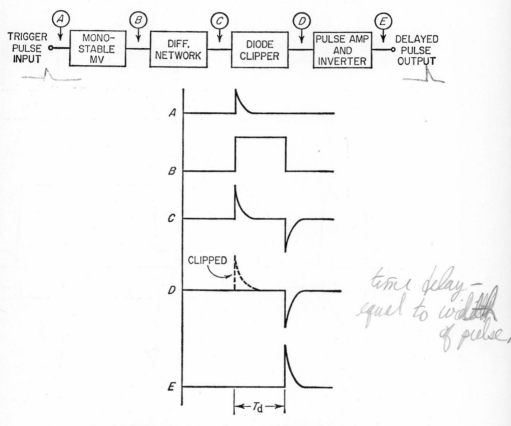

Fig. 9.6 Delay elements and monostable multivibrator.

relative to the input pulse by the delay time (*t*). The delay time is determined by the pulse width of the monostable circuit.

PART II: TRANSISTOR MULTIVIBRATOR CIRCUITS

Transistor multivibrator circuits are counterparts of those using electron tubes. For example, the arrangement of components in the astable transistor circuit shown in Fig. 9.7 is identical with that shown in the vacuum-tube equivalent in Fig. 9.3*c*.

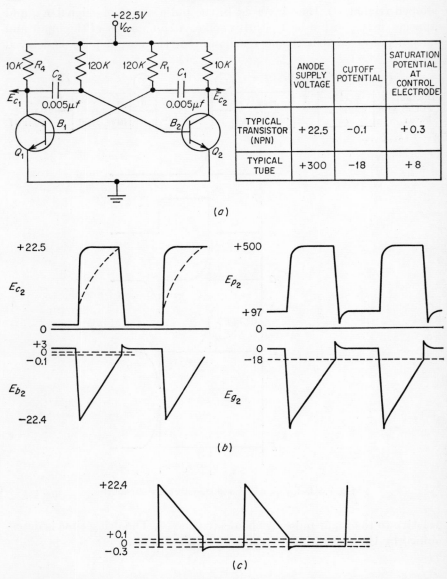

Fig. 9.7 (a) Transistor astable multivibrator. (b) Comparison of waveforms. (c) PNP base waveform.

A comparison of the operating waveforms of the two types (Fig. 9.7) indicates that circuit action is also identical. For this reason the discussion of transistor multivibrators presented in the following paragraphs is brief. Emphasis is placed on circuit characteristics which differ from those of the vacuum-tube counterpart. Where details of circuit action are not given, reference is made to the discussion of the vacuum-tube equivalents.

Although both PNP and NPN transistors are used in practical work, the NPN type is shown in most illustrations in this chapter. This practice facilitates the understanding of circuit action since the NPN is more nearly analogous to the triode vacuum tube. For example, the anode supply voltage for both the NPN transistor and the triode is positive. Also, in the two amplifier types a positive potential applied to the input will cause saturation current and a negative potential of sufficient magnitude will produce cutoff. The most significant difference between the two amplifiers is the operating potentials normally encountered in practical work. These are compared in the table in Fig. 9.7.

Collector-coupled Astable (Free-running) Multivibrator

The transistor circuit shown in Fig. 9.7, like its counterpart (Fig. 9.3c), functions as a relaxation oscillator. The state of conduction in each transistor alternately changes from cutoff to saturation. Conduction of one transistor causes cutoff of the other so that when one is on, the other is off. Oscillations are self-starting when power is applied and continue until power is removed.

The function of each component in the transistor multivibrator shown in Fig. 9.7 is identical with that performed by the corresponding component in the vacuum-tube circuit. For example, R_1–C_1 and R_2–C_2 are the coupling elements and also determine the pulse width and the pulse repetition rate of the output waveform. In this circuit, the value of R_1 or R_2 is much smaller than the input impedance of the transistor at cutoff. A typical value for input resistance is 250,000 ohms. In special cases, when this value differs, the parallel combination of R_1 and the input resistance must be considered in calculating the pulse width and the pulse repetition frequency. The circuit shown in Fig. 9.7 may be used in a test set to produce a train of pulses for checking computer components.

The operating waveforms of the collector-coupled transistor multivibrator and the plate-coupled vacuum-tube multivibrator are compared in Fig. 9.7b. There is a definite similarity between the two. Two differences can be observed, however. Notice that the output-voltage swing in the transistor is more nearly equal to the supply voltage. When the transistor conducts, only 0.1 volt is dropped across it since the resistance from collector to emitter is less than 50 ohms. Compare this with the voltage drop of 97 volts across the 10,000-ohm resistance of the conducting vacuum tube. Obviously, the transistor acts more nearly like an ideal switch. Also, there is an apparent absence of undershoot distortion in the collector waveform of the transistor multivibrator. The undershoot is actually present; but, because of the low impedance of the conducting transistor, it has a magnitude of only millivolts and is therefore not significant. When low collector supply voltages are used or when the multivibrator is designed to operate at high frequencies, "tilt" in the collector waveforms will be observed. This is shown by dashed lines in the waveforms in Fig. 9.7b and is due to slowing of the cutoff process by minority-carrier storage.

If the polarity of the supply voltage is reversed in the circuit shown in Fig. 9.7, a PNP transistor may be substituted for the NPN transistor shown, with no significant change in circuit action. C_1 and C_2 charge and discharge through the same paths previously explained for the vacuum-tube equivalent, but the direction of both the charge and discharge paths will be opposite to that of the vacuum-tube circuit. This, of course, is due to the negative source potential and the opposite bias characteristics of PNP transistors when compared with NPN transistors and triode tubes.

The base waveform associated with the circuit shown in Fig. 9.7a when PNP transistors are used is illustrated in Fig. 9.7c. This waveform, sometimes confusing to the technician experienced with vacuum-tube circuits, is seen to be an inverted mirror image of the NPN waveform (Fig. 9.7b) and is caused by C_2 discharging in the opposite direction.

Transistor Monostable (One-shot) Multivibrator

A basic transistor multivibrator of the one-shot type is shown in Fig. 9.8. The circuit and its operating waveforms are identical with those of the vacuum-tube equivalent in Fig. 9.5.

As was true in the vacuum-tube counterpart, coupling between stages is accomplished through the use of a coupling resistor instead of a capacitor to reduce overshoot and roll-off distortion. Accordingly, the outputs at V_2 and B_1 corresponding to P_2 and G_1 in Fig. 9.5 are essentially rectangular and distortion-free. A brief description of circuit action is now given.

In the circuit of Fig. 9.8, Q_2 is biased positively by the collector supply voltage V_{cc} through R_2, and Q_1 is biased negatively by its base-bias supply V_{bb}. Initially, therefore, the circuit rests in a stable state with Q_2 conducting saturation current and Q_1 cut off (time 1, Fig. 9.8b). A positive trigger pulse of sufficient amplitude to overcome the negative bias at B_1 will forward-bias Q_1 and cause it to conduct. Conduction of Q_1 due to the positive trigger pulse initiates an abrupt transition to the opposite state and is caused by the regenerative feedback previously described.

With Q_2 cut off and Q_1 conducting saturation current, the circuit rests in its quasi-stable state (time 2, Fig. 9.8b).

During the rest period, C_2 discharges toward the low collector potential of Q_1. The discharge current flowing through R_2 biases Q_2 negatively, well below the cutoff level of the transistor. Q_2 remains cut off until the nega-

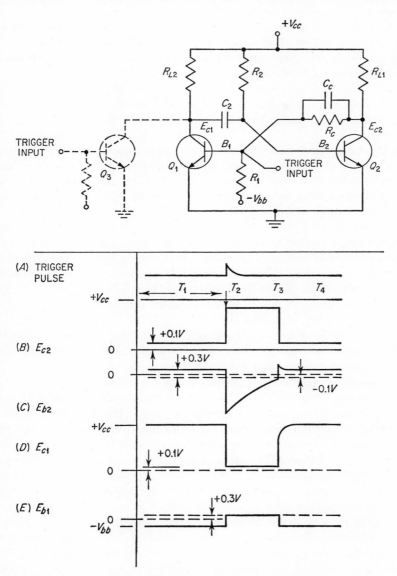

Fig. 9.8 NPN monostable multivibrator and waveforms.

tive potential at B_2 decreases to the conduction level of the transistor (approximately 0.2 volt positive).

When Q_2 conducts, an abrupt switching action again occurs and the initial stable state is reestablished. C_2 is a small commutating capacitor (approximately 50 $\mu\mu$f) and serves to increase the response time of the circuit as previously described.

The transistor monostable multivibrator, like its vacuum-tube counterpart, may be triggered by a positive pulse at B_1 or V_2 or by a negative pulse at B_2 or V_1. The same considerations concerning loading by the trigger source apply when the transistor circuit is triggered. The most reliable triggering is accomplished through the use of a separate trigger stage as shown in Fig. 9.9. Q_3 provides the voltage amplification of the trigger pulse and prevents loading of the multivibrator circuit by the trigger source.

A practical example of a monostable multivibrator using a PNP transistor is shown in Fig. 9.9. The circuit is used to stretch the duration of an input pulse from 0.4 to 2 μsec. This is a modification of the basic circuit shown in Fig. 9.8. It represents a circuit simplification impossible in the vacuum-tube equivalent.

In comparing Figs. 9.8 and 9.9, note that a direct connection is made between the collector of Q_2 and the base of Q_1. There are no coupling resistors or capacitors, and the cutoff bias supply for Q_2 has been eliminated. Despite these changes, the action in the circuit in Fig. 9.9 is nearly identical with that of the basic circuit in Fig. 9.8. The only difference between the two concerns the limits of conduction in Q_1 during operation. Q_1 is never cut off. Consider the base potential of Q_1 during cutoff and saturation of Q_2. When Q_2 is cut off, its collector-to-ground potential, and therefore the base potential of Q_2, is approximately -0.3 volt since most of the supply voltage V_{cc} is dropped across R_3 because of the low base-to-emitter resistance of the conducting transistor Q_1.

The negative 0.3 volt at the base of Q_1 forward-biases the PNP transistor and causes a saturation current of approximately 3 ma. When Q_2 conducts, however, its collector-to-ground potential drops to -0.1 volt. Since a positive voltage of approximately 0.2 volt is required to produce cutoff, Q_1 still conducts. The amount of conduction, however, is extremely small, approximately 85 μa. Hence, Q_1 is assumed to be cut off for all practical purposes. Action in the circuit in Fig. 9.9 is briefly described in the following paragraphs.

Resistor R_2 is chosen so that when power is applied, the base current of Q_2 is sufficient to hold Q_2 on. When Q_2 conducts saturation current, the collector-to-ground potential of Q_2 equals -0.1 volt and effectively holds Q_1 off. During this interval, C_1 charges toward the supply voltage of Q_1 through R_2 and the conducting transistor Q_2. Electron flow during the charge of C_1 is shown by solid arrows in Fig. 9.9. With Q_1 cut off and Q_2 conducting saturation current, the circuit rests in a stable state until an external trigger pulse is applied to the base of Q_3.

The base of Q_3 has no significant potential and can be assumed to be 0 volt; hence, Q_3 is initially cut off. A negative pulse at the base of Q_3 causes it to conduct saturation current. The current of Q_3 flowing through R_1 increases the collector-to-ground potential of Q_1 to -0.1 volt. C_1 then

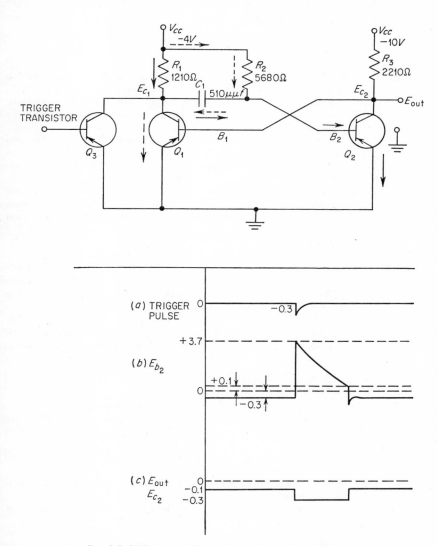

Fig. 9.9 PNP monostable multivibrator and waveforms.

discharges positively toward this potential through R_2. The discharge current of C_1 biases the base of Q_2 positive with respect to ground and cuts it off. The discharge path of C_2 is shown in dashed lines in Fig. 9.9.

The circuit rests in this semistable state until the potential at the base of Q_2 decays to 0 volt. At this time Q_2 begins to conduct, and the circuit returns abruptly to its initial stable state with Q_2 conducting saturation current and Q_1 effectively cut off.

Since PNP transistors are used, rather than NPN transistors, the waveforms associated with Fig. 9.9 are inverted images of those of the basic circuit.

Summary

The multivibrator is a two-stage regenerative amplifier having two conducting states. In one state, one amplifier conducts heavily and holds the other cut off. In the opposite state, the reverse occurs. Because of its bistable nature, the multivibrator finds many applications in digital computer circuits. It may be used to store binary information or to generate, shape, and delay pulses.

The three types of multivibrators in current use are the astable, monostable, and bistable circuits. The astable multivibrator is a free-running oscillator whose output waveform is essentially rectangular. This type is frequently used to generate pulses for testing digital circuitry. The monostable or one-shot multivibrator does not oscillate, but rests permanently in a stable state (one tube on and the other off) until externally triggered. This type produces one complete rectangular pulse for each applied trigger pulse. The monostable circuit is used to develop accurately timed gating signals, to increase or decrease the width of a pulse, or to introduce a time delay between two circuits. The bistable multivibrator, often called the flip-flop, is primarily used in storage and counting applications; it is discussed in the next chapter.

Multivibrators may employ vacuum-tube or transistor amplifiers as their basic switching elements. The type of amplifier used, however, does not alter the basic operating principles. Transistor multivibrator circuits are counterparts of those using electron tubes, and circuit action in each is identical. The most significant difference between transistor and vacuum-tube multivibrators is the operating potentials normally encountered in practical work. The output waveforms of transistor multivibrators, although smaller in amplitude, are similar in shape to those of the vacuum-tube type.

QUESTIONS

9.1 List the three classifications of multivibrators and the uses of each.

9.2 What factors determine the operating frequency of a free-running multivibrator?

9.3 What modification can be made on the basic free-running multivibrator to improve frequency stability?

9.4 What components determine the output pulse width of a monostable multivibrator?

9.5 Is it possible to obtain an inverted and a noninverted output from a monostable multivibrator? Show how this may be done.

9.6 Can the output pulse of a monostable multivibrator be shorter than the input pulse? Explain.

Chapter **10**

The Bistable Multivibrator (Flip-flop)

Two stable states

The bistable type of multivibrator circuit is the one most frequently used in the computer field. As its name implies, the circuit has two stable states of conduction. It can rest in either of its stable states and can be switched from one state to the other by applying a trigger

not switch until trigger comes in

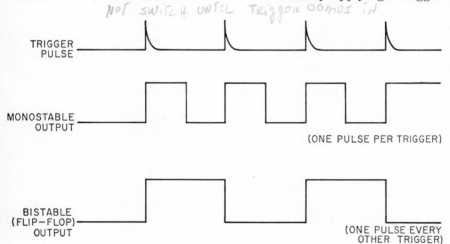

Fig. 10.1 Comparison of waveforms of bistable and monostable multivibrators.

pulse to the input. In computer work, the bistable circuit is referred to as the *logical flip-flop*. One trigger pulse "flips" the state of the circuit, and the second "flops" the circuit back to its initial condition.

Since the bistable multivibrator remains in one of its stable states until triggered, it can be thought of as having a storage capacity. Because it has two stable states, it can be used effectively to store the 1 and 0 digits used in the binary system of counting.

Functioning as binary storage devices, flip-flops in various arrangements are used in digital equipment to perform such logical operations as addition, subtraction, multiplication, and division of binary numbers.

Like the monostable multivibrator, the bistable circuit can also be used to generate a rectangular pulse. In this case, however, two trigger pulses are required. Figure 10.1 compares the trigger requirements and output waveforms of the flip-flop with those of the monostable circuit.

The basic circuit from which all bistable multivibrators are developed is termed the *Eccles-Jordan trigger circuit*. In the following paragraphs, the operating principles of this circuit are explained. This is followed by a discussion of the circuit modifications necessary to convert the basic circuit to the logical flip-flop. Transistor circuits are treated in Part II of this chapter.

PART I: VACUUM-TUBE BISTABLE CIRCUITS

Eccles-Jordan Trigger Circuit

The Eccles-Jordan trigger circuit is illustrated in Fig. 10.2. It is similar to the basic free-running multivibrator circuit and is essentially a two-stage voltage amplifier with the output of each stage connected to the

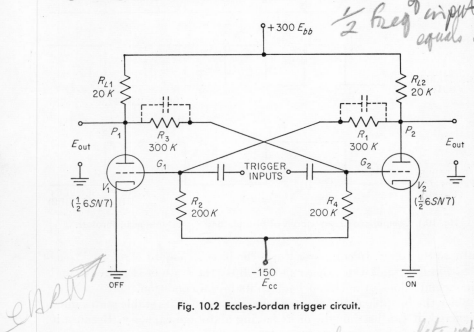

Fig. 10.2 Eccles-Jordan trigger circuit.

input of the other. With the output voltages coupled in this manner, a current increase in one tube results in a current decrease in the other. The circuit is regenerative because the current decrease in the second tube further increases the current in the first.

In both the Eccles-Jordan and the free-running multivibrator circuits, regeneration results in a rapid switching action when power is applied; one tube moves rapidly toward saturation while the other moves toward cutoff. After the end states are reached, however, action in the two circuits is no longer similar. The Eccles-Jordan circuit will rest permanently in the end state until externally triggered. There are two reasons for this circuit behavior:

1. Resistors rather than capacitors are used for coupling.
2. The grid resistors are returned to a negative-bias source.

In such a circuit arrangement, the grid of each tube is excited by two voltage sources, one positive (E_{bb}) and the other negative (E_{cc}). Both source potentials appear across a voltage divider consisting of the series combination of R_{L_2}, R_1, and R_2 for V_1; and R_{L_1}, R_3, and R_4 for V_2. For this reason, the grid-to-ground potential at G_1 or G_2 is always equal to the algebraic sum of the potentials contributed by each source.

Component values in the voltage dividers are chosen so that the grid-to-ground potential at G_1 or G_2 varies between a positive value sufficient to drive the tube into grid clamp and a negative value of a magnitude well in excess of that required to cut the tube off. For example, when V_2 is conducting saturation current, the voltage drop across R_{L_2} reduces the positive voltage available for division across R_1 and R_2. The negative voltage contributed by the source E_{cc}, therefore, predominates; and the grid-to-ground potential at G_1 drops far below the cutoff potential of the tube.

Conditions in the stable state are best understood if the magnitudes of the coupling voltages at G_1 and G_2 are determined. It is not difficult to calculate these voltages.

Consider the component values shown in Fig. 10.2 and assume V_1 is cut off by the regenerative action that occurs when power is applied. To calculate the voltages at G_1 and G_2 which hold V_1 cut off and V_2 at saturation, consider first the potential at G_2. Since two sources contribute to this potential, the method of superposition may be used to calculate the potential contributed by each source separately. These potentials are then added algebraically.

The grid-to-ground potential at G_2 contributed by the source E_{bb} is found by first assuming that E_{cc} is shorted to ground. If this is assumed, E_{bb} is applied across a voltage divider consisting of the series combination of R_{L_1}, R_3, and R_4. Accordingly,

$$E_{R_4} = 300 \times {}^{200}\!/_{520} = +115.4 \text{ volts}$$

If we proceed in a similar manner, the potential at G_2 contributed by the source E_{cc} is found by assuming E_{bb} is shorted to ground.

$$E'_{R_4} = -150 \times {}^{320}\!/_{520} = -92.3 \text{ volts}$$

where E'_{R_4} equals the grid-to-ground potential contributed by the source E_{cc}. The net potential with respect to ground at G_2, then, is

$$E_{G_2} = +115.4 + (-92.3) = +23.1 \text{ volts}$$

Since the impedance between grid and cathode is less than 1,000 ohms when the grid is positive, the 23-volt potential calculated above actually never appears at G_2, but acts as a driving force that clamps the grid to approximately ground potential. V_2 is held firmly at saturation because of the cutoff tube V_1.

The same procedure is followed to determine the potential that holds V_1 cut off. The plate-to-ground potential of the conducting tube V_2, however, must first be found. This is done by drawing a 20-kilohm load line on the characteristic curves of the tube plate. On the tube shown in Fig. 10.2, the plate-to-ground potential at P_2 when G_2 is 0 volt is approximately $+100$ volts. The grid-to-ground potential at G_1, then, is

$$E_{G_1} = 100 \times {}^{200}\!/_{500} + (-150) \times {}^{300}\!/_{500} = -66 \text{ volts}$$

Since the cutoff potential of the 6SN7 is -18 volts, conduction of V_2 drives V_1 far beyond cutoff, and the circuit will remain in this stable state indefinitely.

Triggering. To accomplish switching in the Eccles-Jordan circuit, the tube in the cutoff state must be raised to the conduction level. Once conduction begins, regenerative action completes the switching process. If V_1 is cut off, it may be raised to the conduction level by applying a positive pulse at G_1 or P_2 or a negative pulse at G_2 or P_1. Since pulses of short duration are ordinarily used for switching, commutating capacitors (shown in dashed lines in Fig. 10.2) are employed to improve the response time and ensure reliable triggering (see Chap. 9).

While a pulse of either polarity may be used, the circuit is more sensitive to a negative pulse. For instance, in the cited example a positive pulse in excess of 30 volts is needed at G_1 to bring V_1 to the conduction level. If a negative pulse is applied at G_2, however, only 3 volts is required. The negative pulse decreases the conduction of V_2, is amplified and inverted by V_2, and is coupled to the grid of V_1 through the commutating capacitor. If we assume a stage gain of 10 for V_2, the amplified pulse developed at G_1 is equal to 30 volts and is sufficient to bring V_1 to the conduction level and initiate the switching process. An alternative method of triggering, called *negative pulse steering*, is shown in Fig. 10.3. This method is used when repeated switching of the flip-flop by pulses of one polarity is desired. A train of negative trigger pulses is applied to both

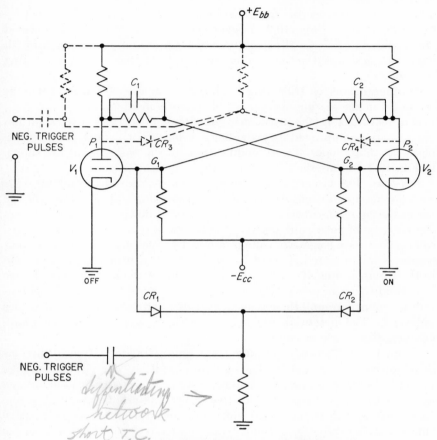

Fig. 10.3 Negative pulse steering with diodes.

grids through pulse-steering diodes CR_1 and CR_2. The steering diodes direct the input pulse to the appropriate tube. For example, assume that V_1 is cut off and V_2 is conducting. The negative bias, which holds V_1 off, will reverse-bias CR_1, and the negative input pulse will not appear at G_1. Since G_2 is at approximately ground potential at this time, CR_2 will be forward-biased by the same negative input pulse and will direct the pulse to the conducting tube. After switching, V_2 is cut off and V_1 is conducting. The bias conditions of CR_1 and CR_2 are now reversed, and the next input pulse is directed to V_1. In this manner a continuous train of negative pulses will accomplish repeated switching of the flip-flop.

While the steering diodes in Fig. 10.3 could be eliminated by applying negative pulses to G_1 and G_2 directly, such a procedure would delay the switching time.

Negative pulse steering may also be applied to P_1 or P_2, as shown by the dashed lines in Fig. 10.3. Trigger action is similar to that described above; but in this case the negative trigger pulse, after passing through diode CR_3, is coupled to the conducting tube V_2 through the commutating capacitor C_1.

Another means of triggering is through the use of trigger tubes as discussed in the section on monostable circuits in Chap. 9.

Modifications to the basic trigger circuit. The basic Eccles-Jordan circuit may be improved by providing self-bias for V_1 and V_2 and adding plate-catching diodes. These modifications to the basic circuit are shown in Fig. 10.4 and are discussed separately.

Self-bias. The circuit arrangement shown in Fig. 10.4 eliminates the need for a separate negative source by providing self-bias through the use of the common-cathode resistor R_k. Current flowing through R_k biases the cathode of each tube positive relative to ground. Since this has the same effect as a negative voltage applied to the grids, a negative-bias source is not required. Except for the method of providing bias, action in the circuit in Fig. 10.4 is identical with that in the basic circuit. To see how conduction in one tube holds the other cut off, consider the potentials developed around the circuit in Fig. 10.4, with the component values indicated. The potentials shown in the figure apply when the plate-catching diodes are disconnected.

When V_2 conducts saturation current (approximately 10 ma), the bias developed at the cathode of V_1 is 70 volts positive. The voltage coupled to G_1 is one-fourth of the plate potential of P_2. The grid-to-ground voltage at V_1 is therefore 42.5 volts positive. Since the cutoff potential of the tube used is approximately 20 volts and the grid of V_1 is less positive (more negative) than its cathode by 28 volts (70 − 42), V_1 is held in the cutoff state by the conduction of V_2.

The cathode bypass capacitor C_3 has no effect during the stable state but prevents degeneration during the transition between states. If this capacitor is omitted, the gain of each stage will be greatly reduced and the circuit will not respond to low-amplitude trigger pulses.

Plate-catching Diodes. The plate-catching diodes connected as shown in Fig. 10.4 will clip the output waveform at P_1 and P_2 and reduce the peak-to-peak amplitude from 120 to 80 volts. CR_1 and CR_3 limit the positive excursion to 280 volts, and CR_2 and CR_4 limit the negative excursion to 200 volts. The clipping levels are shown in Fig. 10.4b. Because these

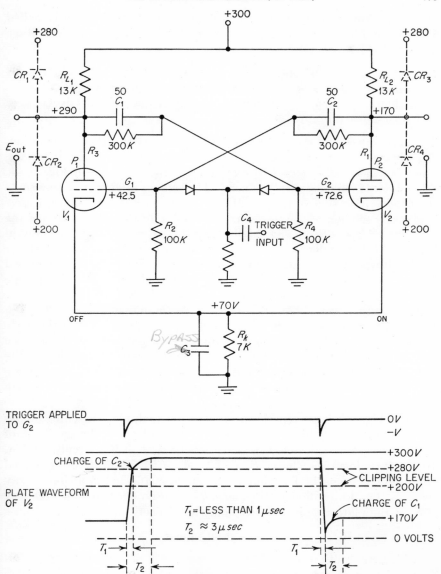

Fig. 10.4 Modified Eccles-Jordan and waveforms.

diodes determine the output voltage levels, they are frequently called
level-setting diodes. There are two reasons for limiting the plate voltage
in this manner:

1. To provide a constant output amplitude despite any reduction of
   cathode emission due to tube aging or changes in temperature
2. To improve the recovery time of the circuit and permit triggering at
   higher repetition rates

This last function of the plate-catching diodes needs further explanation.
The time required for a bistable circuit to switch from one state to the
other is called the *resolving time* of the circuit. As shown in Fig. 10.4b,
this interval is divided into two parts. The smaller interval (t_1) represents
the regeneration time of the circuit and usually occurs in less than 1 μsec.
The major portion of the resolving time is due to the charge time of the
commutating capacitors and may be called the *recovery time*. This interval
is labeled t_2 in the diagram. The commutating capacitors charge and discharge during the switching interval in a manner similar to that described
for the coupling capacitors of the astable multivibrator. The charge current produces the overshoot and roll-off shown in Fig. 10.4b.

The total resolving time (t_1 plus t_2) limits the maximum rate at which
the circuit can be triggered. For example, the resolving time of the plate
circuit in a typical bistable multivibrator is on the order of 4 μsec (see
Fig. 10.4b). Approximately 1 μsec is required for the completion of the
regenerative switching action, and 3 μsec is necessary for C_2 to complete
its charge. For reliable operation, the interval between trigger pulses in
this case must not be less than 4 μsec.

When higher trigger repetition rates are desired, plate-catching diodes
are used to reduce the time required for C_1 and C_2 to charge. This, of
course, results in a decrease in the recovery time of the circuit. In Fig.
10.4, CR_1 reduces the charge time of C_1 since R_{L_1} is effectively removed
from the charge path. The charge time of C_2 is affected in a similar way
by CR_3. The lower diodes CR_2 and CR_4 have no effect on the recovery
time of the plate circuit and serve only a level-setting function.

Logical Flip-flop

A bistable multivibrator used for the purpose of storing binary information in logical machines is called a logical flip-flop. The logical flip-flop
shown in Fig. 10.5 is identical with that shown in Fig. 10.4 but includes
several input and output circuits that make it more effective in counting
and storage applications. These circuit additions are shown enclosed by
dashed lines in Fig. 10.5. Before the additional circuitry shown in the
figure is discussed, some conventions regarding terminology will be
covered.

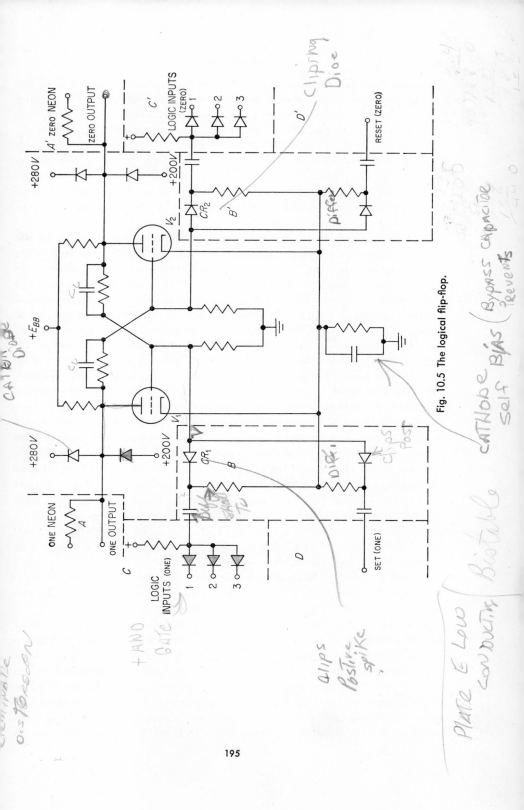

Fig. 10.5 The logical flip-flop.

195

Logical flip-flop terminology. It has been previously shown that the flip-flop has two stable states of conduction. In one state, V_1 is conducting and V_2 is cut off. In the second state, V_2 is conducting and V_1 is cut off. The two states of conduction are shown diagrammatically in Fig. 10.6a and b. Since the flip-flop remains in one of its stable states until triggered, it can be thought of as having a storage capacity. When at rest in one stable state, the circuit is considered to be storing a binary 1, or, simply, to be in the ONE state. If the circuit is triggered to the opposite state of conduction, it is considered to be storing a binary 0, or, simply, to be in the ZERO state.

An indication of the state in which the flip-flop rests is provided by the voltage levels at its output terminals. It will be shown in a succeeding paragraph that the output of only one tube could be used to indicate the state of the flip-flop. In the logical flip-flop, however, both outputs are used for this purpose. The output voltage from one of the tubes is used to indicate that a binary 1 is stored in the flip-flop, while the output of the other tube indicates the storage of a binary 0. This is shown diagrammatically in Fig. 10.6c. Although the output of V_1 has been chosen in the diagram to represent the 1, the choice is purely arbitrary. V_2 could be used for the 1 indication, and $V1$ for the 0 indication. Once the choice is made, however, the components associated with the tube selected are designated the ONE-side components of the flip-flops and the output from this side is designated the ONE-side output. Conversely, the other side of the flip-flop is designated the ZERO side and its output is designated the ZERO-side output. This is shown in Fig. 10.6d.

Consider for the moment a computer system in which the presence of a signal is indicated by a high (most positive) voltage level. A low output voltage level would then indicate that a signal is not present. This logic will be applied to a flip-flop designated as shown in Fig. 10.6d. Both conduction states shown in Fig. 10.6a and b will be considered to show how the ONE-side and ZERO-side outputs determine whether a binary 1 or a binary 0 is being stored.

Consider first the stable state shown in Fig. 10.6a. This state of conduction is redrawn in Fig. 10.6e with the outputs appropriately marked. Since V_1 is cut off, its output voltage is more positive than that of V_2; that is, the ONE-side output is high, and the ZERO-side output is low. If this type of logic is assumed, the flip-flop is obviously in the ONE state since a 1 is present in the output and a 0 is not present.

Similar reasoning will show that when the flip-flop is switched to the opposite state, both outputs will indicate the storage of a binary 0. Consider the drawing in Fig. 10.6b. This figure shows a state of conduction opposite to that in Fig. 10.6a. The flip-flop is redrawn in Fig. 10.6f with the outputs appropriately marked. Since V_2 is off, its ZERO-side output is

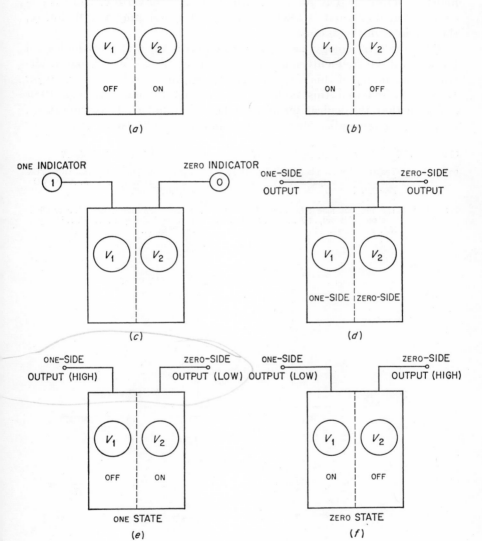

Fig. 10.6 States of conduction.

Reset 0 side insures in 0

high; therefore, a 0 is present in the output. Conversely, since V_1 is conducting, its output is low; therefore, a 1 is not present. Obviously, the circuit is in the ZERO state.

Since the terminology used above to describe the states of the logical flip-flop will be frequently employed in future discussions of logical circuits, a summary of this terminology is given in the table of Fig. 10.7a. It is suggested that this table be used in conjunction with Fig. 10.6e and f so that the logical terms used become familiar. It is important, however, to remember that this terminology applies only to systems

CIRCUIT STATE	ONE-SIDE TERMINOLOGY	ZERO-SIDE TERMINOLOGY
ONE state	The ONE-side tube is CUT OFF or OFF. The ONE-side output is HIGH. A binary 1 is PRESENT.	The ZERO-side tube is CONDUCTING or ON. The ZERO-side output is LOW. A binary 0 is NOT PRESENT.
ZERO state	The ONE-side tube is CONDUCTING or ON. The ONE-side output is LOW. A binary 1 is NOT PRESENT.	The ZERO-side tube is CUT OFF or OFF. The ZERO-side output is HIGH. A binary 0 is PRESENT.

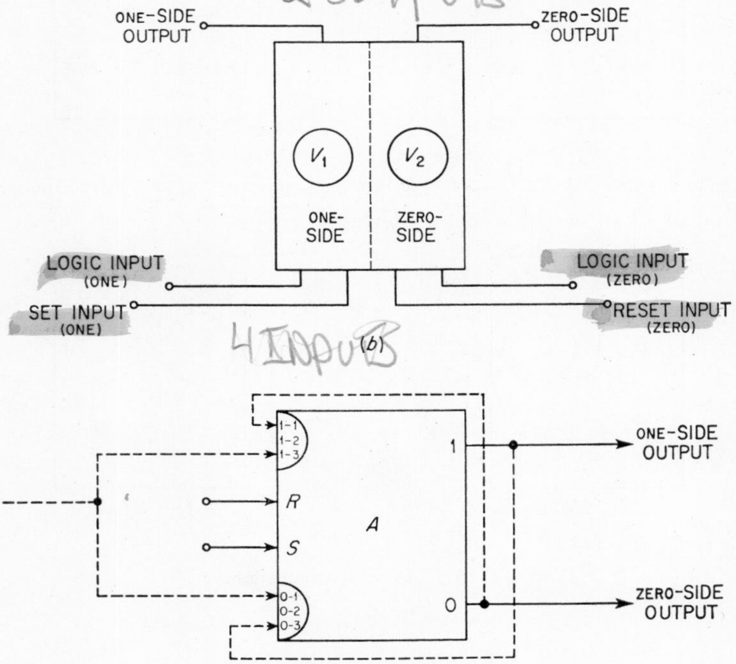

Fig. 10.7 Flip-flop terminology and symbols. (a) Terminology associated with the logical flip-flop in a positive logic system. (b) Simplified logical symbol. (c) Complemented flip-flop symbol.

employing the most positive voltage level to indicate a 1, or presence of a signal.

A question is often raised concerning the reason for providing two outputs, rather than one, to indicate the state of the logical flip-flop. An explanation for this practice is given in the following paragraph.

When two outputs are employed, both the ONE state and the ZERO state are indicated by a high voltage level. In the ONE state, the high level is available from the ONE-side output; in the ZERO state, the high level is available from the ZERO-side output. The two high levels are used to an advantage when the logical function of AND or OR is to be performed. For example, assume that outputs of two flip-flops are to be given the AND function. Assume, further, that a high level is to be produced in the 'output of the AND circuit when a binary 1 appears in flip-flop A and a binary 0 appears in flip-flop B. Since high outputs are available from both flip-flops, this logical function can be conveniently performed. A system employing flip-flops with only one output, however, would be at a distinct disadvantage. To see that this is true, consider a flip-flop whose states are described by Fig. 10.6e and f, and assume that the flip-flop has only one output, the output of V_1. As shown in Fig. 10.6e and f, the ONE state would be indicated by a high output from V_1; but the ZERO state would necessarily be indicated by a low output. Then to perform the logical AND function described above, the output of the flip-flop storing the binary 0 must first be inverted before being applied to the AND-gate input. Since thousands of similar operations are performed in a complex computer, the added expense of providing inverter circuits would be prohibitive.

While a logical flip-flop has only two outputs, it ordinarily has four inputs, two to each side. These inputs are shown in Fig. 10.7b. There is no electrical difference between the LOGIC inputs on the ONE side and the SET input. Trigger pulses applied to either input will switch the flip-flop to the ONE state. The LOGIC inputs on the ZERO side and the RESET input are also identical electrically. Trigger pulses applied to either of these inputs switch the flip-flop to the ZERO state. The outputs of logical switching circuits, such as AND or OR gates, are applied to the LOGIC inputs of the flip-flop, causing the storage of a 1 or a 0 to be conditional on the performance of certain logical operations. The SET and RESET inputs are used to initially preset the flip-flop to some predetermined state prior to the performance of these logical operations. In effect, the SET and RESET inputs clear the flip-flop of information previously stored and set up what could be called *start* conditions.

The logical flip-flops shown in Fig. 10.5 may now be discussed. Since the circuit shown in Fig. 10.5 is identical with that shown in Fig. 10.4, circuit analysis will be limited to an examination of the component additions at the input and the output. The input and output circuits shown enclosed in dashed lines in Fig. 10.5 are designated A, B, C, and D. These inputs are associated with the ONE-side output and the ONE-side input to the flip-flop. To the right of the diagram, input and output circuits corresponding to those on the left are designated A', B', C', and D'. The explanations given for components in A, B, C, and D in the paragraphs below apply equally to the corresponding blocks A', B', C', and D'.

Two outputs from the ONE side and two outputs from the ZERO side of the flip-flop are shown in blocks A and A' in Fig. 10.5. One terminal is the logic output and provides information on the state of the flip-flop for use by other components in the computer. The other terminal, designated ONE NEON and ZERO NEON, is connected to a neon indicator panel used for troubleshooting purposes. The neons on the panel are usually connected in banks conveniently arranged so the technician can tell at a glance the condition of each flip-flop in the various counters and registers of the computer.

In order to make the flip-flop usable in a system employing square waves, the ONE-side and ZERO-side inputs are usually composed of a diode and a differentiating network similar to that shown in Fig. 10.8. These components convert the square-wave input to the negative spike required for efficient triggering of the binary circuit. A square-wave input at A is differentiated by the short-time-constant RC network so that at point B the leading edge appears as a positive spike and the trailing edge as a negative spike. The positive portion of the differentiated waveform reverse-biases the diode and is effectively prevented from appearing at point C. The negative spike, however, forward-biases the diode and is passed on to the grid of the flip-flop to initiate the switching process.

In block B in Fig. 10.5, two input circuits similar to those shown in Fig. 10.8 are connected in parallel. One input is the LOGIC input and, in this particular flip-flop, is fed by a three-input AND gate (block C). The other input is the SET input (block D). Since switching is accomplished at all inputs in a similar way, only the SET action will be explained.

Assume the flip-flop is storing a binary 0 and it is desired to switch the flip-flop to the ONE state. Since the flip-flop initially rests in the ZERO state, its ZERO-side output is high. Therefore, the ZERO-side tube (V_2) is cut off and the ONE-side tube (V_1) is conducting. A pulse applied to the SET input (block D) is differentiated and clipped by the input circuits (block B) and appears as a negative spike at the grid of V_1. This negative spike decreases conduction in V_1 and initiates the switching process. After switching, V_1 is cut off; its output connected to the ONE side is high. Thus, the circuit has been set to the ONE state.

Flip-flops differ chiefly in the type of gate circuits provided at the LOGIC inputs. Frequently, an OR gate is substituted for the AND circuit (block C), and in other flip-flops a gate that provides both the AND and the OR function is used.

The schematic diagram in Fig. 10.5 is represented more simply on logical diagrams by using a symbol like the example shown in Fig. 10.7c.

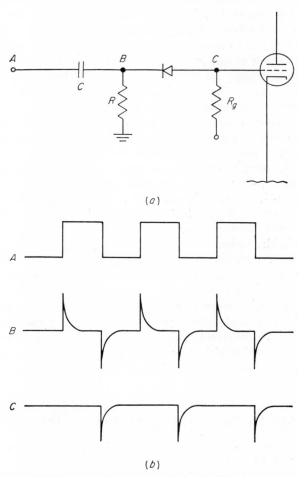

(a)

(b)

Fig. 10.8 (a) Differentiator and diode to generate negative spike. (b) Associated waveform.

When several flip-flops are connected to form counters and registers, each flip-flop is identified by a capital letter. The flip-flop shown in Fig. 10.7c would accordingly be designated flip-flop A.

The inputs shown on the left of the flip-flop symbol correspond to the inputs drawn in the schematic diagram in Fig. 10.5 (blocks C and C').

The AND gates are designated 1, 2, and 3 and prefixed by 1 or 0, depending on the side. The SET and RESET inputs are designated S and R, respectively.

As previously stated, the logical flip-flop may be used for storage applications or for performing counting functions. The input circuits of the logical flip-flop are arranged so that either function can be performed conveniently and effectively. As an example, consider the circuit in Fig. 10.5 to be used to perform a counting function. In this application, repeated switching of the flip-flop is accomplished by applying a continuous train of trigger pulses simultaneously to both the ONE-side and the ZERO-side input. Since the input pulses are applied to both sides simultaneously, some means must be provided to direct the input pulse to the correct tube. This is accomplished conveniently through a method of connection called *complementing*. Complementing serves a pulse-steering function and proves reliable when trigger pulses at high repetition rates are used. Complementing is accomplished by applying the ONE-side output of the flip-flop to the AND gate associated with the ZERO side. Also, the ZERO-side output is returned to the AND gate at the ONE-side input. Trigger pulses, called clock pulses, are then applied simultaneously to both AND-gate inputs. This method of connection is shown by the dashed lines in the logical diagram in Fig. 10.7c. To see how complementing ensures that each successive trigger pulse is directed to the correct tube, assume the flip-flop is in the ZERO state when a clock pulse appears at both the ONE-side and ZERO-side AND gates. Since the flip-flop is in the ZERO state, the high output from the ZERO side renders the ONE-side AND gate permissive, and the clock pulse is allowed to pass. The ZERO-side AND gate is nonpermissive at this time because the low output from the ONE side acts as an inhibiting force upon the gate. In this way, the clock pulse is directed to the ONE-side input and switches the flip-flop to the ONE state.

PART II: TRANSISTOR BISTABLE CIRCUITS

As pointed out in Chap. 9, most transistor multivibrator circuits are counterparts of those using electron tubes. A comparison of the basic transistor flip-flop shown in Fig. 10.9 with its vacuum-tube equivalent shown in Fig. 10.2 indicates that the transistor bistable circuit is no exception. Corresponding components in the two circuits serve similar functions, and circuit operation in the two is identical.

The major point of difference between the transistor flip-flop and its vacuum-tube equivalent concerns the time required for switching between the two stable states. In the case of the vacuum tube, it was shown that this interval, called the resolving time, is divided into two parts:

the regeneration time and the recovery time (due principally to the charge time of the commutating capacitors). In the transistor flip-flop, one additional factor contributes to the duration of the switching interval. If the transistor is permitted to remain saturated during the stable state, minority-carrier storage will increase the time required to turn the transistor off. For this reason, when transistor flip-flops are designed to operate with high trigger repetition rates, nonsaturating techniques are employed (see Chap. 7). An example of a transistor flip-flop using non-

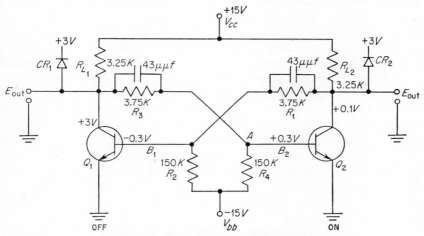

Fig. 10.9 Basic flip-flop using NPN transistors.

saturating techniques to decrease the resolution time of the circuit is given later in this chapter.

Basic NPN Flip-flop

The basic circuit of a flip-flop using NPN transistors is shown in Fig. 10.9.

Although the circuit operation is identical with that of the Eccles-Jordan circuit discussed earlier, a brief description of circuit action is repeated. When power is applied to the circuit shown in Fig. 10.9, a rapid switching action occurs because of regenerative feedback common to all multivibrators. One transistor moves rapidly toward saturation while the other moves toward cutoff. Once the end states are reached, the circuit will rest in this stable condition until an external trigger pulse is applied.

In the stable state, one transistor is held at saturation while the other is held beyond cutoff. These stable conditions are maintained because of the voltages developed at B_1 and B_2 through the voltage-dividing action of the coupling resistors.

In Fig. 10.9, the approximate collector and base potentials developed in the stable state are shown. Q_1 is assumed to be cut off and Q_2 in the conducting state. With Q_2 conducting saturation current, its collector-to-ground potential is approximately 0.1 volt positive. This value is typical for the transistor types normally used in this application. A portion of this voltage is coupled to the base of Q_1 because of the action of the voltage divider, R_1 and R_2. Also contributing to the base-to-ground potential at B_1 is a portion of the negative-bias supply (V_{bb}). Calculation by superposition will show that the net potential contributed by these two sources is approximately 0.3 volt negative. Since the cutoff potential of this NPN transistor is approximately 0.1 volt negative, Q_1 is definitely cut off. The base-to-ground potential at B_2 is calculated in a similar manner by determining the net potential contributed by the positive 3-volt collector potential of the cutoff transistor (Q_1) and the negative-bias source (V_{bb}). The sources are applied across the voltage divider, R_3 and R_4. If the effect of the conducting transistor is disregarded, calculation will show that the net potential at B_2 is approximately 2.5 volts positive. This forward bias causes saturation current in Q_2. Since the low base-to-emitter resistance shunts point A, this positive voltage does not actually appear at B_2 but becomes a driving force that clamps the base to approximately 0.3 volt positive.

It is clear, therefore, that Q_2 holds Q_1 in the cutoff state and Q_1 holds Q_2 at saturation.

Diodes CR_1 and CR_2 in Fig. 10.9 perform the same functions as the plate-catching diodes associated with the vacuum-tube flip-flop. They limit the positive excursion of the output signal, provide amplitude stability, and improve the recovery time of the circuit.

Triggering considerations discussed earlier for the vacuum-tube circuit apply also to the transistor flip-flop. Examples of diode and triode triggering, as well as trigger pulse steering through complementing, are given in the following development of the logical flip-flop.

Transistor Logical Flip-flop

The basic transistor flip-flop shown in Fig. 10.9 is converted to a logical flip-flop by the addition of input and output circuits. These are shown enclosed in dashed lines in Fig. 10.10a. Since NPN transistors are used, the input and output components function exactly as their corresponding components in the vacuum-tube equivalent (see Fig. 10.5). Details of circuit action are repeated in the following paragraphs for emphasis.

If we again assume the most positive voltage level to represent 1, when Q_1 is cut off the flip-flop is in the ONE state. This is true because the ONE-side output is high (3 volts positive), indicating that a binary 1 is present. Also, since Q_2 is conducting at this time, the ZERO-side output is low (0.1 volt), indicating that a binary 0 is not present.

The ONE-side and ZERO-side outputs (blocks A and A') provide information on the state of the flip-flop for use by other circuits in the computer. The other output terminal at the ONE side or ZERO side is connected to a neon indicator through a voltage amplifier. Voltage amplification is necessary since approximately 90 volts is required to ionize a neon bulb and only 3 volts is present when this terminal is high.

Block B in Fig. 10.10 comprises a differentiating network and a diode clipper. These components produce the negative pulses required for triggering when rectangular pulses of long duration are applied to the input. C_1 and R_2 differentiate signals applied to the LOGIC inputs, and C_2 and R_2 perform the same function at the SET input. CR_2 removes the positive spike after differentiation of the input pulse.

A two-input AND gate is provided in this particular flip-flop at the LOGIC inputs (block C). The single-ended SET input (block D) permits presetting of the flip-flop to the ONE state to set up start conditions. The RESET input (block D') permits presetting of the flip-flop to the ZERO state when desired. A block diagram of the circuit in Fig. 10.10a is shown in Fig. 10.10b. This diagram shows the function of the input and output terminals. Notice that when NPN transistors are used, the block diagrams of the vacuum-tube flip-flop and the transistor flip-flop are identical (Fig. 10.7b).

Complementing of the transistor logical flip-flop is accomplished in the same manner as that described for the vacuum-tube flip-flop. The ONE-side and ZERO-side outputs are returned to the AND gates at the LOGIC inputs. This is shown in Fig. 10.10c. Notice that the logic symbol of the complemented transistor flip-flop is identical with that shown for the vacuum-tube flip-flop (Fig. 10.7c).

A logical flip-flop employing PNP transistors, rather than NPN transistors, is shown in Fig. 10.11a. The circuit is identical with the NPN flip-flop in Fig. 10.10a except for the following changes:

1. All source potentials have opposite polarity.
2. The positions of the cathodes and anodes of CR_1, CR_2, CR_3, and CR_4 are reversed.
3. Input designation is reversed. For example, the inputs associated with the ONE-side output are now applied to the ZERO side.

All the above changes are necessary because of the opposite bias requirements of the PNP transistor when compared with the NPN transistor or the triode tube. Changes 2 and 3, however, require elaboration and are explained in the following paragraph.

Earlier it was explained that diodes CR_1 and CR_3 reduce the charge time of the commutating capacitors by bypassing the load resistors. This occurs when the transistors are switched off. Since the potential toward which the capacitors charge is now negative (V_{cc}), both the polarity of the clipping level and the position of the diodes must be reversed.

The positions of diodes CR_2 and CR_4 are also reversed because of the opposite characteristics of the PNP transistor. Earlier it was shown that the flip-flop circuit is more sensitive to trigger pulses that drive the conducting amplifier toward cutoff. For this reason, negative trigger pulses are used in flip-flops employing NPN transistors or triode tubes. Since

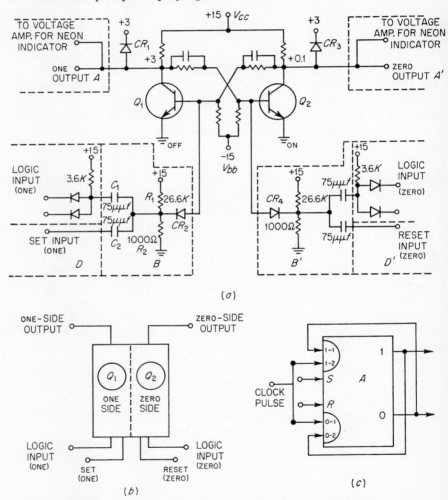

Fig. 10.10 (a) Logical flip-flop using NPN transistors. (b) Block diagram logical flip-flop. (c) Logical symbol of complemented transistor flip-flop.

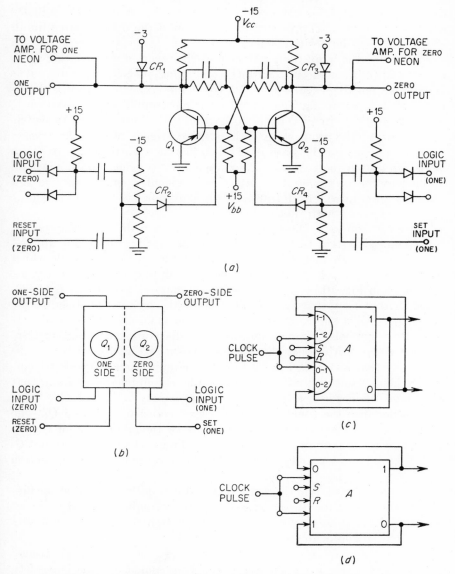

Fig. 10.11 (a) Logical flip-flop using PNP transistors. (b) Input and outputs. (c) Logical symbol. (d) Alternative logical symbol.

the positive potential is now required to accomplish cutoff, CR_2 and CR_4 must be arranged to clip the negative portion of the differentiated input signal and pass the positive spike.

To see why the input designations must be reversed, assume that Q_2 is cut off and Q_1 is conducting. With Q_1 conducting, its collector potential is at its most positive excursion (-0.1 volt). The ONE-side output is therefore high and, assuming logic where a 1 is represented by the most positive voltages, the circuit is in the ONE state. If it is now desired to switch the circuit to the ZERO state with positive trigger pulses, the trigger must be applied to the base of the conducting transistor Q_1. In other words, to switch the circuit to the ZERO state, the trigger pulse must be applied to the ONE side. This latter requirement is emphasized in the block diagram for the PNP transistor flip-flop shown in Fig. 10.11b. Compare this diagram with that in Fig. 10.10b.

The PNP transistor flip-flop is complemented in the same way as the NPN transistor; that is, the ONE-side and ZERO-side outputs are applied to AND gates at the LOGIC inputs. Two examples of logic symbols which may be used to represent the complemented flip-flop on logical diagrams are shown in Fig. 10.11c and d. The logical diagram shown in c is identical with that previously given. The alternative symbol of d shows the actual relative positions of the ONE-side and ZERO-side inputs and outputs. Both symbols, however, indicate the same complementing function.

Input circuit variations. The flip-flop shown in Fig. 10.12a is a modification of that shown in Fig. 10.11a. This circuit features triode triggering at the SET and RESET inputs and includes a simplified logic input that eliminates the need for a separate AND-gate input.

Consider first the function of the trigger transistors Q_3 and Q_4. The circuit is initially preset to the desired state by the application of a negative pulse to the SET or the RESET input. Trigger transistors Q_3 and Q_4 are affected by a negative pulse in a similar way; hence, only the action of the SET input need be explained.

Assume the circuit is in the ZERO state and it is desired to preset the flip-flop to the ONE state. In the ZERO state, Q_2 is conducting and Q_1 is cut off. A negative pulse at the SET input will switch the circuit to the ONE state as described in the following paragraphs.

Trigger transistor Q_3 is cut off during the interval between trigger pulses because CR_1 is conducting at this time and biases the base of Q_3 slightly positive. Since both V_3 and V_1 are cut off, the collector potential of Q_1 is 3 volts negative. A negative pulse at the SET input reverse-biases CR_1 and removes the cutoff bias at Q_3. The negative pulse appearing at the base of Q_3 provides forward bias, and Q_3 conducts saturation current. When Q_3 conducts, the collector of Q_1 swings positive from -3 volts toward ground potential. This positive pulse is coupled through the commutating capacitor and appears at the conducting transistor Q_2. Conduction in Q_2 decreases, and regenerative action switches the circuit to the ONE state.

The LOGIC inputs on both the ONE and ZERO sides consists of an RC network and a series diode. These components perform a dual function. The

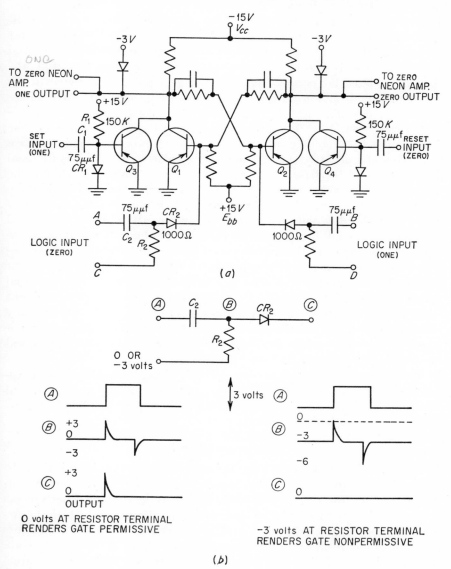

Fig. 10.12 (a) Modified PNP logical flip-flop. (b) Permissive and nonpermissive modes.

first function is to convert rectangular input pulses into positive pulses required for triggering the flip-flop. This function is identical with that performed by corresponding components at the LOGIC inputs of all flip-flops previously explained. Under appropriate input conditions, however, these components also function as a two-input AND gate. The capacitor terminal is considered one input to the gate and the resistor terminal, the other input. The gate is rendered permissive or nonpermissive by the application of the appropriate voltage to the resistor terminal. If the resistor terminal is returned to ground (0 volt), the gate becomes permissive and a trigger pulse is passed. When returned to a negative potential, the gate is rendered nonpermissive, and no trigger pulse is delivered to the flip-flop. Circuit action during the permissive and nonpermissive modes is illustrated in Fig. 10.12b. Consider first the conditions shown on the left. When ground, or 0 voltage, is applied to the resistor terminal, the input pulse is differentiated by C_2 and R_2 and appears at point B as a positive and a negative spike. The positive spike forward-biases CR_2 and is passed on to the base of the transistor to accomplish switching. The negative spike reverse-biases CR_2 and is effectively removed. This action is identical with that described previously. It is important to note, however, that the differentiated signal (B) swings above ground potential only because point B is at ground potential at the time the input pulse appears. In this case, the differentiated waveform swings above and below a 0-volt reference level. During the nonpermissive mode, the resistor terminal is returned to -3 volts, and point B is biased at this potential when the input signal is applied. For this reason, the differentiated input now rides above and below a reference level of -3 volts. As shown by waveforms B and C on the right in Fig. 10.12b, neither the positive nor the negative spike swings above 0 volt; hence, CR_2 does not conduct and no trigger pulse is passed.

To complement the circuit shown in Fig. 10.12a, clock pulses are applied simultaneously to the capacitor terminals (points A and B), and the ONE-side and ZERO-side outputs of the flip-flop are applied to the resistor terminals (points C and D).

Nonsaturated Flip-flop

In all previous examples of the logical flip-flop, no provision is made to prevent transistor saturation during the stable state. Consequently, minority-carrier storage effects introduce a delay in the switching process and result in a reduction in the maximum repetition rate at which the circuit may be triggered. In the circuit shown in Fig. 10.13, the transistors are prevented from entering the saturation region in the stable state through the use of diodes CR_1 through CR_4. CR_1 and CR_2 prevent saturation current in Q_2, and CR_3 and CR_4 perform the same function for Q_1.

To understand how these diodes prevent saturation current, consider the circuit action during the stable state when Q_1 is cut off and Q_2 is conducting. These conditions are shown in Fig. 10.13b.

CR_1 conducts continuously during both the switching interval and the stable state since the base of Q_2 and, therefore, the anode of CR_1 are near

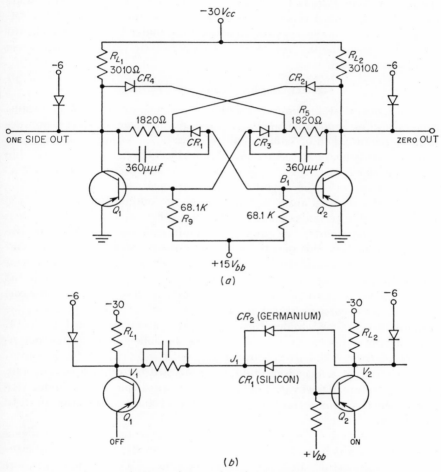

Fig. 10.13 (a) Nonsaturating flip-flop. (b) Diode limiting action.

ground potential. CR_2, however, is reverse-biased during most of the switching interval and does not conduct until the load current through R_{L_2} causes the collector potential to swing more positive than the potential at J_1. When this occurs, CR_2 conducts and bypasses a portion of the base current to the collector. Limited to this extent, the base current is never sufficiently great to cause saturation current in Q_2. For correct operations, component values must be chosen so that the collector of Q_2 is prevented from becoming forward-biased during the stable state. This is usually accomplished by selecting a silicon diode for CR_1 and a germanium diode for CR_2. In a typical case, the forward voltage drop across the silicon diode CR_1 is 1.2 volts, and that across the germanium diode CR_2 is 1 volt. During the stable state when both diodes conduct, the difference in the voltage drops across the two diodes causes the collector voltage of Q_2 to be 0.2 volt negative with respect to base, and reverse bias is maintained.

Direct-coupled Transistor Flip-flop

While most bistable circuits employ resistor coupling between states, direct coupling is possible and, when used, results in a considerable reduction in the number of components required. An example of a direct-coupled bistable circuit is shown in Fig. 10.14. This circuit has two stable states in which one transistor is in saturation and the other is nearly at cutoff. Operation of the circuit will now be explained.

When power is first applied, both transistors conduct since the negative source potential provides forward bias. Because of variations in the tolerances of components, one transistor conducts more heavily than the other. The instant this occurs, positive feedback between collectors and bases of the transistors results in a rapid switching action; one transistor is driven toward saturation and the other toward cutoff. The circuit reaches a stable state when saturation current flows in one transistor. Assume Q_2 becomes saturated. The approximate collector and base potentials developed under these conditions are shown in Fig. 10.14.

Saturation current through R_{L_2} reduces the collector-to-ground potential of Q_2 from -0.3 to approximately -0.1 volt. Since this potential is negative with respect to ground, Q_1 is forward-biased and cannot be in the cutoff state. However, this value of forward bias is low enough to reduce the collector current of Q_1 to less than $100\mu a$, and Q_1 is assumed to be cut off.

With Q_1 cut off, its collector potential rises toward V_{cc} and provides a forward bias which is more than sufficient to enable Q_2 to remain saturated. The collector voltage of Q_1 never reaches -10 volts, however, but is clamped at -0.3 volt because of the low emitter-to-base resistance of Q_2.

Although the output-voltage swing of this circuit is only 0.2 volt peak-to-peak, this value is sufficient to turn transistor switches on and off.

The components shown in dashed lines in Fig. 10.14 convert the basic circuit to a logical flip-flop. The circuit is preset to the ONE or the ZERO state by a negative pulse at the SET or the RESET input. The parallel transistors at the LOGIC inputs function as two-input AND gates. These gates deliver a positive trigger pulse to the base of the flip-flop transistors when the inputs to the gates are satisfied. Consider the ZERO logic input gate on the left of the diagram. The gate is rendered permissive when

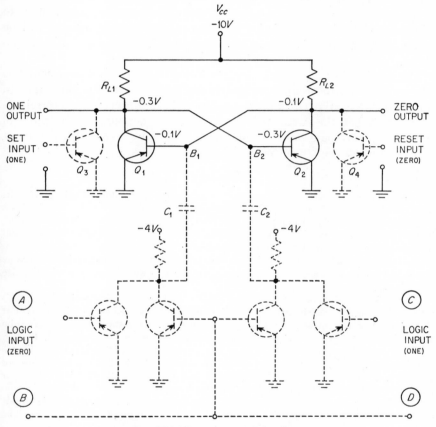

Fig. 10.14 Direct-coupled flip-flop.

both input terminals (A and B) are at 0 volt when a negative trigger appears. If either input terminal A or input terminal B is at -3 volts when the trigger appears, the gate is rendered nonpermissive.

To understand the action of this gate, assume that the flip-flop is in the ONE state. When this is true, Q_1 is conducting and Q_2 is cut off. To switch the circuit to the ZERO state with positive pulses, the pulse must be applied to B_1. This may be accomplished by applying a negative trigger pulse at the ZERO LOGIC inputs when the gate is permissive.

If both terminals A and B are at 0 volt before the trigger appears, both gate transistors are off and the collector potential is -4 volts. A negative trigger of -3 volts applied to terminal A drives the left transistor into saturation. Its collector potential swings positively toward 0 volt, and a positive pulse is coupled through C_1 to the base of Q_1. The flip-flop switches to the ZERO state.

If input terminal B is at -3 volts before the trigger appears, the gate will be nonpermissive. This is true because the right transistor will be conducting at this time, and the negative trigger pulse will have no effect.

The flip-flop in Fig. 10.14 is complemented in the conventional manner. The ONE-side output is applied to terminal A, and the ZERO-side output to terminal C. Negative clock pulses are applied simultaneously to terminals B and D. When the circuit is in the ONE state, the ZERO-side output will render the ONE logic inputs nonpermissive because terminal C will be at -3 volts when the trigger appears.

Summary

Most bistable multivibrators are variations of the Eccles-Jordan trigger circuit. This circuit consists of two voltage amplifiers connected in cascade. The output of one amplifier is connected to the input of the other. Although the circuit is regenerative, it does not oscillate, because of external bias applied to the amplifiers. This external bias provides the circuit with two stable states.

The Eccles-Jordan trigger circuit can rest permanently in either of its two stable states and can be switched from one state to the other by application of a trigger pulse to its input.

While trigger pulses of either polarity can be used to accomplish switching, multivibrators are more sensitive to pulses which are applied to the conducting tube. For this reason negative pulses are used for triggering multivibrators using vacuum-tube and type NPN transistor amplifiers, while positive pulses are used with type PNP.

When repetitive switching by pulses of one polarity is desired, some system of pulse steering is employed to ensure that each successive pulse is directed to the proper amplifier. Common pulse-steering methods make use of pulse-steering diodes or employ a system of pulse steering called *complementing*.

The transistor flip-flop is similar to its vacuum-tube counterpart. The basic circuit configuration and operating principles are identical in the two types of circuits. The major points of difference between transistor and vacuum-tube multivibrators are:

1. Direct coupling between amplifier stages can be used in transistor flip-flops. This type of coupling is not possible in the vacuum-tube circuit.
2. When extremely high-speed switching is desired, nonsaturating techniques must be employed in the transistor circuit to minimize the adverse effects of minority carrier storage.

Because of the bistable nature of the multivibrator, it is used in data-processing equipment as a binary storage device and forms the basic element in circuits designed to perform logical and arithmetic operations. When used in this way, the multivibrator is referred to as the *logical flip-flop*.

The logical flip-flop circuit is similar to the basic Eccles-Jordan trigger circuit but includes several modifications that make it more effective in counting and storage applications. Modifications to the basic circuit usually include the following:

1. Logical switching circuits such as AND and OR gates at the input to the flip-flop
2. Provisions for presetting the flip-flop to either of its two stable states
3. Differentiating circuits to make the flip-flop usable in a system employing square waves
4. Output circuits to give a visual indication of the state in which the flip-flop rests

Terminology and symbols associated with the logical flip-flop are summarized in the table of Fig. 10.7a and the drawings of Fig. 10.7b and c.

QUESTIONS

10.1 What is the basic difference between the free-running multivibrator and the Eccles-Jordan trigger circuit?

10.2 Why are the coupling resistors bypassed with capacitors?

10.3 What is the purpose of the pulse-steering network?

10.4 What are four practical uses of flip-flops?

10.5 How can the output levels of a flip-flop be controlled?

10.6 What modifications are made to the basic Eccles-Jordan circuit to change it to a logical flip-flop?

10.7 How is the state of a flip-flop determined?

10.8 What is complementing and how is it accomplished?

10.9 In a transistor flip-flop, how is minority-carrier storage avoided?

10.10 Why are flip-flops more sensitive to pulses of the polarity which cuts off a conducting tube or transistor than they are to pulses of the polarity which brings these elements into conduction?

Chapter 11

Schmitt Trigger

The problem of discriminating between signal and noise pulses is always present in digital computers and data processors. The greater the distance and time between signal origin and use, the greater the possibility of noise pulses intermingling with the data. Noise waveforms of varying frequency and amplitude not only affect the regions between successive signal pulses but also distort signal pulses. Since the computer circuitry is necessarily designed to respond to signals of very specific shape, amplitude, and duration, something must be done to re-form these distorted pulses and to reject any intervening noise pulses between one signal pulse and the next.

Detecting and reshaping of pulse or sinusoidal waveforms is accomplished by the Schmitt trigger circuit (sometimes referred to as the *binary cathode-coupled circuit*). The output of the Schmitt trigger is a rectangular waveform.

Circuit Operation

The Schmitt trigger circuit is amplitude-sensitive and is designed to produce an output only when the input signal is at, or in excess of, a prescribed amplitude or reference level. This reference level is maintained through cathode biasing. With the use of a variable bias control, the amplitude required to trigger the circuit can be altered.

The duration of the output waveform is equal to the period of time that the input signal remains at, or in excess of, the specified reference level. Figure 11.1 illustrates the ability of this circuit to differentiate between signal and noise voltages.

The Schmitt trigger is a two-stage pulse-shaping circuit. The output pulse will be of constant amplitude because the input stage will become

216

saturated by any signal above the reference level. The second stage will be driven into the cutoff region by the signal occurring at the plate of the first stage. The circuit is, in effect, a bistable multivibrator; thus, it can function as an amplitude comparator, indicating by one or the other of its two stable states whether the input signal is above or below the specified level.

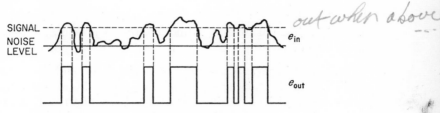

Fig. 11.1 Signal detection with Schmitt trigger.

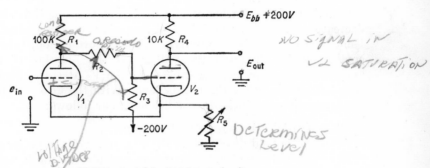

Fig. 11.2 Typical Schmitt trigger circuit.

Figure 11.2 is the schematic diagram of a Schmitt trigger circuit with a sinusoidal input. An examination of this circuit will reveal that it is actually a cathode-coupled bistable multivibrator. Coupling between the first stage (V_1) and the second stage (V_2) is accomplished by resistors R_1, R_2, and R_3. Regenerative feedback is obtained through an unbypassed common-cathode resistor (R_5). Resistor R_5 is adjusted to obtain the desired operating level.

Static conditions. Resistors R_1, R_2, and R_3 form a voltage-dividing network between +200 and −200 volts. With ground as a reference, a positive potential appears at the junction of resistors R_2 and R_3 when tube V_1 is cut off. The positive potential is applied to the grid of tube V_2, causing it to conduct. Current flowing in the tube V_2 will develop a positive voltage across the common-cathode resistor R_5. This voltage causes tube V_1 to be biased beyond cutoff.

The static conditions of the circuit are as follows:

1. E_{in} is absent or below the trigger level.
2. Tube V_2 is conducting because of the positive voltage on its grid from voltage divider R_1, R_2, and R_3.
3. Tube V_1 is held at cutoff by the bias voltage developed across cathode resistor R_5.
4. Plate voltage of tube V_2 is low because of its conduction.
5. Plate voltage of tube V_1 is high because it is held at cutoff by the bias voltage of resistor R_5.

Positive trigger. When an input signal of sufficient amplitude is applied, tube V_1 conducts. As tube V_1 conducts, its plate potential becomes less positive, causing the grid voltage of tube V_2 to become less positive. Tube V_2 conducts less, and the somewhat positive voltage that was present across R_5 becomes even less positive. This negative-going voltage is also felt on the cathode of V_1. The resulting increase in the conduction of V_1 further decreases its plate potential which further decreases the grid potential of V_2, causing V_2 to conduct even less. Hence, this action is cumulative. After a short period, tube V_1 will be conducting heavily, and the voltage at the junction of resistors R_2 and R_3 will become negative, biasing tube V_2 at cutoff until the input signal E_{in} drops below the trigger level. With the grid of tube V_1 above the trigger level, the circuit conditions are as follows:

1. E_{in} potential causes tube V_1 to conduct.
2. Tube V_2 is held at cutoff by the negative voltage on its grid and by the bias voltage developed across resistor R_5. Both potentials are generated as a result of the conduction of tube V_1.
3. Plate potential of tube V_1 is low because of its conduction.
4. Plate potential of tube V_2 is high, nearly equal to E_{bb}.

The conditions just described remain unchanged as long as the input signal is above the specified trigger level.

Reverse trigger. When the input signal E_{in} begins to fall below the trigger level, the conduction in tube V_1 decreases and its plate voltage starts to rise toward E_{bb}. This rise in plate voltage is applied to the grid of tube V_2. When the grid potential of tube V_2 is brought above the cutoff point, reverse triggering takes place. At this time tube V_2 begins to conduct, causing an increase in the current flow through the common-cathode resistor R_5. This increase in current flow increases the bias on tube V_1. An increase in bias on tube V_1 causes this tube to conduct less and its plate potential to rise still further. This rise is again applied to the grid of tube V_2, which allows tube V_2 to conduct more heavily. An increase in the conduction of tube V_2 causes more current to flow through resistor R_5, placing more bias on tube V_1. This action is also cumulative and continues until tube V_1 is completely cut off and tube V_2 is conducting at saturation. At the completion of the reverse trigger, the circuit is returned to its original operating condition and awaits the next input signal.

The switching action described above takes place rapidly. It causes the output waveform to have steep and well-defined leading and trailing edges. *CAUSED IN DIFFERENCE IN BIAS BETWEEN TUBES*

Reverse trigger delay. Since the upclock and downclock of the squarewave output from V_2 have been explained as a result of the increase and decrease of a positive sine-wave input to V_1, it seems to follow that the voltage levels at which these two events take place would be the

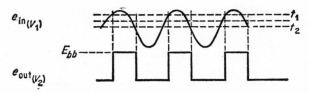

Fig. 11.3 Typical Schmitt trigger waveforms.

same. This is not quite true, however. As shown in Fig. 11.3, the downclock of E_{out} occurs at a lower input voltage level than that which causes the upclock. Compare t_1 and t_2 in Fig. 11.3. This difference in voltage levels is necessary so that the square-wave output of V_2 may be terminated.

The reason for this is as follows: It has been observed that the alternate cutoff and conduction of V_2 yield high and low outputs, respectively. The cutoff and conduction of V_2 are caused by the conduction and cutoff of V_1. When V_1 is cut off, V_2 conducts heavily and produces a low output. Current flow through R_5 due to the conduction of V_2 biases the cathodes of both V_1 and V_2 positively with respect to ground. This positive bias at the cathode of V_1 necessitates a positive signal of certain amplitude on the grid of V_1 before V_1 will conduct and cut off V_2. When V_2 cuts off, the current will then flow through V_1, R_1, and R_5. Since R_1 has ten times the resistance of R_4, the voltage now dropped across R_5 is less than when V_2 was conducting. Consequently, the positive bias on the cathodes is now less than when V_1 was cut off.

In the meantime, the positive sine-wave input has (1) gone sufficiently positive to cause V_1 to conduct, (2) increased to its maximum, and (3) decreased from maximum to the point where its voltage level is equal to that which is necessary to bring V_1 into conduction. This would be the point where V_1 might be expected to cut off; but now its cathode is at a lower positive potential, so V_1 now requires a lower positive voltage on its grid to suppress the electron flow from its cathode and effectively cut it off.

It can be seen that the delay in the cutoff of V_1, caused by its lowered positive cathode bias, results in a slight increase in the length of the square-wave output at V_2. This delay is called *hysteresis*, or *backlash*.

Transistorized Schmitt Trigger

Now that the operation of a vacuum-tube Schmitt trigger has been described, the transistorized version of the same circuit can be more easily explained. (Refer to Fig. 11.4.)

The operation of the transistorized Schmitt trigger is essentially the same as that of the vacuum-tube trigger circuit. An output will be produced only during the time the input signal is equal to, or in excess of, a definite reference level.

If a static or quiescent condition is assumed, E_{in} is not present. Transistor Q_1 is cut off, and its collector voltage is almost equal to $-V_{cc}$.

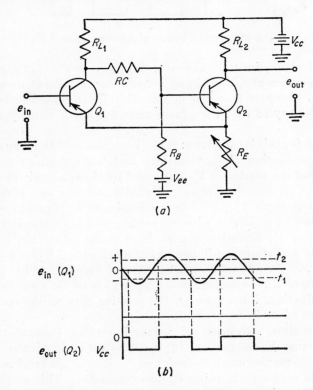

Fig. 11.4 (a) Transistorized Schmitt trigger. (b) Associated waveforms.

Resistors R_L, R_C, and R_B form a voltage-dividing network between $-V_{cc}$ and $+V_{ee}$. With Q_1 cut off, a voltage negative with respect to ground is present at the junctions of resistors R_C and R_B and turns on transistor Q_2. The conduction of transistor Q_2 causes current to flow through the common-emitter resistor R_E. This current flow places a reverse bias on the emitter of transistor Q_1, holding it at cutoff. The static conditions then are as follows:

1. E_{in} is not present or is above trigger level.
2. Transistor Q_2 is conducting because of the negative collector potential of transistor Q_1.
3. Transistor Q_1 is cut off because of bias developed across resistor R_E from the conduction of transistor Q_2.
4. Transistor Q_1 collector potential is equal to $-V_{cc}$.
5. Transistor Q_2 collector is nearly at ground potential because of its heavy conduction.

When a negative signal of sufficient amplitude (Fig. 11.4b) is applied to the base of transistor Q_1, it will overcome the reverse bias present from R_E and allow transistor Q_1 to conduct. The conduction of transistor Q_1 causes its collector potential to become less negative. This less negative signal is applied to the base of transistor Q_2, causing a decrease in the conduction of that transistor; consequently, less reverse-bias voltage is developed across resistor R_E. This allows transistor Q_1 to conduct more, further decreasing its collector potential and causing Q_2 to conduct less. The regenerative action is cumulative and will continue until transistor Q_1 is conducting near the saturation region and transistor Q_2 is held at cutoff by the low collector voltage of transistor Q_1. The condition of the Schmitt trigger circuit during the time the input signal is equal to, or less than, the specified reference level is as follows:

1. E_{in} is equal to, or less than, the reference level.
2. Transistor Q_1 is conducting in or near the saturation region.
3. Transistor Q_2 is held at cutoff by conduction of transistor Q_1.
4. Collector voltage of transistor Q_1 is nearly 0 volt.
5. Collector voltage of transistor Q_2 is $-V_{cc}$.

This new stable condition is maintained until the input signal begins to rise (becomes more positive). The positive-going signal places a reverse bias on the base of transistor Q_1, decreasing its conduction and causing its collector voltage to become more negative. This more negative signal applied to the base of transistor Q_2 allows it to conduct and causes more current to flow through common-emitter resistor R_E. This increases the reverse bias applied to transistor Q_1, causing less conduction in that transistor; hence, its collector potential becomes still more negative.

This more negative signal is applied to the base of transistor Q_2 and allows Q_2 to conduct more heavily, generating a greater bias voltage for transistor Q_1 across resistor R_E. This action is also cumulative and continues until transistor Q_1 is cut off and transistor Q_2 is conducting in the saturation region.

Summary

It can be seen that vacuum-tube Schmitt trigger circuits yield no output until the input signal is of a sufficiently positive potential. When this occurs, the output rises abruptly to a previously adjusted positive amplitude. When this input signal swings back through a somewhat lower positive potential, the output signal is abruptly terminated. The transistorized Schmitt trigger circuit differs in that the inputs are negative-going signals which yield negative output signals of a previously adjusted amplitude.

The Schmitt trigger circuit is in fact a cathode-coupled bistable multivibrator with resistive coupling between stages. The main uses of the circuit in digital computers and data processors are waveshaping and signal detection. The circuit can be used to reshape distorted signals or to convert sinusoidal waveforms to pulse waveforms. The output of the Schmitt trigger is a rectangular wave whose pulse width is equal to the length of time the input signal remains at or exceeds some specified reference level. Since the Schmitt trigger is a two-stage bistable device, the output can be taken from either stage. In the examples discussed, however, the output has been from the second stage.

QUESTIONS

11.1 What is the main function of the Schmitt trigger?

11.2 Which type of multivibrator is the Schmitt trigger most similar to? Explain the difference.

11.3 What determines the output pulse width of the Schmitt trigger?

11.4 Why is the variable resistor R_5 in Fig. 11.2 not bypassed with a capacitor?

11.5 What polarity will the output waveform of an NPN transistorized Schmitt trigger have when an input signal is applied?

Chapter 12

Blocking Oscillators

A blocking oscillator is any oscillator which cuts itself off after one or more cycles of its oscillating frequency. There are two classifications of blocking oscillators: single-swing and self-pulsing. Both types can be triggered or free-running. The output waveforms produced by blocking oscillators are illustrated in Fig. 12.1. The output waveform shown in Fig. 12.1a is generated by a single-swing blocking oscillator. In this type, the amplifier is cut off after one oscillating cycle is complete. In Fig. 12.1b, the output of a self-pulsing blocking oscillator is shown. Cutoff in this type occurs after two or more cycles have been completed.

Like multivibrators, blocking oscillators can be arranged in either astable or monostable circuits. In the astable (free-running) circuit, a period of rest occurs between each oscillating interval, and the circuit performs as a relaxation oscillator (Fig. 12.1a and b). The monostable or triggered circuit is held initially at rest by external bias and remains in a stable state until an external triggering pulse is applied. When this occurs the circuit oscillates briefly, then abruptly cuts off until retriggered. The output waveforms of monostable blocking oscillators are shown in Fig. 12.1d and e.

The type having the widest application in digital computers is the monostable single-swing blocking oscillator. The output waveform of this circuit is shown in Fig. 12.1d. With correct design, the monostable single-swing blocking oscillator can produce output pulses as narrow as 0.05 μsec. For this reason, the circuit is often used for reshaping broad, rounded input pulses into narrow output pulses with sharp leading and trailing edges. This circuit may also be used in frequency division and counting applications. This chapter is limited to a discussion of the single-swing blocking oscillator. The monostable (triggered) circuit is most fre-

223

quently used, but the astable type will be presented first to introduce important principles. Transistor blocking oscillators will be covered in Part II of this chapter.

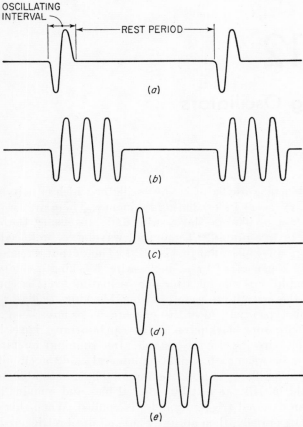

Fig. 12.1 Blocking-oscillator output waveforms. (a) Free-running single-swing blocking-oscillator waveforms. (b) Free-running self-pulsing blocking-oscillator waveforms. (c) Trigger pulse. (d) Triggered single-swing blocking-oscillator waveform. (e) Triggered self-pulsing blocking-oscillator waveforms.

PART I: VACUUM-TUBE BLOCKING OSCILLATORS

Single-swing Blocking Oscillator (Astable Type)

The basic circuit of the free-running single-swing blocking oscillator is illustrated in Fig. 12.2. The circuit functions as a relaxation oscillator and periodically generates a series of narrow pulses.

As shown, the circuit consists of a triode tube, a pulse transformer with unity turns ratio, and an RC network. The components are arranged to provide voltage amplification and regenerative (positive) feedback. The regenerative action in the blocking oscillator is similar to that which occurs in a multivibrator but is accomplished with one amplifier instead of two. The polarity inversion provided by the second amplifier in the multivibrator is accomplished in the blocking oscillator through the use of a pulse transformer.

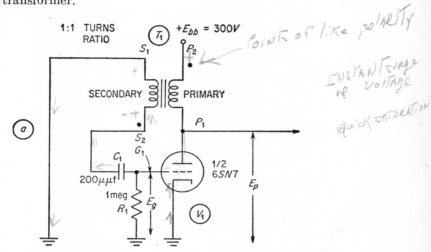

Fig. 12.2 Astable (free-running) blocking-oscillator basic circuit.

To understand regenerative action in this circuit, assume that there is a voltage increase in the positive direction at the grid of V_1. The increase is reinforced by feedback from the output of the amplifier as described in the following paragraphs.

An increase in the grid-to-ground potential at G_1 results in a current increase through V_1 and the primary of T_1. As the primary current through T_1 increases, the magnetic flux surrounding the primary also increases and results in an increase in the potential difference developed across its terminals. Because of the direction of current during the increase, the instantaneous polarity of the dot side of the primary is positive relative to its nondot side. Since the dots at each winding indicate identical polarities, the increase in the potential difference developed across the secondary terminals by flux linkage has an instantaneous polarity at S_2 that is positive relative to S_1 and ground.

The potential at S_2 represents the feedback voltage and is coupled through C_1 to the grid of the tube. Since the feedback voltage swings positive relative to ground, it reinforces the initial potential at G_1. The regenerative action described above causes an abrupt switching action when power is applied to the circuit. As current increases, feedback drives the tube into saturation. Once saturation is reached, a slight decrease in plate current results in a second switching action, and the tube

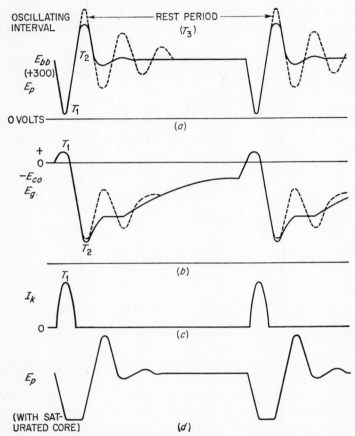

Fig. 12.3 Astable blocking-oscillator operating waveforms. (a) Plate (E_p) waveform. (b) Grid (E_g) waveform. (c) Cathode (I_k) waveform. (d) Plate (E_p) waveform—core saturated.

is abruptly cut off. This cycle of events is repeated after an interval determined by circuit time constants.

Typical waveforms of plate voltage, grid voltage, and cathode current are shown in Fig. 12.3. These waveforms are helpful toward providing an understanding of the circuit action explained in the following paragraphs.

When power is first applied, the grid-to-ground potential is 0 volt and V_1 conducts heavily. Positive feedback drives V_1 abruptly toward saturation. During this interval, the grid of V_1 swings positive with respect to ground, and the plate voltage swings negatively toward 0 volt. When the grid is driven positive, grid current charges C_1 through the path shown in Fig. 12.4a, and electrons accumulate on the capacitor plate nearest the grid. The accumulation of electrons causes the grid to become less positive. This reduces the rate at which the plate current increases, which, in turn, reduces the magnitude of the feedback voltage.

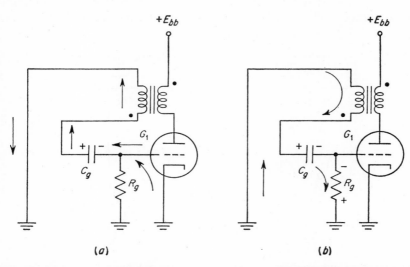

Fig. 12.4 Charge and discharge path of C_1. (a) Electron flow during charge of C_g. (b) Electron flow during discharge of C_g.

The action is cumulative and ends when both the rate of plate-current increase and the feedback voltage are reduced to 0. That point in time is represented by t_1 in the waveforms shown in Fig. 12.3. Since plate current has reached its maximum value and is no longer changing, feedback to the grid circuit ceases and C_1 begins to discharge through the path shown in Fig. 12.4b. As C_1 discharges, the potential at G_1 swings in the negative direction and plate current decreases. At the instant this occurs, regenerative action reinforces the negative swing at G_1, and the grid is driven far beyond the cutoff potential of the tube. With a 1:1 turns ratio, the negative excursion of G_1 is approximately equal to the peak-to-peak swing of the plate voltage. This point in time is indicated by t_2 in Fig. 12.3. The tube remains at cutoff for an interval determined by the discharge time of C_1–R_1. The cutoff interval is called the rest period (t_3 in Fig. 12.3) and is much longer in duration than the oscillating interval (t_1 plus t_2) because of the long time constant of the discharge path.

During the rest period, C_1 discharges through R_1, and the voltage at G_1 approaches the conduction level of the tube (E_{co}). When this level is reached, V_1 conducts and the cycle of events just described is repeated. Oscillation in this manner continues until power is removed.

As shown in the plate waveform in Fig. 12.3, the plate voltage rises above E_{bb} when the tube current is cut off. This is due to the inductance of the transformer windings. Current continues to flow in these windings when the tube current ceases, because the magnetic field surrounding the primary turns collapses at this time. The resultant inductive current flows

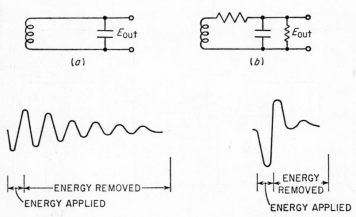

Fig. 12.5 Damped oscillations in a shock-excited resonant circuit. (a) High Q. (b) Low Q.

in the same direction as the initial plate current and charges the capacitance of the transformer windings to a voltage in excess of E_{bb}.

The output waveform at the plate of V_1 (Fig. 12.3a) is approximately sinusoidal since the circuit tends to oscillate at a frequency determined by the inductance of the transformer windings and the distributed and circuit capacitances. These components form a resonant circuit that becomes shock-excited when V_1 conducts. Oscillations are not continuous, but decay exponentially to zero since energy is no longer supplied to the resonant circuit when the tube cuts off. The exponential decay in a shock-excited tank circuit is shown in Fig. 12.5.

As shown in the figure, the rate at which the oscillations decay is a function of circuit Q. In low-resistance (high-Q) circuits, the decay is relatively slow (Fig. 12.5a). If series or shunt resistance is added to the circuit as shown in Fig. 12.5b, the Q is lowered. The energy in the tank circuit is then quickly dissipated, and the decay is abrupt.

In a correctly designed single-swing blocking oscillator, the pulse transformer is chosen so that core losses sufficiently reduce the circuit Q, and oscillations cease after approximately one cycle. This results in the plate waveform shown in solid lines in Fig. 12.3a. The dashed lines in Fig. 12.3a and b result when the core losses in the transformer are too low. When this occurs, an external resistance must be shunted across the transformer in order to reduce circuit Q and provide the correct damping factor. The usable output pulse of this circuit is made up of the negative excursion of the plate waveform (Fig. 12.3a) or the cathode-current waveform (Fig. 12.3c). Pulse width depends upon the resonant frequency of the tank circuit described previously. A high resonant frequency results in a narrow pulse width. Since C_1 shunts the resonant circuit when V_1 conducts, it has a pronounced effect on pulse width; for narrow pulses the value of C_1 should be made as small as possible. Pulse width is also affected by the degree of core saturation in the transformer. If tube conduction causes core saturation, the pulse shape becomes rectangular and pulse duration increases (see Fig. 12.3d).

Output terminals. The basic circuit shown in Fig. 12.2 has been modified in Fig. 12.6 to show the methods commonly used to provide an output pulse.

Four outputs are shown: A, B, C, and DD'. In a given application usually only one of the outputs is provided. For example, if output A is desired, the tertiary winding L_t and the cathode resistor are omitted from the circuit. If output DD' is desired, both RP and R_k are omitted. The output chosen depends upon voltage polarity, pulse amplitude, and impedance requirements of the succeeding stage.

Voltage waveforms available at all terminals are shown in Fig. 12.6 (A through D'). Pulse outputs at terminals A and C assume the shape of the cathode current in the waveform illustrated in Fig. 12.3. Since no inductive current flows through RP or R_k, outputs at these terminals are free of overshoot and may be preferred rather than pulses at B and DD'. Pulse amplitude and output impedance, however, are relatively low; when pulses at a higher impedance or greater amplitude are required, either the plate waveform at B or the output of the tertiary windings at DD' is used. The output at B consists of a negative pulse with a positive overshoot caused by transformer inductance. Overshoot may be removed through the use of diode limiter CR_2 and current-limiting resistor R_L, shown in the figure. An ungrounded output is provided by using the tertiary winding L_t. This output has the same shape as the plate waveform at B. This arrangement provides a pulse of either polarity. For example, if terminal D' is grounded, a positive pulse is available at terminal D. If terminal D is grounded, a negative pulse is available at D'. Diode CR_1 can be used to remove inductive overshoot. The tertiary winding also provides d-c isolation and, if the correct turns ratio is selected, any one of a wide range of impedance and voltage levels can be obtained.

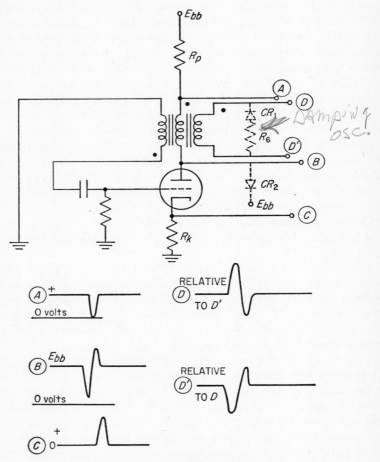

Fig. 12.6 Output terminals and waveforms.

Monostable (Triggered) Blocking Oscillator

A free-running blocking oscillator can be converted to a monostable or triggered type by returning the grid resistor to a voltage source sufficiently negative to prevent tube conduction. When this is done, the circuit remains quiescent until externally triggered. Upon application of an external trigger pulse, the circuit generates one output pulse, then returns to its initial stable state until retriggered.

The monostable circuit shown in Fig. 12.7 is identical to the astable circuit in Fig. 12.2 except for the negative-bias source E_{co} and the input capacitor C_2. Although operation of the monostable circuit is similar to that of the free-running type, a brief explanation of circuit action is given here.

As shown by the grid waveform of Fig. 12.7c, the bias source E_{co} holds the grid below cutoff, and the circuit is initially at rest in a stable state.

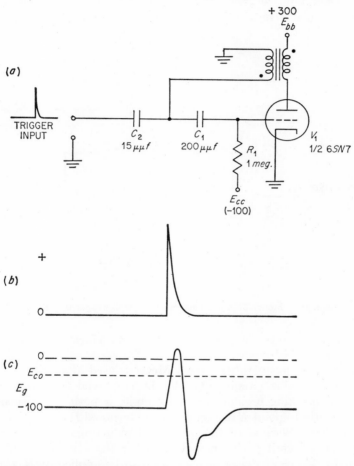

Fig. 12.7 Monostable blocking oscillator and waveforms. (a) Circuit diagram. (b) Trigger pulse. (c) Grid waveform.

A positive trigger pulse of sufficient amplitude to bring the grid potential to conduction level (E_{co}) results in conduction of tube V_1. When this occurs, the trigger pulse is no longer needed to sustain conduction. An abrupt switching action due to regenerative feedback drives the tube toward saturation. During this interval, C_1 charges to approximately 300 volts. When saturation is reached, the plate current settles at a constant value, feedback ceases, and C_1 discharges. The discharge of C_1 initiates a second switching action, and the grid is driven well beyond the cutoff potential of V_1. As C_1 discharges, the grid-to-ground potential increases toward the conduction level of the tube. Conduction level is never reached, however, because of the cutoff source E_{cc}. For this reason the circuit remains in a quiescent state until the next trigger pulse is

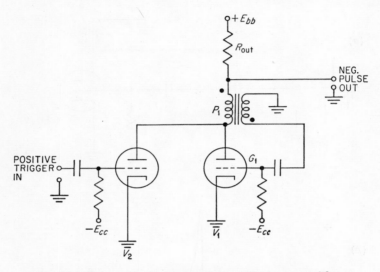

Fig. 12.8 Monostable blocking oscillator with trigger amplifier.

applied. Plate-voltage and cathode-current waveforms are identical to those of the astable circuit.

Triggering the monostable circuit. Methods used to provide an output pulse in the astable circuit may also be employed for triggering the monostable blocking oscillator. For example, a positive pulse may be applied directly to point E in Fig. 12.6 or to terminal D if a tertiary winding is included. Because of the phase-inversion properties of the pulse transformer, triggering with negative, rather than positive, pulses can be used. In this case, the negative pulse can be applied at B, C, or D'. Obviously, when triggering is executed through one of these means, a different set of terminals must be used to extract the output pulse. Since the grid draws current during the generation of the output pulse, the input and output impedances of the blocking oscillator are extremely low (less than 1,000 ohms) during the trigger interval. For this reason, triggering by the stated methods requires low-impedance trigger sources capable of generating large-amplitude pulses. Because of the low-impedance requirements, sources of this type are adversely affected by circuit action in the blocking oscillator. To overcome this problem, a trigger amplifier as shown in Fig. 12.8 is frequently employed. The relatively high plate impedance of V_2 (approximately 9,000 ohms) provides isolation between the trigger source and the blocking oscillator. Also, since V_2 provides voltage gain, lower-amplitude trigger pulses may be used.

In operation, both V_1 and V_2 are held below cutoff by E_{cc} during the interval between triggers. A positive pulse applied at the trigger input causes V_2 to conduct, and the plate voltage at P_1 decreases. The negative excursion is inverted by the pulse transformer and appears as a positive voltage at G_1 to initiate the blocking-oscillator cycle.

PART II: TRANSISTORIZED BLOCKING OSCILLATOR

A monostable single-swing blocking oscillator using a PNP transistor is shown in Fig. 12.9. The circuit arrangement is identical with that of the vacuum-tube blocking oscillator shown in Fig. 12.2. Operation of both transistor and vacuum-tube oscillators is so nearly identical that only differences in operation are emphasized in this section. Collector and plate waveforms of the two oscillators are compared in Fig. 12.9. The collector waveform is inverted relative to the plate waveform because the bias characteristics of the PNP transistor are opposite to those of the vacuum tube. Waveforms a and b occur when the pulse-transformer core is not excessively saturated during the conducting interval. Waveforms c and d show the change in pulse shape and pulse duration which occurs when the core is permitted to saturate.

Waveforms a and b emphasize the major point of difference between the two oscillators. In the transistor circuit, minority-carrier storage effects delay turn-off time and result in wider, more rectangular pulses. The inductive overshoot occurring during the cutoff period, however, is identical in the two blocking oscillators. The output of the transistor blocking oscillator is usually provided through the use of a tertiary winding on the pulse transformer. As was true in the vacuum-tube circuit, a diode limiter, (CR_1 in Fig. 12.9) is used to remove the inductive overshoot. In some circuits, the diodes shown by dashed lines are added to the circuit shown in Fig. 12.9 to limit collector voltage excursions on both positive and negative swings. Diode CR_2 prevents the collector voltage from swinging more negative than supply voltage V_{cc}. (This ordinarily occurs during the inductive overshoot period.) Limiting negative excursion in this manner ensures that the maximum permissible reverse voltage is not exceeded and prevents collector breakdown. Ordinarily this is no problem in vacuum-tube circuits since the plate can withstand much greater voltages before breakdown occurs.

Diode CR_3 reduces the effect of minority-carrier storage by preventing the collector from becoming forward-biased during conduction.

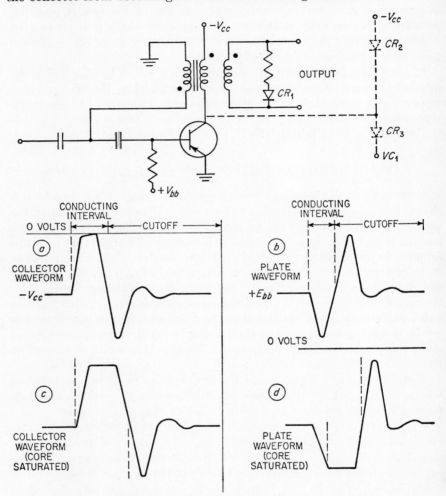

Fig. 12.9 Transistorized monostable blocking oscillator and waveforms.

Summary

The blocking oscillator is a sine-wave oscillator which cuts itself off after one or more cycles of its oscillating frequency. Cutoff in the single-swing type occurs after completion of one oscillating cycle. The self-pulsing blocking oscillator generates two or more cycles prior to cutoff.

Blocking oscillators can be classified as either astable (free-running) or monostable (triggered) circuits. Free-running types operate continuously and perform as relaxation oscillators in that a rest period occurs between each oscillating interval. The monostable type oscillates only when triggered and then cuts itself off abruptly until retriggered.

The circuit with the widest application in digital computers is the monostable single-swing blocking oscillator. This circuit generates one narrow output pulse for each input trigger pulse and is used in pulse-forming and shaping applications.

The monostable single-swing circuit consists of an amplifier, a pulse transformer, and an *RC* network. The pulse transformer and circuit capacitance form a resonant circuit which becomes shock-excited when the amplifier conducts. Oscillation is but momentary, however, since regenerative feedback sharply cuts off the amplifier, and energy is no longer supplied to the resonant circuit. When correctly designed, the pulse transformer is chosen so that core losses sufficiently reduce the circuit Q and oscillations cease after approximately one cycle.

In pulse-forming and shaping applications, the usable output pulse from this circuit is made up of the negative excursion of the plate waveform. The width of this pulse depends primarily on the resonant frequency of the circuit but is affected by the degree of core saturation in the pulse transformer. The input capacitor (C_1) also has a pronounced effect on pulse width since it effectively shunts the resonant circuit when the amplifier conducts. For narrow pulses, the value of this capacitor should be made very small.

Triggering of the monostable circuit can be accomplished by both positive and negative pulses. The input trigger may be applied to the grid, cathode, or plate circuits. Because of the low impedance of the blocking oscillator during the generation of the output pulse, trigger amplifiers are employed between the trigger source and the blocking oscillator to provide isolation.

While the output pulse may be taken from the plate, cathode, or grid circuits, a tertiary winding on the pulse transformer is usually used for this purpose. The ungrounded tertiary winding provides a pulse of either polarity, ensures d-c isolation between the oscillator and the succeeding stage, and provides means of selecting wide ranges of impedance and voltage levels through choosing the correct turns ratio.

Blocking oscillators employing transistors are identical as to both circuit configuration and operating principles when compared with the vacuum-tube type. The major point of difference between the two is the minority-carrier storage effect associated with transistor amplifiers. Minority-carrier storage delays turn-off time and results in a wider, more rectangular pulse. To overcome this effect, conventional nonsaturating techniques can be used.

QUESTIONS

12.1 What are the two classifications of blocking oscillators? Describe each.

12.2 What causes undesirable oscillations to occur when the tube or the transistor is driven to cutoff?

12.3 How are these undesirable oscillations suppressed?

12.4 If the transformer and B+ in a free-running blocking-oscillator circuit are fixed, how can the frequency of the blocking oscillator be varied without changing the width of the output pulses?

12.5 What determines the width of the output pulses? Explain.

12.6 What determines the output frequency of a synchronized blocking oscillator?

12.7 List some uses of the blocking oscillator.

Chapter **13**

Timing Oscillators

Digital computers solve problems by following a detailed system of instructions called a *program*. Each instruction contained in the program must be performed by the computer at the correct time and in the correct sequence. To do this, two components must be incorporated in the computing system: (1) a timing oscillator to divide time into small, equal intervals; and (2) a clock to record the number of timing intervals that have passed since the start of the program. The timing oscillator and clock synchronize all functions performed by the computer and ensure that each function occurs precisely on time.

Program Synchronization

The timing oscillator is the heart of the synchronizing system in a computer. It generates the basic timing interval and determines the rate at which the computer processes information. To see how this is done, consider the simplified block diagram in Fig. 13.1. As shown in the diagram, the output of the timing oscillator (signal A) is a continuous sine wave. A period of one cycle of this oscillating waveform establishes the basic timing interval. In a typical computer, the free-running frequency of the timing oscillator is 200 kc; therefore the basic timing interval (duration of one cycle) is 5 μsec. The output of the timing oscillator is delivered to a pulse-forming-and-shaping circuit which produces one output pulse (called a clock pulse) for each input cycle (signal B).

The clock shown in Fig. 13.1 is an electronic counter. This clock records the number of timing intervals which have passed since the start of the program by counting the number of clock pulses delivered to its input. At a predetermined count or timing interval, the computer performs a function determined by an instruction contained in the program unit.

The simplified program illustrated in Fig. 13.1 contains three instructions. When the counter or clock contains a count of ten, the computer adds the information present at input A to that present at input B. At time interval 20, input C is subtracted from the sum of A plus B; and at timing interval 30, the computer stores the result of the subtraction in its memory unit.

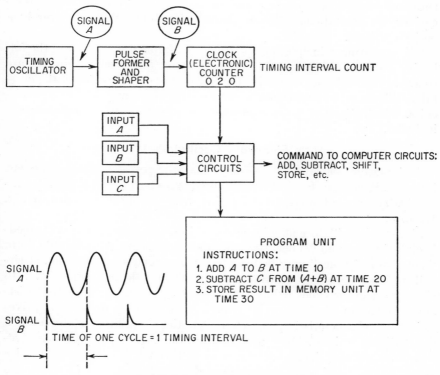

Fig. 13.1 Program synchronization.

In modern computers thousands of instructions are contained in the program unit. The time required for the computer to execute each instruction depends, of course, on the nature of the instruction. A shift-to-storage instruction, for example, can be executed more quickly than an add instruction. If the execution time for the average instruction is 10 timing intervals, a computer with a 200-kc timing oscillator can perform 20,000 operations a second.

While the above example illustrates the chief use of timing oscillators in computer systems, often more timing oscillators are used in auxiliary equipment at the input or output of the computer. For example, an additional timing oscillator would be included in the range-tracking equipment of a missile-guidance computer. This timing oscillator would be termed the *range oscillator*. Regardless of specific application, however, the purpose of all timing oscillators is the same: to divide an interval of time into small equal and precisely measured time increments.

Since the basic timing interval generated by a timing oscillator will change if its frequency drifts, frequency stability is an important characteristic of such devices. In many cases, oscillators used in these applications are crystal-controlled to provide frequency stability over long periods of time.

The operating principles of sine-wave oscillators are covered in the following pages. Feedback oscillators employing LC resonant circuits are treated first. This treatment is followed by the development of the crystal oscillator from oscillators controlled by conventional LC-type circuits. Illustrations of both transistor and vacuum-tube oscillators are included.

Sine-wave Oscillators

A sine-wave oscillator is a device capable of converting direct current into an alternating current at a frequency determined by circuit constants. The output waveform of a sine-wave oscillator is shown in Fig. 13.2*a*.

Sine-wave oscillators may be classified into two broad groups: (1) feedback oscillators and (2) negative-resistance oscillators. Although the term "negative resistance" may be used to account for the cancellation of circuit resistance in any continuously oscillating device, when used to classify oscillator types it has a more specific meaning. Negative-resistance oscillators employ special circuit elements that display negative-resistance characteristics, or characteristics opposite to those of a conventional resistor. For example, when the voltage across a negative-resistance element increases, the current through it decreases and vice versa. Examples of negative-resistance devices are screen-grid tubes, gas diodes, and tunnel diodes. The negative-resistance oscillator is rarely used in timing-oscillator applications. For this reason, this discussion will be limited to feedback oscillators.

The block diagram of a feedback oscillator is shown in Fig. 13.2*b*. As shown in the diagram, the oscillator contains three essential parts: (1) a frequency-determining element, (2) a power amplifier, and (3) a feedback loop with a feedback element. The frequency-determining element, usually a resonant circuit, limits oscillations to a single frequency and supplies a varying signal at this frequency to the power amplifier. The power amplifier increases the power of the signal applied to its input. Part of the output power from the amplifier is supplied to the load and part is returned as feedback power to the input of the oscillator. The power fed back to the input must be returned in phase with the input power. This is called *regenerative*, or *positive*, feedback. The feedback power is used to overcome resistance losses in the frequency-determining element and for this reason is said to contribute an element of negative resistance to the circuit. The feedback element provides coupling be-

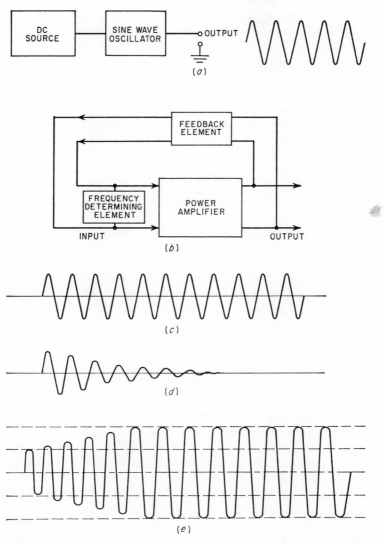

Fig. 13.2 Sine-wave oscillator. (a) Block diagram and output waveform. (b) Feedback oscillator. (c) Proper amount of feedback. (d) Insufficient feedback. (e) Excessive feedback.

tween the output and input of the oscillator and controls the amount of energy fed back to the input. When the feedback power is just sufficient to overcome the resistance losses in the feedback loop, the circuit oscillates continuously at a constant amplitude. If an excessive amount of feedback energy is returned to the input, the amplitude of the output signal will continuously increase until it is limited by circuit saturation. If insufficient feedback is provided through the coupling element, the circuit will oscillate only momentarily and oscillations will decay exponentially to zero in a relatively short period of time. The three conditions of feedback are shown in Fig. 13.2. The ratio of the feedback power to the power delivered to the input of the amplifier is termed the *loop gain* of the circuit. To provide continuous oscillations in the output, the loop gain of the circuit must be greater than unity.

The usable output power of any feedback oscillator is reduced by the amount of power fed back to the input to sustain oscillations. For this reason, losses in the feedback loop must be kept at a minimum, and the feedback circuit must be designed to match the input and output impedances of the amplifier. These requirements are particularly important in power oscillators and in oscillators designed to operate at extremely high frequencies.

Sine-wave oscillators employing feedback principles are often classified in accordance with the type of frequency-determining element used in the oscillator. Included in this classification are *LC* resonant oscillators, crystal-controlled oscillators, and resistance-capacitance-controlled oscillators. Oscillators whose frequency is controlled by *RC* networks find their widest use as audio-frequency generators and are not covered. *LC* resonant and crystal-controlled oscillators, however, are frequently employed in timing applications and are discussed in the following paragraphs.

LC Resonant Oscillators

LC resonant oscillators utilize the resonating properties of an inductor-capacitor combination to control the frequency at which the circuit oscillates. When power is momentarily applied to such a combination of components, the circuit becomes shock-excited and oscillates for a short time. To understand how oscillations originate in an *LC* network, consider the circuit shown in Fig. 13.3.

When switch S_1 is thrown to the left, capacitor C_1 charges to the applied voltage with the polarity shown. During the charge, energy is stored in the electric field between the plates of the capacitor. When the battery is removed and switch S_1 is thrown to the right, the capacitor discharges through the inductor. During the discharge, energy in the electric field of the capacitor is transferred to the magnetic field that builds up around the inductor because of the flow of current. When the capacitor is completely discharged, all the energy originally contained between the plates of the capacitor is stored in the magnetic field of the inductor. At this point, with no moving charge to support it, the magnetic field collapses. The collapsing magnetic field induces a voltage across the coil, and the capacitor becomes charged in the opposite direction.

The circuit action described above is repetitive. Energy is alternately exchanged between the capacitor and the inductor as C_1 charges and discharges through L. Oscillation in this manner continues until all the en-

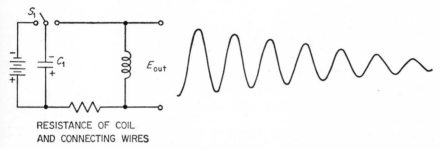

RESISTANCE OF COIL
AND CONNECTING WIRES

Fig. 13.3 *LC* network.

ergy received during the initial charge of C_1 is dissipated in the form of heat caused by circuit resistance. As shown in the figure, the output voltage, taken across the inductor, is sinusoidal in shape and decays exponentially to zero as energy in the circuit is dissipated.

The frequency at which the circuit oscillates is a function of the product of $L \times C$ and can be determined through the use of the formula

$$F = \frac{1}{2\pi \sqrt{LC}}$$

The circuit shown in Fig. 13.3 would oscillate continuously were it not for the circuit resistance. In feedback oscillators, circuit resistance is overcome through use of a power amplifier and regenerative feedback. A simple circuit to accomplish this is shown in Fig. 13.4*a*.

The circuit is a self-excited amplifier circuit since its output is fed back to its input. L_s and C_1 form a parallel resonant circuit whose characteristics are similar to those described above. These elements determine the frequency at which the circuit oscillates. C_2 and R_1 provide grid-leak bias and establish the operating point on the characteristic curve of the tube. V_1 is in a common-cathode circuit and provides phase inversion in addition to power amplification. L_p is the feedback element and consists of a small number of turns wound on the same core as L_s. L_p is termed a *tickler coil,* but in conjunction with L_s it functions as a phase-inverting transformer. C_3 is a bypass capacitor that provides a low-impedance path to ground for the oscillating signal.

Circuit operation. When power is applied to the circuit shown in Fig. 13.4*a*, current through V_1 increases toward saturation. The plate-current

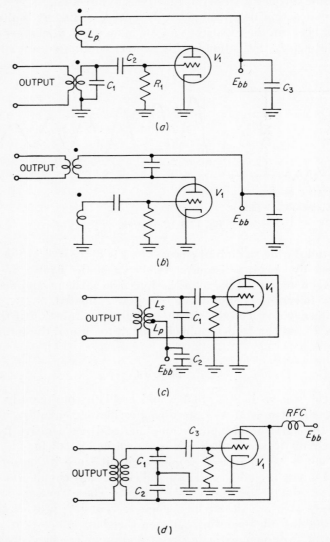

Fig. 13.4 Typical oscillators. (*a*) Armstrong oscillator (tuned-grid tickler-feedback). (*b*) Meissner oscillator (tuned-plate tickler-feedback). (*c*) Hartley oscillator. (*d*) Colpitts oscillator.

increase is accompanied by an expanding magnetic field which surrounds the tickler coil L_p. An expanding magnetic field induces a voltage in the secondary coil L_s. If we assume that the transformer secondary is connected to provide phase inversion, the instantaneous polarity at the dot side of L_s is positive relative to ground. This positive voltage is coupled through C_2 to the grid of V_1 and furthers the plate-current increase. Circuit action constitutes regenerative (positive) feedback and is cumulative. Current through V_1 continues to be supported by positive feedback until saturation is reached.

During this interval C_1 charges, and energy supplied by the induced voltage is stored in the electric field of the capacitor. When saturation is reached, current through the tickler coil no longer increases and the induced voltage in the secondary winding is reduced to zero. Since the source of energy to the tuned circuit is removed, C_1 discharges through L_s, and the resonant circuit oscillates in a manner previously described.

Since the oscillating voltage across C_1 is coupled to the grid of V_1, plate current varies in step with the natural oscillations of the resonant circuit. The phase-inverting properties of both amplifier and transformer provide in-phase feedback and ensure that energy is induced in the resonant circuit at the correct time to support oscillations.

The circuit just described is called the *Armstrong oscillator*, named after its inventor. It is also referred to as the *tuned-grid tickler-feedback oscillator* because of the location of the resonant circuit and the type of feedback element used.

Many variations of this basic feedback oscillator are possible. Examples of circuit variations frequently encountered in practical application are shown in Fig. 13.4b to d. Notice that each of the amplifiers in the examples shown is arranged in the common-cathode circuit configuration. This is not a strict requirement. Any of three circuit configurations— common-grid, common-cathode, or common-plate—can be used in the design of a feedback oscillator. The common-cathode configuration, however, is employed because of its high power gain and its superior impedance characteristics. This configuration displays a high impedance in both the input and the output circuit. For this reason, there is little loss in the feedback loop because of mismatch.

The frequency-controlling element in feedback oscillators can be placed at any point in the feedback loop. The Meissner oscillator shown in Fig. 13.4b is a typical example. In this oscillator the resonant circuit is in the plate circuit, and regenerative feedback is provided through a tickler coil at the input to the power amplifier. The Meissner oscillator is but one example of many so-called tuned-plate oscillators. Tuned-cathode oscillators are also possible.

Feedback in the oscillators shown in Fig. 13.4a and b is accomplished through the transformer action of a tickler coil. Other means of providing the correct regenerative feedback are shown in Fig. 13.4c and d. Feedback in the Hartley oscillator shown in Fig. 13.4c is accomplished through the use of a tapped inductor or autotransformer. Fluctuations in plate current supply energy to the resonant circuit through the feedback path from ground through V_1, the primary coil L_p, and the signal bypass capacitor C_2. The signal current through L_p induces a voltage in the secondary winding (L_s) in the correct phase to sustain oscillations.

The Colpitts oscillator shown in Fig. 13.4d is similar to the Hartley oscillator except that a split capacitor rather than a tapped coil is employed as the feedback element. Energy is supplied directly to the capacitor of the tank circuit through C_2. The feedback path is from ground, through V_1 and C_2, and back to ground. The r-f choke in the plate lead prevents the oscillating signal from being shunted by the low impedance of the power source.

The operating frequencies of the LC oscillators described above change with variations in the supply voltage, variations in the load on the oscillator, and changes in temperature. These factors affect the frequency of the oscillator because all alter the total circuit capacitance that shunts the parallel resonant circuit. Despite the inherent frequency instability of the LC resonant oscillator, frequency drift can be considerably reduced through correct design. Frequency stability sufficient for most applications can be achieved through use of regulated power supplies, buffer amplifiers to isolate the oscillator from its load, and positive-temperature-coefficient capacitors to compensate for capacitance changes caused by temperature.

When the frequency of feedback oscillators must be held to close tolerances, crystal control is usually employed. The operating principles of crystal oscillators follow.

Crystal Oscillators

The frequency stability of a feedback oscillator may be improved by using a quartz crystal as the frequency-controlling element. The frequency drift in a correctly designed oscillator may be held to less than one cycle each megacycle. This excellent frequency stability is due to the fact that oscillation depends on the mechanical properties of the crystal and is only slightly affected by circuit capacitance.

Crystalline substances like quartz have the same series and parallel resonant properties as electric circuits containing inductance, because of the piezoelectric characteristics of such materials.

When quartz is subjected to mechanical strain, a difference of potential is generated at opposing surfaces of the crystal (see Fig. 13.5a). In addition to this effect, the reverse is also true; that is, if an external potential is applied across the surfaces of the crystal, its shape will become altered. For this reason, an alternating voltage applied across the crystal causes the crystal to vibrate mechanically. Maximum vibrations occur when the frequency of the applied voltage is equal to the natural vibrating frequency of the crystal. At this frequency, the crystal behaves electrically like a series resonant circuit.

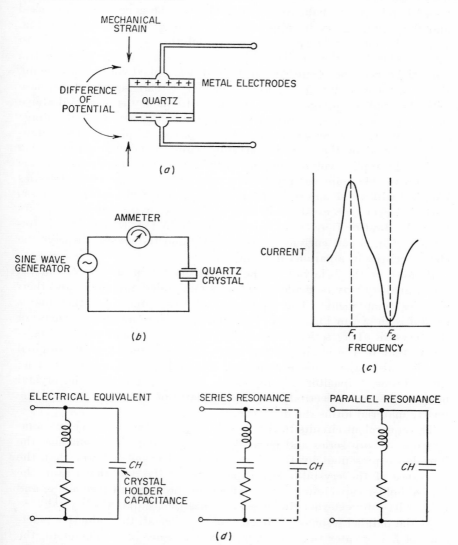

Fig. 13.5 Resonant properties of quartz crystal. (a) Piezoelectric effect. (b) Effect of resonant properties. (c) Crystal current characteristics. (d) Equivalent circuits.

246

COMPUTER CIRCUITS

The resonant properties of a quartz crystal may be demonstrated with the circuit in Fig. 13.5b. The curve in Fig. 13.5c shows how the current in the circuit varies as the frequency applied to the circuit is increased.

When the frequency of the generator is well below mechanical resonance, the crystal vibrates weakly and the current recorded by the ammeter is relatively small. As the frequency of the generator is increased and the vibrating crystal approaches mechanical resonance (F_1 in Fig. 13.5c), the current begins to increase and the crystal mass tends to vibrate ahead of the applied voltage. At this point the piezoelectric potential causes the circuit current to lead the applied voltage, producing the effect of capacitance. At F_1, the current is maximum and in phase with the applied voltage. As the generator frequency is increased above mechanical resonance, vibrations tend to lag behind the applied voltage and the current decreases rapidly. At this point, the piezoelectric potential developed by the vibrating crystal causes the circuit current to lag behind the applied voltage, producing the effect of an inductance. Notice that up to this point the crystal has displayed electrical characteristics identical with those of a series LC resonant circuit. Unlike its LC counterpart, however, the crystal will also oscillate at a frequency above its natural vibrating frequency (F_2 on the curve in Fig. 13.5c). At this frequency (F_2), circuit current drops abruptly and the crystal displays the characteristics of a parallel resonant circuit.

Because of the behavior of the quartz crystal in electric circuits, a direct analogy may be made between its mechanical properties and their electrical equivalents. The equivalent electric circuit for the quartz crystal is shown in Fig. 13.5d. The inductance L represents the mass of the crystal. The series capacitance C is equivalent to the elasticity, that is, the ability of the crystal mass to return to its original position when the stress is removed. The resistance R represents frictional losses. Capacitor CH represents the capacitance of the crystal holder. The metal electrodes act as the plates of the capacitor, and the quartz material forms the dielectric.

The equivalent circuits to the right in Fig. 13.5d show the active components at both series and parallel resonance. At series resonance, the impedance presented by the vibrating crystal is much lower than the reactance of the crystal-holder capacitance (CH). For this reason the crystal-holder capacitance has no effect on the resonant frequency, and neither has any external circuit capacitance that shunts the crystal.

At the parallel resonant frequency of the crystal, the inductive reactance of L is greater than the capacitive reactance of C. Therefore, the combination of L and C appears as net inductance. This is shown in the equivalent circuit at the extreme right in Fig. 13.5d. This net inductance

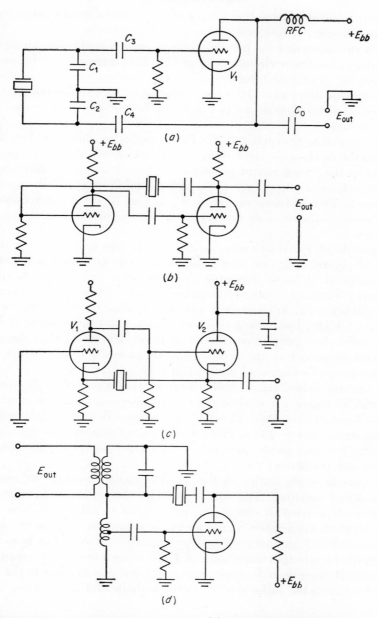

Fig. 13.6 Typical vacuum-tube crystal oscillators. (a) Pierce oscillator (parallel resonance). (b) Two-stage RC-coupled oscillator (series resonance). (c) Grounded-grid RC-coupled oscillator with cathode follower output (series resonance). (d) Crystal-controlled Meissner oscillator.

forms a parallel resonant circuit with the crystal-holder capacitance and any external circuit capacitance shunted across it.

Both the series and the parallel mode of crystal operation can be used in feedback-oscillator circuits. Figure 13.6 illustrates circuits frequently encountered in practical work.

The crystal shown in Fig. 13.6a performs at its parallel resonant frequency, whereas those shown in Fig. 13.6b through d operate in the series resonant mode.

The operating principles of the Pierce oscillator shown in Fig. 13.6a are similar to those of the Colpitts oscillator shown in Fig. 13.4d. The crystal in the Pierce circuit performs the function of the inductance in the Colpitts oscillator and resonates with C_1 and C_2 at its parallel resonant frequency. The grid-leak capacitor (C_3 in Fig. 13.4d) is not required in the Pierce oscillator since the crystal-holder capacitance performs this function.

Figure 13.6b illustrates one possible way in which the series resonant mode of crystal operation may be used. The circuit shown in Fig. 13.6d is a modified Meissner oscillator (compare with Fig. 13.4b). Increased frequency stability is obtained in this circuit by inserting a crystal in the feedback path. At frequencies above and below resonance, the crystal displays a high impedance and reduces the amount of feedback at these frequencies. This prevents oscillation at frequencies other than the series resonant frequency of the crystal. The frequency stability of most LC oscillators can be improved in a similar way.

It was stated in Chap. 9, Multivibrators, that a two-stage RC-coupled amplifier is regenerative when the output of one amplifier is connected to the input of the other. This principle is used in the crystal-oscillator circuit shown in Fig. 13.6c. The crystal in the feedback loop operates in its series resonant mode and ensures that regenerative feedback occurs at only one frequency.

The circuit configuration in Fig. 13.6c is also a two-stage RC-coupled regenerative amplifier. The circuit provides the optimum in frequency stability. It is used in one of the most stable oscillators in existence. Interelectrode capacitance is reduced to a minimum through the use of a grounded-grid amplifier (V_1). The cathode follower (V_2) is used to match the high output impedance of V_1 to its own low input impedance. The crystal operates in its series resonant mode and appears in the feedback loop from the cathode of V_2 to the cathode of V_1.

Feedback Oscillators Employing Transistor Amplifiers

The operating principles of transistor oscillators are identical with those of the vacuum-tube types described above. Representative circuit

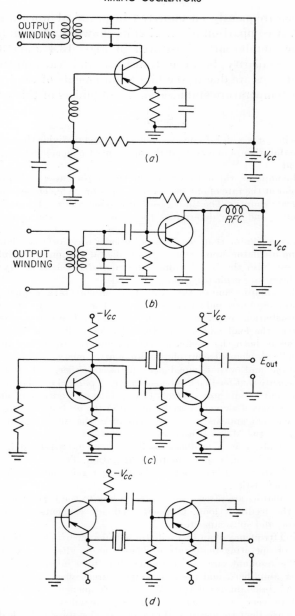

Fig. 13.7 Typical transistorized crystal oscillators. (a) Transistorized Meissner oscillator (tuned-collector tickler-feedback). (b) Transistorized Colpitts oscillator. (c) Two-stage RC-coupled oscillator. (d) Grounded-base RC-coupled oscillator with emitter-follower output.

configurations frequently encountered in practical work are illustrated in Fig. 13.7. A comparison of the circuits shown in this figure with their vacuum-tube counterparts illustrated in Figs. 13.4 and 13.6 will emphasize the similarity between transistor and vacuum-tube circuits. Circuit differences are due to the bias requirements of the transistor and the need for temperature stabilization in amplifiers of this type.

Summary

A timing oscillator is a high-frequency generator used to divide time into small equal segments. The duration of one cycle at the operating frequency determines the length of each segment.

In a digital computer, the output from the timing oscillator is shaped into narrow pulses that occur at the rate of one pulse each oscillator cycle. These pulses are used to clock the program counter. The timing oscillator synchronizes all functions performed by the computer and also determines the rate at which the computer processes information.

Although any oscillator that generates a periodic waveform continuously may be used in timing-oscillator applications, most digital computers employ sine-wave oscillators to establish the basic timing interval. LC resonant or crystal-controlled feedback oscillators are ordinarily used.

All feedback oscillators contain three essential components: a frequency-determining element, a power amplifier, and a feedback circuit. The frequency-determining element ensures that oscillations occur at only one frequency. The power amplifier supplies output power to the load and also feedback power to its own input to overcome resistance losses in both the feedback network and the frequency-determining element. The feedback element controls the amount of energy fed back to the input, matches the input and output impedances of the amplifier, and often contributes a phase shift to ensure that feedback is regenerative. A parallel resonant circuit made up of an inductor and a capacitor controls the operating frequency of an LC resonant oscillator. The resonant element may be placed in the grid, cathode, or plate circuit. The resonant element appears in the grid circuit in the Armstrong oscillator and in the plate circuit of the Meissner oscillator.

The power amplifier in a feedback oscillator may be arranged in the common-cathode, common-grid, or common-plate configuration. The common-cathode circuit, however, is ordinarily used because of its high power gain and superior input-output impedance characteristics.

Feedback oscillators are often classified according to the type of feedback element employed in the feedback loop. Common feedback elements are the tickler coil, tapped inductor, and split capacitor.

The operating frequency of an LC oscillator will change with variations in the supply voltage, load, or operating temperature. These factors alter the circuit capacitance that shunts the resonant circuit. To reduce drift to a minimum, regulated power supplies, buffer amplifiers, and positive-temperature-coefficient capacitors are often employed in LC resonant oscillators. When the frequency of a feedback oscillator must be held to very close tolerances, crystal-controlled feedback oscillators are employed. The excellent frequency stability of the crystal oscillator is due to the fact that oscillation depends on the mechanical properties of the crystal and is only slightly affected by circuit capacitance. This is particularly true when the crystal is operated in its series resonant mode.

The operating principles of transistor oscillators are identical with those of the vacuum-tube types. Circuit differences are due to the bias requirements of the transistor and the need for temperature stabilization in amplifiers of this type.

QUESTIONS

13.1 Why are timing oscillators so vital to the operation of digital computers and data processors?

13.2 What device is generally used in conjunction with the timing oscillator for program synchronization?

13.3 Are timing oscillators sinusoidal or nonsinusoidal? Explain why.

13.4 List the three essential sections of the feedback oscillator and describe the function of each.

13.5 What factors affect the operating frequency of an LC oscillator?

Chapter **14**

Special-purpose Amplifiers

Computing machines require many types of nonlogical special amplifier circuits to perform numerous tasks. Special-purpose amplifiers are used to increase the signal amplitude or change the shape of a pulse waveform, isolate one stage of a circuit from another, control the lighting of neon indicators, and control relays which perform a wide variety of operations. These are but a few of the many functions amplifiers perform in modern computing systems.

An understanding of the operating principles of these amplifier circuits is important if computer operations are to be thoroughly understood.

Pulse Amplifiers

The pulse-amplifier circuit has a variety of functions in a computing system. It can be used to generate a pulse-output waveform from either a square-wave input or a spiked differentiated input waveform. This pulse output can be used to supply drive to the various shift registers and counters in the system.

With a slight modification, the pulse amplifier becomes adaptable as a gating circuit and can be used to perform some of the logical functions required in a computer system.

Circuit operation. Figure 14.1 is an electrical schematic diagram of a typical vacuum-tube pulse-amplifier circuit showing input and output waveforms.

The waveforms indicate that this particular circuit is used to generate a pulse output from a square-wave input. The output pulse width is determined by the characteristics of the pulse transformer T_1. Pulse amplitude is kept nearly constant by allowing tube V_1 to conduct at saturation when the input signal is applied.

252

With no input, tube V_1 is biased well beyond cutoff through its negative grid return. No current flows in its plate circuit.

With the application of an input signal, tube V_1 conducts heavily through the primary winding of transformer T_1. This current generates a large magnetic field which induces an output voltage in the secondary winding. This output will appear only when the magnetic flux is changing.

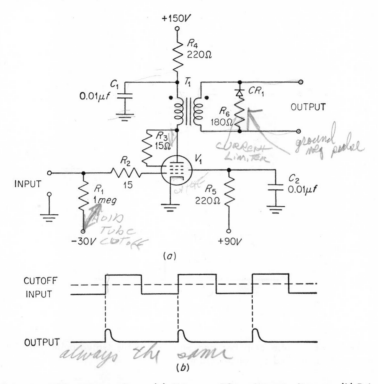

Fig. 14.1 Pulse amplifier and waveforms. (a) Pulse-amplifier schematic diagram. (b) Pulse-amplifier waveforms.

It can be seen then that the output pulse width is determined by the time required to saturate the primary of transformer T_1 and not by the width of the input signal. When T_1 becomes saturated, the magnetic field generated remains constant, and no voltage is induced in the output winding.

When the input signal is removed, tube V_1 will cut off, and the magnetic field stored in the transformer winding will collapse. Resistor R_6 and diode CR_1 prevent undesirable "ringing" in the secondary winding when the input signal falls below cutoff. Ringing is a result of the collapsing magnetic field, tending to induce a voltage of opposite polarity in the secondary winding. If this were to happen, diode CR_1 would conduct and shunt the secondary. R_6 limits the current through the diode and protects it from an overload.

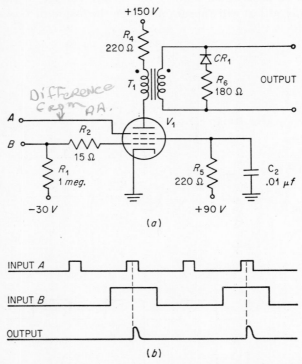

(a)

(b)

Fig. 14.2 Gated pulse amplifier and waveforms. (a) Gated-pulse-amplifier schematic diagram. (b) Input and output waveforms.

It was previously stated that with a slight modification the pulse amplifier could be converted to a gating circuit. Figure 14.2 shows this change.

In the static condition, tube V_1 is again held at cutoff by the bias voltage on its control grid. With the suppressor grid no longer returned to the plate of tube V_1, an input applied only to the control grid will not bring this tube into conduction. In order for V_1 to conduct, both inputs must appear in coincidence. Input A or B alone is not sufficient to overcome the large negative bias applied to the control grid of the tube. If both inputs are present, tube V_1 will conduct and produce an output in the secondary winding of pulse transformer T_1. The width of the output pulse again will be determined by the time required to saturate the primary winding, not by the length of time tube V_1 conducts. It can be seen then that this pulse amplifier can be used as a logical gating circuit producing an output only if both input signals are present. This circuit is sometimes referred to as a *coincidence amplifier.*

Transistorized Current Driver

The previous paragraphs have described the operation of vacuum-tube pulse amplifier circuits capable of producing a pulse output to the logic circuits in a computer. The transistorized pulse amplifier, more commonly termed the *current driver,* will now be examined. This circuit also generates an output current pulse capable of driving transistor logic circuits in a computer.

Figure 14.3 shows a transistorized current driver with its input and output waveforms.

Circuit operation. Transistor Q_1, a triggered blocking oscillator, is held at cutoff by a positive reverse bias on its base from the voltage divider (consisting of resistors R_6 and R_3) between ground and the positive 15-volt supply. Transistor Q_2, used for isolation and amplification, is held at cutoff by the positive voltage appearing at the junction of resistors R_4 and R_5.

When an input pulse is applied, its leading edge will immediately turn transistor Q_1 on. This causes collector current to flow in winding W_1 of transformer T_1, generating a large magnetic field. The field induces a voltage in windings W_2 and W_3 of transformer T_1. The voltage induced in W_3 is coupled through capacitor C_2 and resistor R_1 to the base of transistor Q_1 and is in phase with the input signal. This causes even more collector current to flow through W_1 of the transformer and generates an even larger magnetic field. This action is cumulative and continues until W_1 of transformer T_1 becomes saturated, allowing no further change in magnetic field density to take place.

The voltage induced in W_2 is determined by the magnetic flux generated and also the turns ratio of the transformer. With the correct turns ratio, enough base current is supplied to transistor Q_2 through coupling network R_4 and C_4 to cause it to saturate. The collector of transistor Q_2 changes then from -15 to nearly 0 volt. This voltage change of almost 15 volts is impressed across the primary winding of T_2. Transformer T_2 is a step-down transformer with a turns ratio of approximately $4.3:1$. The primary winding contains 60 turns, and the secondary winding contains 14 turns. With a 15-volt change across a 60-turn winding, the figure of four turns for each volt is obtained. Using the ratio of 4 turns for each volt, we can see how the voltage induced in the 14-turn secondary winding of T_2 will be 3.5 volts. This is a large decrease in voltage; however, a step-down in voltage causes a step-up in current by the same ratio. Therefore, the output current is quite large, actually 4.3 times greater than that appearing in the primary winding of transformer T_2.

The output pulse width is determined by the length of time required to saturate transformer T_1 in the collector circuit of transistor Q_1. Once this condition is reached, the signal on the base of transistor Q_2 falls off

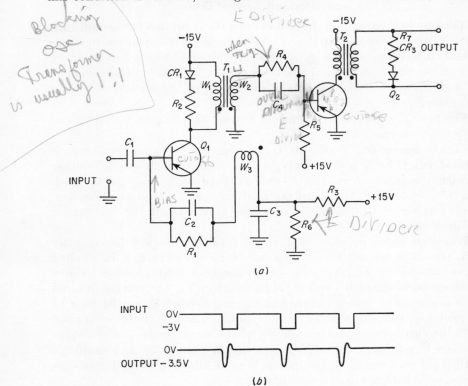

Fig. 14.3 Transistorized current driver and waveforms. (a) Transistorized-current-driver schematic diagram. (b) Current-driver waveforms.

and the d-c bias voltage appearing at the junction of resistors R_4 and R_5 turns transistor Q_2 off. This transistorized circuit generates a high-current pulse of short duration capable of driving many logic circuits in the computer.

Buffer Amplifier

The buffer amplifier is a very important part of every computing and data-processing system. It is used for isolation, power amplification, and impedance matching. The need for buffer amplifiers can be understood more clearly if the output of a flip-flop circuit is considered. In a computer this output may become the input to several other circuits, such as other flip-flops, indicator circuits, or logical AND and OR gates. If these other circuits were all connected directly to the flip-flop, they would cause a loading effect. This would cause instability and, therefore, unreliable circuit operation. To prevent this condition, a buffer amplifier is placed between the flip-flop output and these other circuits. Thus, the flip-flop circuit is isolated, ensuring correct and reliable operation.

Since the need for buffer amplifiers has been explained, a buffer typical of those found in present-day computers will be examined. Figure 14.4

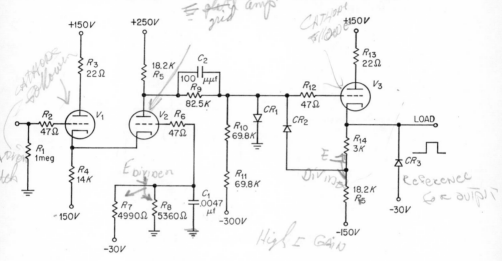

Fig. 14.4 Vacuum-tube buffer amplifier.

shows a vacuum-tube buffer-amplifier circuit. The input signal to the circuit could be the output of a flip-flop or some type of logic gate. Tube V_1 functions as a cathode follower; therefore, it offers a high input impedance which prevents loading of the preceding stage. Tube V_2 functions as a grounded-grid amplifier which amplifies the output of tube V_1 with no phase inversion. Tube V_3 functions as another cathode-follower circuit and matches the relatively high output impedance of the grounded-grid amplifier to the low impedance of the load.

Circuit operation. To understand the circuit operation, assume the input levels to tube V_1 to be -30 volts and 0 volt as shown in Fig. 14.4. With -30 volts as an input, tube V_1 is not conducting heavily, and the bias voltage developed by cathode resistor R_4 is slightly less than -16 volts. The voltage divider consisting of R_7 and R_8 biases the grid of V_2 at -15 volts. With -15 volts on its grid and approximately -16 volts on its cathode, tube V_2 conducts heavily and its plate voltage falls. When

V_2 conducts, point A drops toward -60 volts. This voltage, however, is clamped to approximately -47 volts by diode CR_2 before being applied to the grid of cathode follower V_3. With -47 volts as an input signal, tube V_3 conducts very little, and its cathode potential is clamped at -30 volts by diode CR_3. Note that the output is of the exact phase and amplitude of the original input to tube V_1; the output signal, however, has considerably more power than the original input signal because cathode follower V_3 is actually a power amplifier. Tube V_2 is necessary in order to amplify the output of the first stage to compensate for the voltage loss of cathode follower V_1.

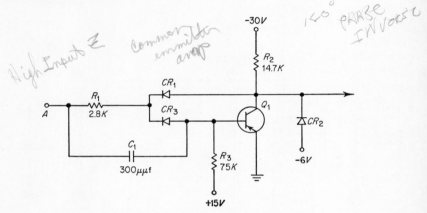

Fig. 14.5 Transistor inverter buffer.

When the signal input rises toward 0 volt, tube V_1 conducts heavily, and the d-c bias generated across R_4 increases to about $+5$ volts. Tube V_2 now has $+5$ volts on its cathode and -15 volts on its grid and is biased nearly at cutoff, causing its plate voltage to rise toward $+250$ volts. The potential at point A begins to increase in the positive direction; however, diode CR_1 clamps this junction at ground potential when this condition is present. With ground potential on its grid, tube V_3 conducts heavily, causing a larger voltage drop to appear across its cathode circuit. Under this condition, the potential at the top of resistor R_{14} is nearly 0 volt with respect to ground. The output is again in phase with the original input signal but has much more power and is capable of driving several other stages.

Now that the operation of the vacuum-tube buffer amplifier has been explained, analysis of a typical transistorized buffer circuit is undertaken. Figure 14.5 shows a transistorized version of another buffer amplifier.

This is a simple one-stage common-emitter amplifier whose output is obtained from the collector of transistor Q_1. Since the input signal is applied to the base circuit, phase inversion will take place. If phase inversion is undesirable, the circuit could be replaced with a common-collector configuration and still retain the buffer effect.

Assume the input logic levels to be 0 and -6 volts. Resistor R_1 supplies a constant current to the base of Q_1 when its input is -6 volts. Capacitor C_1 is a speedup capacitor which allows additional base current to flow in Q_1 during transitions of the input square wave. This additional current decreases the switching time of transistor Q_1, causing sharp leading and trailing edges to appear in the output waveform. Diodes CR_1 and CR_3 provide double-diode clamping action to clamp the collector potential so that it cannot fall below the base voltage to forward-bias the collector junction. This avoids saturation of transistor Q_1 when it is on, thereby decreasing its turn-off time. Diode CR_2 clamps the collector potential of transistor Q_1 to -6 volts when Q_1 is not conducting.

With 0 volt as an input to point A, transistor Q_1 is cut off and its plate potential is clamped at -6 volts. When the input signal is -6 volts, Q_1 is conducting heavily and its collector potential is nearly 0 volt. It can be seen then that the output waveform is 180° out of phase with the input. In most cases, however, this is not a disadvantage. Isolation is obtained for the circuit preceding the buffer because now all outputs to other circuits will come from the collector of transistor Q_1.

Buffer amplifiers are used throughout all computing and data-processing systems to provide isolation between stages. They have many desirable characteristics, such as power amplification, impedance matching, and waveshaping. The buffer amplifier is needed to prevent loading of critical circuits and to provide stable and reliable operation of computer systems.

Neon Amplifier

The neon-amplifier circuit is used to control the firing of neon indicators. These indicators are used extensively in computer systems to display information contained in the various registers and counters throughout the computer. Figure 14.6 shows a transistorized version of a typical neon-amplifier circuit.

The actual neon-amplifier circuit consists of resistors R_1, R_2, and R_3 and transistor Q_2. Transistor Q_1 supplies the input. This input could be from a flip-flop circuit located in a counter or shift register in the computer. The circuit shown in Fig. 14.6 is designed to light the neon indicator whenever the input signal to Q_1 is -0.3 volt. Transistor Q_1 receives its input from the ONE-side output of a flip-flop, and the output levels from the flip-flop are -0.3 volt when it is in the ONE state and -0.1 volt when it is in the ZERO state.

The neon indicator displays the state of the flip-flop by lighting when the flip-flop is in the ONE state and extinguishing when the flip-flop is in the ZERO state.

Circuit operation. Assume the flip-flop supplying the input to transistor Q_1 is in the ONE state; the voltage appearing at the base of transistor Q_1 is then -0.3 volt. This voltage turns on PNP transistor Q_1, causing it to conduct in the saturation region. The collector potential changes to -0.1 volt, which is the input to transistor Q_2. Transistor Q_2 is of the NPN type and, using the circuit configuration shown, requires at least -0.3 volt applied to its emitter in order to turn on. With -0.1 volt applied, transistor Q_2 is turned off and its collector potential, dis-

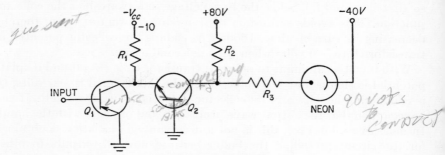

Fig. 14.6 Neon amplifier.

regarding l_{co} is $+80$ volts, which is applied to one electrode of the neon indicator through voltage divider R_2 and R_3.

The opposite electrode of the neon indicator is connected to a -40-volt potential. The voltage across the electrodes then is about 120 volts, which exceeds the firing potential of the neon indicator (which is approximately 90 volts) and causes the indicator to light. Resistors R_2 and R_3 limit the current through the neon indicator once it has fired and drop the collector potential of transistor Q_2 to about $+53$ volts. This voltage may appear to be high for transistor operation; however, transistor Q_2 is a special silicon transistor capable of handling up to $+90$ volts between its collector and base.

Assume now that the flip-flop supplying the input to transistor Q_1 is in the ZERO state. The input voltage is then -0.1 volt. Transistor Q_1 cuts off, and its collector potential begins to approach $-V_{cc}$. When this potential of -0.3 volt is applied to the emitter of Q_2, transistor Q_2 conducts into the saturation region and clamps the collector of transistor Q_1 at the -0.3-volt level. With transistor Q_2 conducting saturation current, its collector potential will be approximately $+2$ volts. This causes a potential of only 42 volts to appear across the electrodes of the neon indicator. The neon indicator is now turned off since there is insufficient voltage across its electrodes to maintain conduction.

It can be seen from the foregoing description that the neon-amplifier circuit, by indicating the state of a flip-flop, performs a useful function in a computer or data-processing system.

Relay Amplifier

The relay-amplifier circuit is used to control the operation of the relays used in a computing system. Usually each relay will have its own relay-amplifier circuit. One of the uses of relays in a computing or data-processing system is to control the starting and stopping of the peripheral

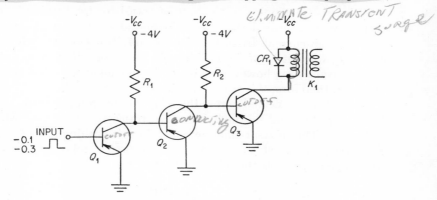

Fig. 14.7 Relay amplifier.

equipment associated with the system. Peripheral equipment consists of equipment external to the computer, such as tape readers, card readers, print-out or punch-out systems, and test equipment.

Relays are also used to actuate various indicators on control panels which indicate to the operator when the computer has finished certain operations or when an error or fault has occurred. Figure 14.7 illustrates a typical transistorized relay-amplifier circuit and shows the output relay winding and the input to the amplifier.

The relay-amplifier circuit consists of transistors Q_2 and Q_3, resistors R_1 and R_2, diode CR_1, and relay coil K_1. Transistor Q_1 supplies the input to the amplifier.

Circuit operation. The signal input will be at one of two logic levels. These levels are assumed to be -0.3 and -0.1 volt. The circuit is designed to actuate the relay when an input of -0.3 volt is applied to the base of transistor Q_1. The 0.3-volt input turns on transistor Q_1 and causes its collector voltage to decrease from approximately -0.3 to -0.1 volt because of current flow through collector resistor R_1. This -0.1-volt level is applied to the base of transistor Q_2, turning it off. Q_2 had previously been conducting because of the negative collector potential of Q_1

on its base. When transistor Q_2 turns off, its collector potential increases negatively. This increase is coupled to the base of transistor Q_3, turning it on. Transistor Q_3 is a high-current driver type of transistor. When Q_3 saturates, its emitter-to-base current clamps the collector of transistor Q_2 to -1 volt. The collector current of transistor Q_3, when it is saturated, is approximately 160 ma. A current of 150 ma flowing through relay coil K_1 is sufficient to energize the relay.

Assume the input to transistor Q_1 to be -0.1 volt. This will turn transistor Q_1 off, causing its collector voltage to rise toward $-V_{cc}$. The negative rise is coupled to the base of transistor Q_2, turning it on. With transistor Q_2 saturated, its collector potential will be -0.1 volt, which biases the high-current driver transistor Q_3 off. The leakage current of transistor Q_3, when it is off, is considerably more than that of a typical low-current transistor; however, it is not large enough to cause relay K_1 to energize; therefore, the armature will not be actuated.

Diode CR_1 connected across the relay coil prevents damage to transistor Q_3 by shunting the high inductive transients generated when Q_3 is turned off. The relay-amplifier circuit, then, is nothing more than a transistorized switch which, when closed, causes a relay to energize and, when opened, causes the relay to deenergize.

Summary

Present-day computers and data-processing machines require a wide variety of special-purpose amplifiers to perform efficient and reliable operations.

The pulse amplifier generates a narrow high-current pulse which can be used as a driver for the logic circuits in the machine. This circuit can be altered slightly to perform gating functions.

The buffer amplifier is used to prevent loading of critical circuits. It also is used as an impedance-matching device and as a power amplifier to provide the necessary currents to the various logic circuits.

The neon amplifier is used to control a neon indicator which informs the computer operator of certain conditions. The amplifier controls the potential across the electrodes of a neon indicator.

The relay amplifier controls the activation of a relay coil in the computer.

These are but a few of the special-purpose amplifiers used today. A computer or data processor designed for one specific use will have special-purpose amplifiers peculiar only to that machine.

QUESTIONS

14.1 Why are nonlogical gates and amplifiers necessary in digital computing systems?

14.2 What are the applications of the nonlogical amplifiers?

14.3 What are the uses of buffer amplifiers in computing systems?

14.4 Why is circuit "loading" undesirable?

14.5 What are the input-output impedance characteristics of buffer amplifiers?

14.6 Why are two transistors required in the neon-amplifier configuration (Fig. 14.6) instead of one?

Chapter **15**

Ferromagnetic Cores

Bistable ferromagnetic cores are widely used in most of the modern, compact digital computers. The square-loop characteristics and microsecond switching time of these cores permit their use in several computer applications. Ferromagnetic cores are easily magnetized and can store binary information for long periods of time without needing external power. They are small and rugged, and they provide reliable operation.

The two major types of ferromagnetic cores used to perform most of the essential functions in computing systems are the ferrite core and the tape-wound bimag core. A recent addition to the ferromagnetic-core class is the multiaperture device (MAD) or transfluxor. The bimag and MAD cores are larger than the ferrite core, and both are used to perform logical operations such as AND, OR, and exclusive OR. Bimag cores are also used in magnetic shift registers, cycle registers, and counters. The ferrite core is used in high-speed coincident-current memory systems.

This chapter presents a detailed explanation of the bimag, transfluxor, and ferrite cores and shows their construction and several circuits. Several applications of the bimag core are shown; the ferrite core is shown in a segment of a coincident-current memory plane.

Core Characteristics

The rectangular hysteresis loop and high switching speed are the characteristics of ferrite materials which make these cores so well suited to computer systems. Figure 15.1 shows the rectangular hysteresis properties of a ferrite core as compared with the hysteresis properties of a core of ordinary steel.

The residual magnetism ($+BR$ and $-BR$) is nearly equal to the maximum magnetization (BM and $-BM$). This property enables the magnetic core to store information reliably. The squareness ratio BR/BM is a measure of the quality of the core; present-day core ratios range from 0.85 to 0.98, depending on the core material.

The usefulness of core material with a square hysteresis loop stems from the fact that once it is magnetized in one direction it will remain in this state until it is magnetized in the opposite direction.

The positive state of residual magnetism $(+BR)$ is generally referred to as the ONE state, and the negative state of residual magnetism $(-BR)$ is referred to as the ZERO state. The state of the material can be sensed

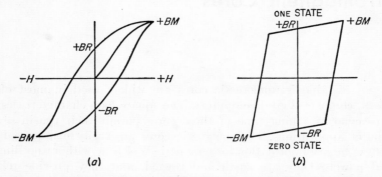

Fig. 15.1 Typical hysteresis loops. (a) Steel hysteresis loop. (b) Ferrite-core hysteresis loop.

by the application of an interrogation pulse. If the core is in one of its two stable states and a pulse of sufficient amplitude and polarity is applied to cause the core to change from one state of residual magnetism to the other, a large flux change occurs, inducing a large voltage in the output winding of the core. On the other hand, if the applied pulse is not of the correct direction, the state of the core remains unchanged, little flux change is produced, and therefore little induced voltage results.

Bimag Core

Ferromagnetic cores are normally toroidal (doughnut-shaped) and may be in either of two forms. The core first discussed is the metallic-tape type shown in Fig. 15.2. This core, through common usage, is called the bimag because of its bimagnetic properties.

The fabrication process of the metallic-tape bimag is shown in Fig. 15.2. The core consists of thin, narrow, molybdenum Permalloy ribbon wound spirally on a ceramic bobbin. After the end of the tape is spot-welded, the core is annealed and then inserted in a plastic sleeve to afford it protection. Next, the core is inserted in its base, and the ends of the windings are soldered to the pins in the base. When this process is completed, the base is inserted in a capsule which is then filled with a solution which, when it hardens, affords shockproof protection to the entire assembly. The basic function of the bimag core is to hold information for a given period of time. This is of no value, however, unless the information can be transferred to other cores and associated circuits. This is accomplished with transfer loops.

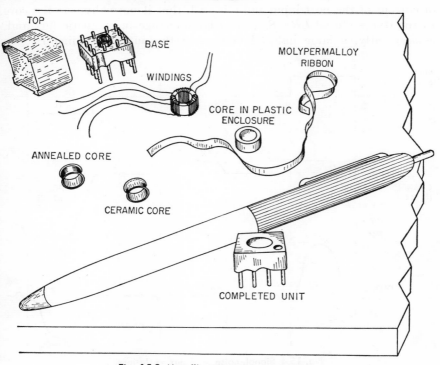

Fig. 15.2 Metallic-tape core construction.

Figure 15.3 shows the elementary bimag circuit. Notice that the flux produced by coil L_1 is linked with coil L_2. This means that a voltage E will be induced in coil L_2 whenever there is a change in flux produced by coil L_1.

The voltage induced into the output winding, coil L_2, must be large if it is to be used to drive other cores and logic circuits. By design it has

Fig. 15.3 Bimag core and windings.

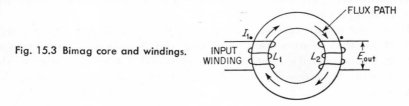

been arranged so that only a complete switch in the core—that is, from $+BR$ to $-BM$ or from $-BR$ to $+BM$—will produce the necessary amount of output voltage to effect the switching of other cores.

Assume the core shown in Fig. 15.3 is already magnetized to $-BR$ on the hysteresis loop. The core is then in the ZERO state. If the direction of current of the next input pulse is such that it normally sets the core to the ONE state $(+BR)$, there is a large change in magnetic flux and, consequently, a large induced voltage in the output winding L_2 (see

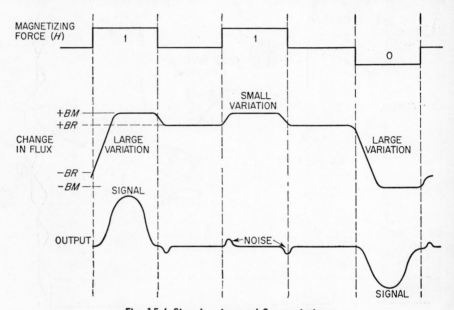

Fig. 15.4 Signal, noise, and flux variations.

Fig. 15.4). If, on the other hand, the core is already in the ONE state when this input pulse arrives, the flux variation is small since the core changes only from $+BR$ to $+BM$ and then back to $+BR$ again when the input is removed. The voltage induced in the output winding is small and is referred to as *noise*.

The bimag core must have at least two coils: one input and one output. However, other functions which can be performed by bimags will require several other coils.

Before going any further with the discussion of bimag circuits, it is important that conventions regarding dot notation be understood. Ambiguity of polarity relating to current and voltages present in the windings of the magnetic core is avoided by using this system of dot notation.

The theory of operation of the bimag core is explained by using conventional current flow (+ to −) rather than electron flow. The arrows in Fig. 15.5, therefore, indicate the direction of conventional current flow. Conventions regarding dot notation are as follows:

1. Conventional current entering the dot side of a winding tends to switch the core to the ZERO state.
2. Conventional current entering the nondot side of a winding tends to switch the core to the ONE state.
3. When a core switches toward the ZERO state, voltages appear with positive polarities at all dot sides of the windings.

If the core is in the ONE state and current enters the dot terminal of winding L_1, a large change in flux takes place and induces a large voltage

Fig. 15.5 Dot notation.

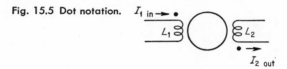

across L_2. In this instance the dot terminal of L_2 is positive, and the nondot terminal is negative. Output current, then, leaves the dot side of winding L_2.

Symbolic representation. The symbol for the bimag core is a circle, as shown in Fig. 15.6. A line with an arrow pointing into the circle

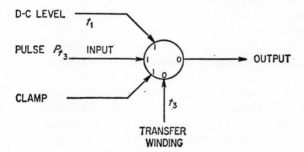

Fig. 15.6 Bimag logical symbol.

represents an input to the core; a current pulse on this line will switch the core to the binary state indicated just inside the circle. Open arrowheads imply pulses; closed arrowheads indicate d-c levels as signals. Double arrowheads of either type indicate that this input will hold the core to that state despite the presence of any other inputs. The symbol on the input line may indicate either the time at which the input occurs (t_1) or the data designation and the time the input may appear (pt_3).

Lines originating at the circle represent output circuits. A signal is present on the line when the core is switched to the state shown nearest the line and on the inside of the circle.

Single-diode transfer loop. The single-diode transfer loop is the basic bimag circuit. It permits indefinite storage of binary information without power dissipation and unconditional transfer of that information to one or more receiving cores when a transfer (advance) current is applied. These transfer pulses are generated by vacuum-tube drivers or thyratron circuits.

The single-diode transfer loop consists of two cores, a diode, and the associated transfer windings. The electrical schematic diagram is shown in

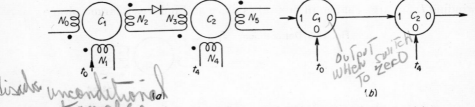

(a)   (b)

Fig. 15.7 Electrical and logical representations of a single-diode loop. (a) Electrical schematic diagram. (b) Logical diagram.

Fig. 15.7 along with the logical representation of the circuit. The purpose of the single-diode transfer loop is to transfer binary information from core C_1 to core C_2.

Assume that core C_1, the transmitting core, is in the ONE state and that core C_2, the receiving core, is in the ZERO state. In order to transfer the 1 from core C_1 into C_2, drive current is applied to the dot side of transfer winding (sometimes referred to as advance winding) N_1. This switches core C_1 to the ZERO state and induces a large voltage E in output winding N_2. Since current enters the dot side of winding N_1, the induced current in output winding N_2 flows from the dot side of the N_2 winding through the low forward resistance of the diode and into the nondot side of winding N_3. Current into the nondot side of N_3 switches core C_2 to the ONE state. Thus the 1 which was in core C_1 is transferred to core C_2. This is called an unconditional transfer of information since the 1 that is in core C_1 is always transferred to core C_2 when the circuit is operated as explained.

The transfer circuit that switches core C_1 from the ONE state to the ZERO state "senses" the core. If core C_1 is in the ZERO state when the next transfer current is applied to N_1, a small change in flux takes place and induces a noise voltage in N_2. This causes insufficient current to flow in the loop to switch core C_2.

The purpose of the diode in the single-diode loop is to prevent the loss of information stored in core C_2 when core C_1 is switched to the ONE state. To visualize this more clearly, assume C_1 is in the ZERO state and core C_2 is in the ONE state. When current I_2 is applied to the nondot side of winding N_0, core C_1 is switched from the ZERO state to the ONE state. This generates a large flux change and induces a large positive voltage at the bottom of output winding N_2. Current would then try to flow from the bottom of winding N_2 into the dot side of winding N_3, attempting to switch core C_2 to the ZERO state. This current, however, is attenuated by the high backward resistance of the diode. This resistance limits the magnitude of the current to a value well below the threshold value for winding N_3, thus keeping core C_2 in the ONE state.

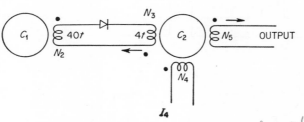

switches *Hig*

no *switch Low*

Fig. 15.8 Single-diode transfer loop. *eliminates*

Thus far, the transfer of a binary 1 from core C_1 to C_2 and the switching of core C_1 back to the ONE state have been explained. Now the effects of transferring the 1 out of core C_2 on the single diode will be examined.

Assume core C_1 is in the ZERO state and core C_2 is in the ONE state. The schematic diagram has been redrawn in Fig. 15.8 to show more clearly the effect of switching core C_2 from the ONE state to the ZERO state.

When a transfer pulse I_4 is applied, current flows into the dot side of winding N_4 and switches core C_2 from the ONE state to the ZERO state. A large flux change is generated and induces a voltage in windings N_5 and N_3. The induced voltage in N_3 is in the forward path of the diode, and current flows into the nondot side of winding N_2, which would appear to switch C_1 to the ONE state and thus transfer the 1 from C_2 back to core C_1. The reverse transfer does not take place, however, because of the turns ratio between N_3 and N_2 and the nonlinear characteristics of the diode. Since the turns ratio is small, the impedance ratio is large; hence, the current induced in winding N_3 is insufficient to switch core C_1.

Magnetic shift register. A magnetic shift register (MSR) is a device in which information may be temporarily stored, then shifted to another location at a predetermined time. A simple MSR can be made by connecting single-diode transfer loops in series as shown in Fig. 15.9. This serial MSR can store a total of two bits of information; hence, it is connected in a two-core-per-bit configuration.

Operation. Assume core A is in the ONE state and all other cores are in the ZERO state. At t_1 time core A is pulsed to the ZERO state, producing an output which sets core B to the ONE state; thus, the information bit of 1 is transferred from core A to core B. At t_2 the 1 is transferred to core C. No output appears from core D at this time since it

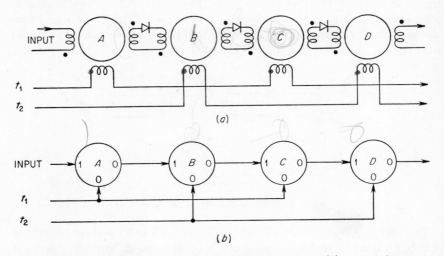

Fig. 15.9 Serial magnetic shift register. (a) Electrical diagram. (b) Logical diagram.

is already in the ZERO state. At the next t_1 time, core A is unaffected, but the 1 in C is transferred to core D. Thus, the 1 originally in core A has been shifted down the register to core D. The next t_2 pulse will shift out the 1 in core D. For serial operation, new information is inserted into core A at any time between t_1 pulses.

In digital data-processing systems the serial MSR serves principally to provide buffer (intermediate) storage of binary information. Binary information from a magnetic drum, tape, or other source can be placed in the register temporarily and delivered to the output circuit whenever desired.

The MSR shown in Fig. 15.9 can, with slight alteration, be used as a modulus 2 counter, that is, a counter that produces one output pulse for every two input pulses. Figure 15.10 is a logical diagram of a mod 2 counter.

The operation starts with a 1 preset into core A. The counter is the same in operation as the MSR except that the output from core D is fed back to core A, thus resetting A at the same time an output is obtained from core D. This makes a complete and continuous loop requiring no external resetting until all cores have been cleared. With this manner of operation, every other t_2 will produce an output, thereby

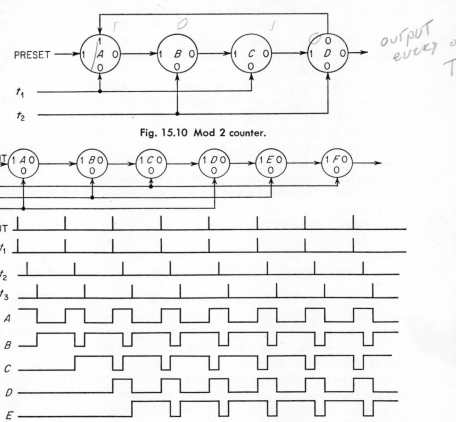

Fig. 15.10 Mod 2 counter.

Fig. 15.11 Timing diagram for serial MSR three-core two bits.

dividing the input pulse by two. Because of this, it is called a mod 2 counter. A mod 3 counter would have the same type of arrangement; however, it would consist of six cores to give an input-output division of three. From this a pattern may be seen for the arrangement of cores for specific counter divisions.

Three-core-per-two-bit MSR. Fig. 15.11 shows a six-core serial MSR that stores two bits every three cores.

Assume all cores are initially in the ZERO state. The first input pulse arrives at core A at the same time as timing pulse t_1 arrives at cores C and F. Core A is then set to the ONE state; and since all other cores are already in the ZERO state, t_1 has no effect on them. When pulse t_2 appears, no change takes place in the register. At t_3 time, the 1 in core A is transferred to core B and core A is returned to the ZERO state. Core D was also sensed at t_3; however, it did not contain a 1.

Before the arrival of the second group of input pulses, cores A, C, D, E, and F are in the ZERO state; and core B is in the ONE state. At t_1 time of the second group of input pulses, a 1 is placed in core A; at this time cores C and F also are interrogated but contain no bits. At t_2 time cores B and E are interrogated; the 1 in core B is then transferred to core C. No transfer takes place at core E since it already is in the ZERO state. At t_3 time cores A and D are sensed; the 1 in core A is then transferred to core B. At the completion of the second group of input pulses, cores B and C contain 1s, and all other cores contain 0s.

At t_1 time of the third input cycle, a new bit is placed in core A; at this time, the 1 in core C also is transferred to core D. At t_2 time the 1 in core B is transferred to core C. At t_3 time two transfers will take place: The 1 in core A is transferred to core B, and the 1 in core D is transferred to core E. At the completion of the third cycle of input pulses, cores B, C, and E contain 1s, and all other cores contain 0s.

When t_1 occurs in the fourth cycle, core A is again set to the ONE state. Also at t_1 time, core C is read out and places a 1 in core D. At t_2 time, the 1 in core B is transferred to core C and the 1 in core E is transferred to core F. At t_3 time, the 1 in core A goes to B and the 1 in core D is transferred to core E.

Before the arrival of the fifth group of pulses, cores B, C, E, and F all contain 1s; cores A and D are in the ZERO state. At t_1 time of the fifth cycle, core A receives a new input, core C transfers a 1 to core D, and core F produces its first output.

The sequence described above is best followed with the use of the waveforms shown in Fig. 15.11.

In the foregoing discussion of the MSRs, a bit was placed in a core and remained there until a transfer pulse shifted it to the next core in line. Then a second transfer pulse, occurring at a different time, shifted the bit to the next core in line.

Sometimes it is desirable to transfer this information through the register with only one transfer pulse. Such an operation is possible if certain provisions are made in the transfer loop to delay the input to each core until after read-out time. This provision, along with its representation, is shown in Fig. 15.12.

Assume 1s to be set in cores A and B. When transfer pulse t_1 occurs, cores A and B are both read out to the ZERO state. The output from core A charges the capacitor since the impedance of this capacitor is less than that of diode CR_2, the input winding of core B, and resistor R. At the termination of the transfer pulse t_1, the capacitor discharges. The discharge path is through the low forward resistance of diode CR_2 into the nondot side of winding L_2 and through resistor R to the opposite plate of the capacitor. Current cannot discharge through winding L_1 because of the high backward resistance of diode CR_1.

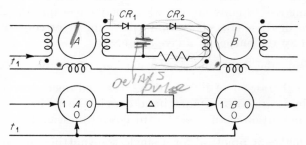

Fig. 15.12 Transfer loop using one driver.

The discharge current of the capacitor entering the nondot side of winding L_2 causes core B to be switched to the ONE state. With this arrangement, then, an MSR can be fabricated using only one transfer pulse. This system has been used successfully in modern computing systems.

The single-diode transfer loop can be used to switch more than one core. This is shown in Fig. 15.13. At present, one bimag core can switch

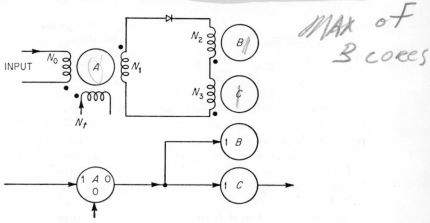

Fig. 15.13 One core switching two cores.

a maximum of only three other cores simultaneously and still operate reliably. If more cores must be switched, a driver is needed.

Split-winding transfer loop. The split-winding transfer loop (sometimes referred to as the *double-diode transfer loop*) was developed to compensate for the shortcomings of the single-diode transfer loop configuration. Disadvantages of the single-diode transfer loop are:

1. Unconditional transfer of information whenever a core is sensed (reset to ZERO state).
2. Cumulative backward flow of information when the cores are read out, giving rise to noise growth which may effect unwanted switching of a core in the chain. This limits the number of cores that can be operated by the output of a given core.

In comparison, the split-winding transfer loop offers these advantages:

1. Conditional transfer of information. (Isolated operations can be performed in a core without affecting others in the chain.)
2. Greater insulation against backward flow of information.

The latter makes it practical for a single transmitting core to switch as many as five or six receiving cores simultaneously.

To understand more clearly the operation of the split-winding transfer loop, it is necessary to reexamine the basic bimag core in terms of impedances (Fig. 15.14). The impedance concept is important here since it is the basic concept upon which the split-winding loop operates.

Assume the core shown in Fig. 15.14b to be in the ONE state. When I is applied, the core will switch; however, a very large counter emf will be

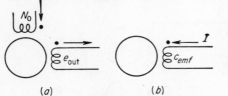

Fig. 15.14 Impedance concept. (a) Core as transformer. (b) Core as variable impedance.

generated in winding N_1, and the core will appear as a relatively high impedance to the drive current I. On the other hand, if the core is already in the ZERO state when I is applied, the counter emf will be very small, and the core will offer very little impedance to the driving source.

Figure 15.15 is a schematic diagram of the split-winding transfer loop. It consists of two cores (A and B), two diodes (CR_1 and CR_2), and a coil (L).

Assume cores A and B to be in the ZERO state when transfer current t_1 is applied. The transfer current will now split into two paths, I_1 and I_2, depending upon the impedance of each branch of the loop. The impedance of both branches is identical since $N_{2A} = N_{2B}$, $CR_1 = CR_2$, and winding N_1 (which does not switch) is balanced by the inductance of the choke coil L. Hence, currents I_1 and I_2 are equal. Current I_1 enters the dot side of winding N_{2A}, and current I_2 enters the nondot winding of N_{2B}. I_1 attempts to switch core B to the ZERO state; I_2 attempts to switch core B to the ONE state. Since the currents are equal, their effects on core B cancel, and core B does not switch.

Assume a 1 to be set in core A and a 0 set in core B. When transfer pulse t_1 is applied, the currents I_1 and I_2 will no longer divide equally in the loop. Winding N_1 appears as a high impedance because of the counter

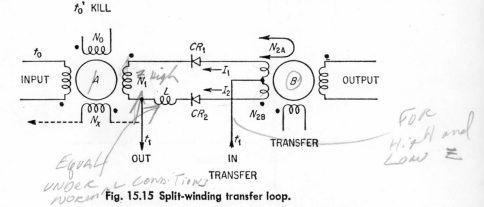

Fig. 15.15 Split-winding transfer loop.

emf when core A is in the ONE state. This limits current I_1 to a small value (although sufficient to switch core A because of the large number of turns in winding N_1). I_2 is now much larger than I_1 since its impedance path is small compared with that of I_1. Since much more current flows into the nondot winding N_{2B} than into the dot winding N_{2A}, core B is switched to the ONE state. The 1 in core A has now been transferred to core B.

A split-winding transfer loop provides for a conditional transfer of information. This point is examined in the next paragraph.

Assume core A in Fig. 15.15 to be in the ONE state and core B to be in the ZERO state. If pulse t_0' is applied to winding N_0, core A switches from the ONE state to the ZERO state. Since current enters the dot terminal of winding N_0, the current induced in winding N_1 tries to leave the dot side; this, however, is in the reverse direction of the diodes. The high backward resistance of the diode prevents any transfer from core A to core B when pulse t_0' switches core A to the ZERO state. The transfer of information from core A to core B then is conditional upon transfer pulse t_1. In the operation just discussed where t_0' reads core A to the ZERO state and no transfer of information took place, pulse t_0' is termed a *kill* pulse. The dotted winding N_x is sometimes used to speed up and ensure reliable switching of core A by pulse t_1. It is referred to as the *helper* winding. Note that the combined currents of I_1 and I_2 flow into the dot terminal of winding N_x which is wound to aid winding N_1 in switching core A back to the ZERO state.

Figure 15.16 shows another method of diagraming the split-winding loop. Notice that not all windings to cores A and B are shown; usually

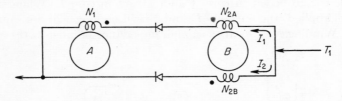

Fig. 15.16 Split-winding driver (T_1) line.

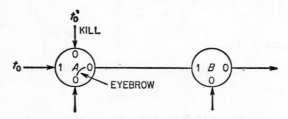

Fig. 15.17 Logical representation of split-winding transfer loop.

only the transfer driver windings (which are actually of most importance for explanation purposes) are shown. Also, many times choke coil L is not shown; however, even though it does not appear on the diagram, a balancing compensator will be used.

The logical symbol for the split-winding transfer loop is shown in Fig. 15.17. Notice the "eyebrow" in core A. It indicates that only that input pulse will initiate a transfer from core A to core B.

The advantages of the split-winding transfer loop over the single-diode transfer loop are absence of noise growth and conditional transfer. That noise growth is not present can be seen by referring to Fig. 15.15. When core B is switched from the ONE to the ZERO state, no current can flow back through the split winding to affect core A because diodes CR_1 and CR_2 obstruct a complete circuit path.

Special Split-winding Loops

Inhibit transfer loop. Figure 15.18 shows both schematic and logical diagrams of an inhibit circuit. On the logical diagram, the inhibit output

is connected by a triangle to the output line it inhibits. In this configuration, the output from core B is not transferred to core C but is used
to prevent the transfer from core A to core C.

Assume cores A and B both contain 1s or 0s and core C contains 0.
When transfer pulse t_1 is applied, currents I_1 and I_2 are equal since the
impedances are equal; therefore, no change takes place in core C. Cur-

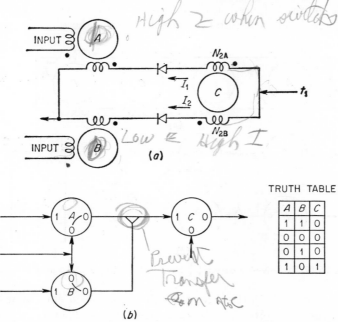

Fig. 15.18 Inhibit circuit. (a) Electrical diagram. (b) Logical diagram.

A	B	C
1	1	0
0	0	0
0	1	0
1	0	1

rents I_1 and I_2 will switch cores A and B back to the ZERO state if they
are in the ONE state.

If core A is in the ZERO state and core B is in the ONE state when
pulse t_1 occurs, no transfer takes place between cores B and C. This is
because the loop is now unbalanced in such a manner as to cause I_1 to
be greater than I_2. Since I_1 enters the dot terminal of N_{2A}, core C remains
in the ZERO state. It must be noted, however, that I_2 is sufficient to
return core B to the ZERO state.

In the final condition, core A contains a 1 and core B contains a 0.
When t_1 is applied, the loop is now unbalanced in such a manner as to
cause I_2 to be greater than I_1. The I_2 current enters the nondot terminal
of winding N_{2B} and, since it is greater than I_1, switches core C to the ONE
state. The conditions necessary to place a 1 in core C can be seen by
examining the truth table in Fig. 15.18. As will be shown later, the in-

hibit loop permits the synthesis of certain logical functions which might otherwise be difficult to visualize.

Exclusive OR. Figure 15.19 shows the schematic and logical diagrams for the bimag exclusive-OR circuit. Its operation is similar to that of the inhibit loop.

In this circuit, as in the inhibit loop, if cores A and B both contain 1s or 0s, the loop is balanced, the application of transfer pulse t_2 will cause an even split in currents, and no switching will take place in cores C or

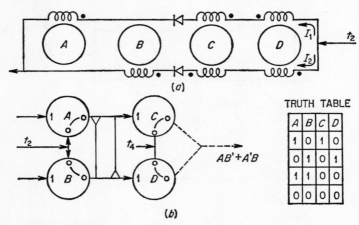

TRUTH TABLE

A	B	C	D
1	0	1	0
0	1	0	1
1	1	0	0
0	0	0	0

Fig. 15.19 Exclusive-OR circuit. (a) Electrical diagram. (b) Logical diagram.

D. If only core A is in the ONE state, the unbalanced current will switch core C to the ONE state since I_2 is now greater than I_1 and enters the non-dot winding of core C. If only core B is in the ONE state, the unbalanced current will switch core D to the ONE state since I_1 is now larger than I_2.

The exclusive-OR result $(AB' + A'B = C + D)$ is obtained by mixing together the outputs from cores C and D. An output will be obtained if either core A or B, but not both, is in the ONE state. This is shown in Fig. 15.19, where cores C and D are alternate outputs.

Inclusive OR. Figure 15.20 illustrates three examples of bimag cores which perform the inclusive-OR function. Diagrams a and b employ single-diode transfer loops; diagram c uses a split-winding transfer loop. In Fig. 15.20a it can be seen that if core A or core B or both are in the ONE state when transfer pulse t_1 occurs, a 1 will be transferred to core C.

Figure 15.20b shows a single-diode transfer-loop arrangement to obtain the inclusive-OR function using two different transfer pulses, t_1 or t_2.

Figure 15.20c shows the split-winding arrangement used to obtain the inclusive-OR function. The circuit is balanced (when cores A and B are in the ZERO state) by the combination of resistor R and coil L. If core A

or core B or both are in the ONE state when transfer pulse t_1 appears, current I_2 will be greater than I_1. Since I_2 enters the nondot terminal of winding N_{2B}, core C will be switched to the ONE state.

The logical symbols shown in Fig. 15.21a, b, and c represent the schematic diagrams shown in Fig. 15.20a, b, and c, respectively.

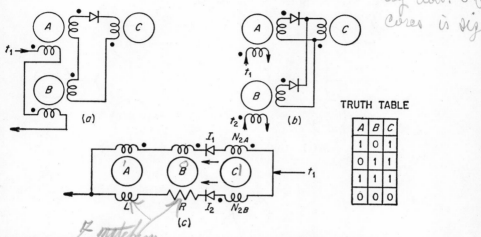

Big adv. of cores is size

TRUTH TABLE

A	B	C
1	0	1
0	1	1
1	1	1
0	0	0

Fig. 15.20 Inclusive-OR circuit. (a) and (b) Single-diode loops. (c) Split-winding loop.

Negation. Figure 15.22 shows the logical symbol for a bimag-core negation circuit. This is a means of performing a logical inversion using bimag cores.

Timing pulse t_1 unconditionally sets the core to the ONE state. If an information pulse (P) is present, it will erase this 1. At the following t_3 time, no output will appear from the core. If, however, pulse P were not present at t_2 time, the 1 would be read out at the next t_3 time. Thus, the circuit has performed a logical inversion; Q appears in the output only if information pulse P is absent.

Bimag AND circuits. The AND function can be understood by using the bimag circuit shown in Fig. 15.23. To produce an output from core B, input P to core A and input Q to core B must both occur at the same t_1 time. When this condition exists, core A switches to the ZERO state at t_2 time and provides an advance current pulse which switches core B to the ZERO state and produces an output R. If only pulse P occurred at t_1 time, and not pulse Q, when core A is read out at t_2 time it would have no effect on core B since it is already in the ZERO state. If only pulse Q occurred at t_1 time, and not pulse P, core A could not supply the advance current to read out core B the following t_3 time, and the 1 in core B would be killed.

With the basic information previously shown, it is possible to construct many different types of core configurations to perform special machine functions.

Serial-parallel MSR. By combining single-diode transfer loops and split-winding transfer loops, it is possible to make a serial-in, parallel-out MSR. This is shown in Fig. 15.24.

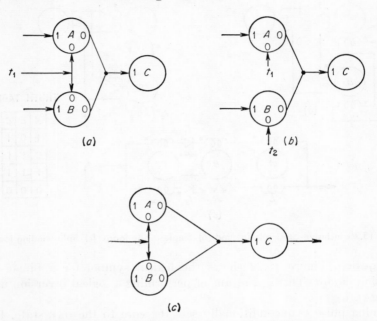

Fig. 15.21 Bimag OR circuits. (a) Single-diode OR using one transfer pulse. (b) Single-diode OR using two different transfer pulses. (c) Split-winding OR circuit.

Cores C_1 through C_6 constitute a two-core-per-bit serial shift register. Cores A, B, and C are the output-register cores. Information is inserted in the register each t_a time shown in Fig. 15.24. During the serial shifting of information, the split-winding loops between the serial register and the output cores prevent the transfer of data to the output. When the

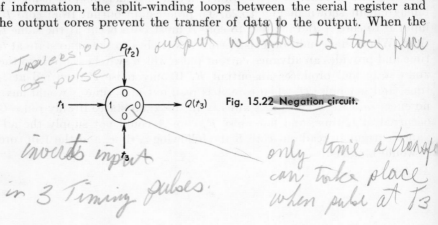

Inversion of pulse

output when the t_2 takes place

inverts input in 3 Timing pulses.

only time a transfer can take place when pulse at t_3

Fig. 15.22 Negation circuit.

last bit of a data word is inserted in core C_1, the preceding bits of that word are in cores C_3, C_5, C_6. A marker pulse is inserted at the beginning of each new word. Core C_6 constantly senses for this marker pulse. When the marker pulse appears in core C_6, it indicates that the entire word is in the register. When pulse t_0 appears, core C_6 is read out and produces transfer driver pulse TP_0, which transfers the input-data word from the serial register to the output register.

TRUTH TABLE

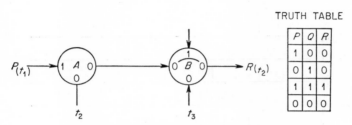

P	Q	R
1	0	0
0	1	0
1	1	1
0	0	0

Fig. 15.23 Bimag AND circuit.

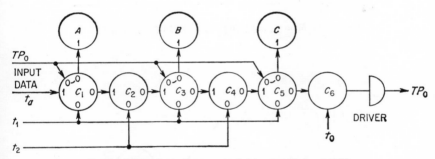

Fig. 15.24 Logical diagram serial-in, parallel-out MSR.

Ping-pong circuit. The bimag-core "ping-pong" circuit is comparable to the vacuum-tube or transistor flip-flop. Upon application of transfer pulses, a binary 1 is transferred alternately between cores C_1 and C_2; hence the name "ping-pong." Figure 15.25 shows the logical representation of a ping-pong circuit, along with its associated timing diagram.

Initially cores C_1 and C_2 are both in the ZERO state. Timing pulses t_1 and t_2 are present but have no effect on the ping-pong configuration since both cores are in the ZERO state. With the application of pulse P_1, which occurs coincident with t_1, core C_1 is switched to the ONE state. At t_2 time core C_1 is read out, transferring the 1 to core C_2 and also generating E_2. At t_1 time the 1 in core C_2 is transferred back to C_1, setting that core and also generating E_1.

The transfer of 1s back and forth between C_1 and C_2 generates outputs alternately at E_1 and E_2 every t_1 and t_2 time, respectively, until the

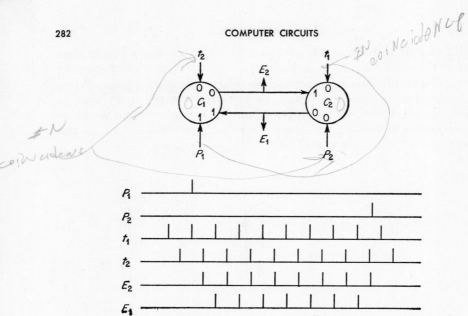

Fig. 15.25 Bimag ping-pong circuit and timing diagram.

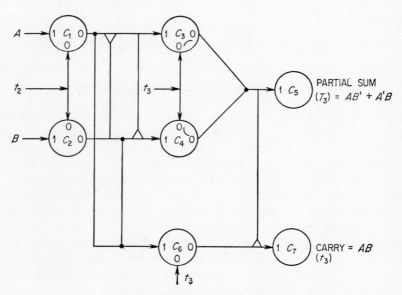

Fig. 15.26 Bimag half-adder circuit.

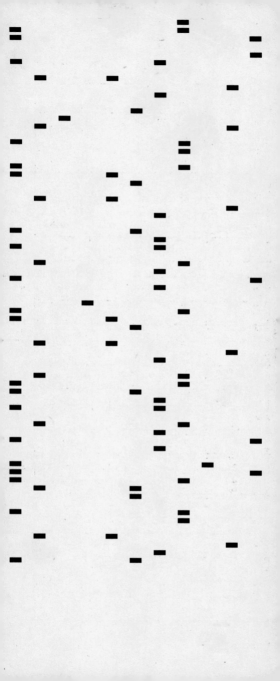

4848

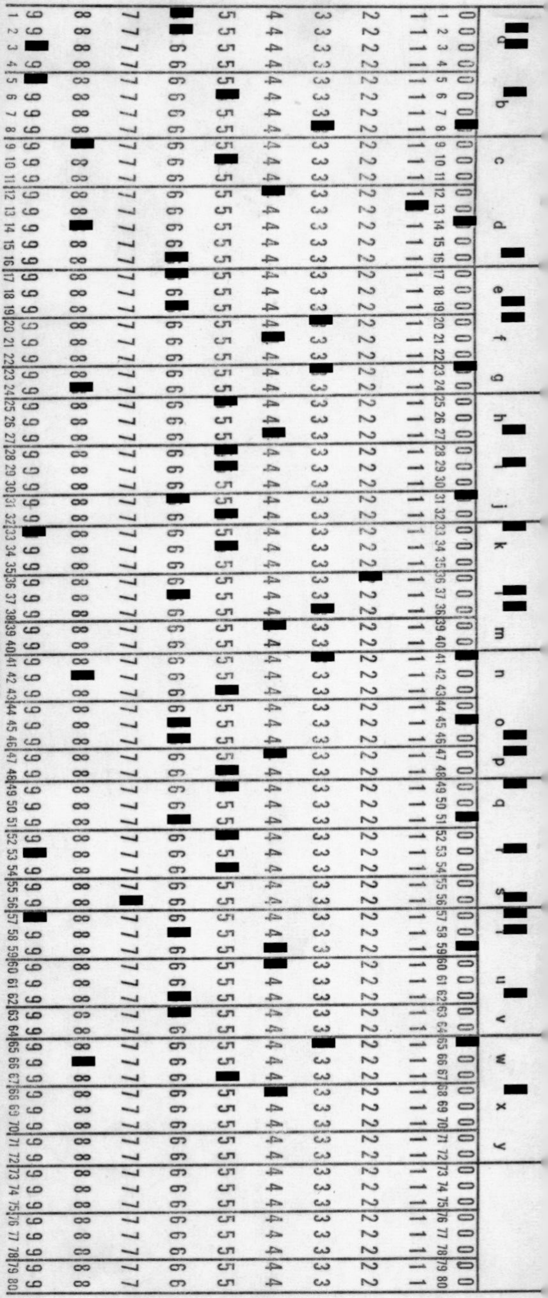

ELECTRIC MACHINERY MFG. CO.

application of pulse P_2. Pulse P_2 occurs in coincidence with transfer pulse t_2.

The effect of these two pulses on core C_2 kills the ping-pong operation. Pulse t_2 attempts to switch core C_2 to the ONE state by the read-out of core C_1; however, at the same time, pulse P_2 attempts to switch core C_2 to the ZERO state. Since the two actions are equal but opposite, core C_2 remains in its original ZERO state.

This type of operation is known as a *coincidence kill*. The coincidence kill must be used if the ping-pong circuit does not incorporate a split-winding loop.

Half-adder. Bimag configurations can also be constructed to perform binary arithmetic. Figure 15.26 is a logical-circuit configuration capable of performing the logical function of half-addition.

The partial sum is obtained by the exclusive-OR circuit, C_1 through C_4. A partial sum appears in core C_5 at t_3 time only if A or B, but not both, are present as an input. To generate a carry in core C_7 requires two steps. Core C_6 is set if either A or B or both are present at cores C_1 and C_2. A carry will be placed into core C_7, however, only if there is no output from the exclusive-OR circuit, because this output inhibits C_6 transfer. Therefore, C_7 will be set to the ONE state only if A and B are both present because at this time there is no output from the exclusive-OR circuit to inhibit the setting of core C_7 by the read-out of core C_6.

Multiaperture Devices

A recent addition to magnetic-core logic is the multiaperture device (MAD). This differs from the conventional bimag core in that it is a ferrite disk and contains more than one aperture. Since there is more than one aperture in the disk, several different flux paths are realized. It is the control of these flux paths that makes MAD operation unique and different from that of the bimag core just studied.

The basic MAD is known as the transfluxor. Figure 15.27 shows the two-hole transfluxor with its associated windings. The apertures, as indicated in the figure, are generally unequal in diameter. Each winding (N_1, N_2, and N_3) encircles a different segment of the disk. Control current of

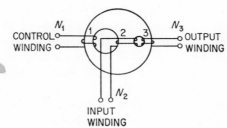

Fig. 15.27 Two-hole transfluxor.

a specified polarity in winding N_1 generates flux paths F_{1a} and F_{1b} as shown in Fig. 15.28. Input current in winding N_2 can generate flux path F_2 or F_{1b}, depending on its amplitude.

The main use of the simple transfluxor is as an a-c gating circuit between the input winding N_2 and the output winding N_3.

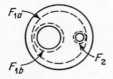

Fig. 15.28 Distribution of flux.

Circuit operation. Assume a control input to winding N_1 of sufficient amplitude to saturate the disk completely with flux. Since the disk is made of ferrite material, it possesses the characteristics of a square hysteresis loop; therefore, even when the control current has been removed, the disk remains completely saturated in its original direction (see Fig. 15.29).

Upon the application of a small a-c input signal to N_2, a changing magnetomotive force is generated which tends to increase the flux in

Fig. 15.29 Transfluxor at saturation.

either core area 2 or core area 3, depending upon the instantaneous signal polarity. Since the core is already saturated, no flux change can take place; therefore, no voltage is induced in output winding N_3. When the core is saturated so that no flux change can take place, the transfluxor is said to be blocked because it prevents any voltage from being induced in winding N_3. In this instance, the gate is closed and no output can be produced.

To open or unblock the transfluxor, a current of opposite polarity to that of the original control pulse must be applied to winding N_1. This is sometimes referred to as a SET *pulse*. The reverse current generates a magnetomotive force which tends to reverse the flux of the disk. However, only a portion of the flux will be reversed; the amount of reversal is dependent upon the amplitude of the SET pulse. This can be seen by examining Fig. 15.30.

Notice that the flux for core area 1 is composed of F_{1a} and F_{1b}. When the SET pulse is applied, path F_{1b} but not path F_{1a} reverses. This is because the magnetic field produced by the SET pulse greatly decreases with the distance measured from the center of the larger aperture. This can be more clearly understood from the following formula:

$$F = \frac{4\pi H}{C} \quad \text{or} \quad FC = 4\pi H$$

where F = magnetic field
C = circumference of flux path
H = magnetomotive force

From this it can be seen that the flux will be reversed from the radius of the larger opening outward. The amplitude of the SET pulse determines

Fig. 15.30 Transfluxor set.

the amount of flux reversal. If the correct SET pulse is used, it is possible to cause the strength of F_{1b} to become great enough to cause a portion of F_2 in core area 2 to reverse also. Setting the flux path in the disk can be compared to biasing a vacuum-tube or transistor circuit.

If an input signal is applied after the flux path has been set, the alternating current in winding N_2 will cause the flux F_2 to reverse back and forth; this, in turn, will induce the varying voltage in output winding N_3. In this instance, then, the gate is opened and allows an output to be produced as long as an input is present to N_2.

The transfluxor is the basic MAD. Other MADs can be produced which contain more than two apertures; these are referred to as *logicors*. Logicors can also be used to perform many of the logical functions necessary in present-day computing systems. The coverage of MADs has been limited to the transfluxor; however, if further information is desired, it is recommended that the bibliography (Appendix II) be consulted.

Ferrite Cores   *Square Hysteris loop*

The ferrite core finds greatest use in coincident-current memory systems. Ferrite cores are small toroids made of brittle ceramic-type material, whose ingredients are iron oxide, manganese, nonmetallic oxides, and an organic binder. Although these materials are not themselves magnetic, the core exhibits strong ferromagnetic characteristics when the substances are combined, bound, heated in a kiln, and cooled. Kiln temperature and length of baking time determine the properties of the ferrite core.

The physics of the ceramic ferrite core have not as yet been explained satisfactorily. The ferrite core is extremely small (see Fig. 15.31). The outside diameter of a typical memory core is 0.083 in.; its inside diameter is 0.050 in.

Point B of the hysteresis loop shown in Fig. 15.31 represents the residual flux remaining in a typical ferrite core after the magnetizing force which brought saturation to A is removed. This is the ONE state of the core. Point E represents residual flux in the opposite direction when a reverse magnetizing force is applied to cause saturation to point D and

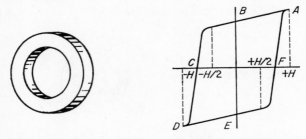

Fig. 15.31 Erasable memory core and hysteresis loop.

is then removed. This is the ZERO state. The hysteresis loop of the ferrite core is more nearly square than the hysteresis loop of an iron core and is considered rectangular.

Assembled into a memory, cores are laid out on a plane matrix lattice of wires, presenting the appearance of a screen. At each major intersection of the wires in this screen, a ferrite core is strung. The cores are strung with an X address wire, a Y address wire, an inhibit wire, and a sensing wire as shown in Fig. 15.32.

There are two reasons for the selection of the ferrite core with its rectangular hysteresis loop in a coincident-current memory system. First, the two residual states of the cores contain much more flux than does iron under equal conditions. When information is stored in the cores and read out, a larger amplitude of output signal and, consequently, a higher signal-to-noise ratio results. Second, a rectangular-type hysteresis loop is preferred because it can, by amplitude selection, discriminate against small switching currents through the conductors threading the core. A small current in a conductor through a ferrite core might generate a magnetizing force of $-H/2$, which is known as *half-select current* (see Fig. 15.31). If the core is in the ONE state (point B), $-H/2$ is not enough to switch the core to the ZERO state. If a core received no other magnetizing forces than $-H/2$ or $-H$, only the full field force $-H$, caused perhaps by the combined time-coincident effects of two half-currents in conductors through the core, could give this switching effect. It will be noted that at some point between $-H/2$ and $-H$, a small additional magnetizing force suddenly switches the core from the ONE state to the ZERO state. However, the core receives only $-H/2$, $-H$, $+H/2$, $+H$, or no force at all.

The metallic core is similar in function to the ceramic core. The metallic core consists of a thin, narrow molybdenum ribbon wound on a steatite bobbin. It is larger than the ferrite core. The metallic core possesses a rectangular hysteresis loop similar to that of the ferrite core but

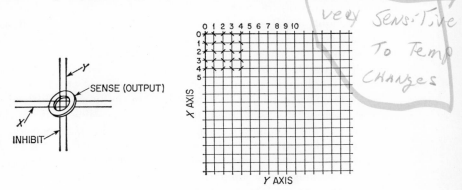

very Sensitive To Temp Changes

Fig. 15.32 Core memory plane.

requires a lower coercive force and is more expensive to make. Recent developments in metal ribbon cores indicate that they compare favorably with ferrites in speed of operation. The switch cores in the memory drivers of a typical computer are metallic cores. They receive a full current in one direction from one half of a 40-turn primary driven by a read driver, and a full current in the opposite direction from the other half of the primary driven by a write driver. The output current from the secondary of 19 turns is used for X address currents and for Y address currents. The square hysteresis loop in this case is used to provide a square-wave output current to the ferrite cores. An ordinary pulse transformer cannot be used since it would not give a square wave of current and it would produce a current reversal when the input drive current decreased. Thus, when a read driver pulses half of the primary, a read pulse is induced in the secondary, of a duration dependent on the hysteresis properties of the switch core and not on the duration of the primary current. When the write driver pulses the other half of the primary, a write pulse opposite in direction to the read pulse is induced in the secondary. The connection between the read-write drivers, the switch cores, and the ferrite cores is elaborated in Chap. 22, Computer Memory Systems.

In production, ferrite cores for computers are tested to meet certain specifications. A typical core may be fabricated to switch on as little as 330 ma (H) and not switch on 200 ma (H/2). Switching time in the ferrite core is roughly inversely proportional to driving current. For example, at a minimum of 330 ma, switching time is 6.5 μsec. At the nominal drive current of 370 ma, switching time is 4 μsec.

The cores are very sensitive to temperature changes, operating maximally at room temperature (70 to 80°F). The hysteresis loop changes shape as a function of temperature. The B dimension of the loop decreases as temperature decreases. Because of the curtailed dimension of the loop along the B axis, the voltage generated on the output winding is not sufficiently large in amplitude and tends to approach a 1:1 signal-to-noise ratio. Decreased temperature also widens the dimension of the loop along the H or horizontal axis. This increased loop dimension reduces the possibility of core switching by the full-select current H, since a larger magnetizing force is required. Eventually, the width of the H dimension may be large enough to make it impossible to drive the core to its new state. Temperature increase causes the H dimension at the loop to become narrow, and flux density along axis B increases. As the H dimension becomes shorter, the core is switched by smaller currents. The core no longer discriminates, and it switches at signals below the value H. In short, at low temperatures the core switches less readily, and at high temperatures it is inclined to switch on any pulse. The problem of temperature control demands the use of air conditioning in the computer.

Summary

Ferromagnetic devices play an important role in the computer and data-processing field. The ferromagnetic cores discussed in this chapter are the bimag core (metallic-tape type); the transfluxor, which is used in logical applications; and the ferrite core, which is used in random-access coincident-current memory systems. Each core discussed is characterized by an almost square hysteresis loop.

The metallic-tape bimag core can perform nearly all the essential logical functions of which transistors and vacuum tubes are capable. The smallness of the bimag core has greatly reduced the physical size and power requirements of the modern computer.

MAD are fairly new components in computing systems and are rapidly gaining popularity.

The ferrite core is widely used in memory systems to provide fast, reliable switching and quick access to stored information.

QUESTIONS

15.1 In what applications are bimag cores and ferrite cores used?

15.2 What does a square hysteresis loop actually represent in terms of switching speed, residual magnetism, and reliability?

15.3 Briefly describe dot notation associated with bimag cores.

15.4 What is the purpose of the diode in the single-winding transfer loop?

15.5 How many bimag cores are required to construct a mod 2 counter? A mod 3 counter?

15.6 What are the advantages offered by a split-winding transfer loop?

15.7 Define conditional transfer and unconditional transfer.

15.8 What does the "eyebrow" in a bimag-core symbol signify?

15.9 What is a transfluxor?

15.10 What is the difference in construction between the bimag core and the ferrite core?

15.11 What is the main application of ferrite cores?

15.12 Describe how information is placed into and removed from ferrite cores.

Chapter **16**

Binary Counters and Decoders

Previous chapters have described various electronic circuits which form the fundamental building blocks of a digital computer. This chapter and the seven following show how these blocks are combined to perform various necessary logical functions.

The logical unit discussed in this chapter is the binary counter. The operation of digital computers and data processors depends greatly on counting and comparing functions. Counters are employed in digital computer control circuits to regulate the sequence in which operations are performed and in data processors to facilitate the recording and modification of information.

The term "binary counter" is self-explanatory. It refers to a device, composed of appropriately connected flip-flops and gates, which performs the function of counting in the binary number system. Either *up-counting* (0, 1, 2, 3, etc.) or *down-counting* (3, 2, 1, 0, etc.) can be accomplished, depending on the logical arrangement employed. The counter output can be used in various ways to perform required functions; for example, it may form a gating voltage which allows information to be transferred from one register to another at the appropriate count.

The two basic counter configurations are the up-counter and the down-counter. Where the counts begin and end depends upon the logical requirements of the computer. There are variations of the basic counters, such as the combination up-down counter, which can count in either direction according to the needs of the computer.

This chapter describes the basic counter configurations. Analogies will be drawn between serial and parallel counters, and the advantages and disadvantages of each will be pointed out. The counters are shown in logical circuitry with external AND-gate inputs to the flip-flops wherever necessary. This is done to allow the substitution of a simple flip-flop logical symbol in the counter circuitry. (Some flip-flops have internal gating with as many as eight inputs.) Consideration then must be given to the trigger-pulse requirements for the flip-flops and gating circuitry actually used in a practical application.

Basic decoders will be discussed and shown in their relationship to counters. Decoders are given a more extensive treatment in Chap. 18, Diode and Transistor Matrices.

For explanatory purposes, the established voltage levels are -20 and 0 volt; hence, the clocking pulse (cp) will vary from 0 to -20 volts, and the output levels of the flip-flops will be 0 and -20 volts. On the flip-flops, the side having an output of -20 volts is referred to as the *low side*, and the side having an output of 0 volt is referred to as the *high side*. The AND gates shown in the circuitry respond to negative inputs; hence, two negative inputs must occur in coincidence before the gate can produce a negative output.

Up-counters

Serial up-counter. A serial up-counter is composed of a group of flip-flops with the ONE-side output of each flip-flop connected to both ONE and ZERO inputs of the next flip-flop in the chain, that is, the flip-flop which contains the equivalent of the next higher binary digit. Figure 16.1 shows a serial up-counter which is capable of counting in binary from 0 (0000) through 15 (1111).

The flip-flops are designed to respond to negative pulses (refer to Chap. 10 for the explanation of flip-flops). The source of negative pulses is normally the trailing edge (designated as downclock) of a clock pulse (designated as cp) or the downclock from either the ONE side or the ZERO side of another flip-flop.

Flip-flop A_1 (Fig. 16.1) changes state every time clock pulse cp is applied; that is, the flip flop switches the high-output voltage from one side to the other. Two pulses are required to cause a flip-flop output to go through a complete cycle, that is, from the ONE state to the ZERO state and back again to the ONE state.

Since a flip-flop changes state only upon the application of a negative pulse, A_2 does not change state until A_1 has switched from the ONE state to the ZERO state. Flip-flop A_2 then cannot change state until A_1 downclocks, that is, until the trailing edge of the pulse from A_1 triggers it. Two input pulses are required to cause A_1 to go through a complete cycle; thus, two complete cycles from A_1 cause A_2 to go through a complete cycle.

In order to produce a complete cycle at the output of A_4, 16 cp's are required. At the downclock of the sixteenth pulse, A_1 will have changed

flipflop change structure
to neg pulses
Trailing edge

state 16 times; A_2, eight times; A_3, four times; and A_4, twice. The binary relationship of the cycles is evident. This configuration of flip-flops is termed a 16:1 up-counter.

The following discussion can be more easily followed if Figs. 16.1 and 16.2 are used as references. In the timing diagram (Fig. 16.2), the dashed vertical lines are inserted to aid in aligning pulses.

clock pulses applied to LSD

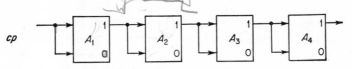

Fig. 16.1 Four-stage serial up-counter.

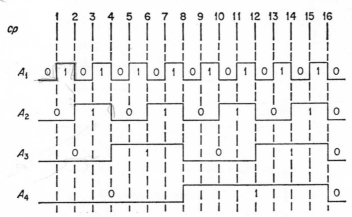

Fig. 16.2 ONE-side outputs of a serial up-counter.

Before the first clock pulse occurs, all four flip-flops (A_1 through A_4) are in the ZERO state; hence, their ONE-side outputs are low (-20 volts) and their ZERO-side outputs are high (0 volt). At the downclock of cp_1, A_1 is triggered from the ZERO state to the ONE state and the ONE-side output becomes high. The binary value in the counter, which should be read vertically from the bottom (most significant digit) to the top (least significant digit) of the timing diagram, is 0001. On the downclock of cp_2, flip-flop A_1 again changes state and the ZERO-side output becomes high. The downclock from A_1 causes A_2 to change from the ZERO to the ONE state. As the result of the changes of state of flip-flops A_1 and A_2, the binary count is now 0010. Timing pulse cp_3 changes A_1 to the ONE state; but since a downclock does not come from the ONE side of A_1, flip-flop A_2 does not change state; it remains in the ONE state. The binary configuration is 0011. On the receipt of cp_4, downclocks are applied simultaneously to A_1, A_2, and A_3, causing A_1 and A_2 to go to the ZERO state and A_3 to go to the ONE state. The resulting binary configuration is 0100.

a gate is enable or inhibited by the voltage ref.

The states of individual flip-flops thus continue to change with successive cp's until the maximum count of 1111 is attained on the receipt of cp_{15}. A count of 1111 (decimal 15) is the highest of which a four-stage counter is capable.

When cp_{16} is received, all flip-flops (A_1 through A_4) change to the ZERO state. The downclock of cp_{16} causes A_1 to go to the ZERO state; and since all flip-flops in the chain are in the ONE state, each generates a downclock to the flip-flop next in line. The downclocks result in a change of count from 1111 to 0000, which was the count present at the beginning of the operation. Each clock pulse following cp_{16} will cause the count to increase by 1 so that cp_{17} causes the count to be 0001, cp_{18} causes the count to be 0010, and so on.

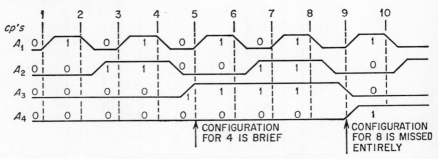

Fig. 16.3 Switching-time error in a serial counter.

The serial counter has one inherent characteristic which is a drawback to its operation at high speeds: The time required for the counter to change states increases proportionately with the number of flip-flops in the counter. Figure 16.3 shows the effect of switching time on the four-stage up-counter.

If the time between successive downclocks of clock pulses is 6 μsec and switching time for each flip-flop is 2 μsec, the following situation arises: When cp_4 is applied to the counter, flip-flops A_1 and A_2 must change state before A_3 can change state. The 2-μsec switching time causes A_3 to go to the ONE state 4 μsec after the downclock of cp_4. Furthermore, A_3 does not complete its change of state for another 2 μsec; therefore A_3 goes to the ONE state coincidentally with the arrival of cp_5. Thus, the counts 0100 and 0101 occur so closely together that any programming process requiring the sampling of 0100 may fail and errors may arise as a consequence. Likewise, when the counter switches from a count of 0111 to 1000, four flip-flops must change state.

Chances are that the count will probably be missed altogether since the switching time for A_1 through A_3 is 6 μsec, and another 2 μsec is required for A_4 to complete its change of state. As a result of this relatively slow switching time in comparison with clock pulse rates, the following outputs could result from the counter, where X equals a missing result: 0000, 0001, 0010, 0011, X, 0101, 0110, 0111, X, 1001, 1010, 1011 X, 1101, etc.

To avoid this fault in a serial counter, it must be designed so that the number of flip-flops is one less than the ratio of the clock pulse repetition time to the flip-flop switching time. This design criterion can be written in the following equation:

$$N = \frac{tp}{ts} - 1$$

where N = number of flip-flops

tp = clock pulse repetition rate, μsec

ts = flip-flop switching time, μsec

If this equation is applied to the preceding problem, it is evident that the optimum of flip-flops in the serial counter is two, as shown in the following equation:

$$N = \frac{6}{2} - 1 = 2$$

Two flip-flops limit the counter to a capacity of binary 11 (decimal 3).

A possible solution to the problem of "lost" counts is to lengthen the pulse repetition rate, but this might slow down the counter and thus reduce its effectiveness. Another solution, more difficult to achieve, is to decrease flip-flop switching time.

The most reliable solution to the problem, however, is the use of a parallel up-counter, which effectively reduces the problem of loss of counts due to cumulative switching times.

Parallel up-counter. A parallel up-counter is composed of a chain of flip-flops whose individual ONE-side outputs are applied to every flip-flop of higher order. Also, the input pulse (cp) is applied directly to every flip-flop in the chain. As has been shown, the flip-flops in a serial up-counter are caused to change state by a downclock from the flip-flop of the next lower order or, in the case of the least significant flip-flop, by the downclock of a cp. The parallel up-counter, however, changes state only when it receives the combined outputs of all flip-flops of a lower significance and the cp. The flip-flop of the lowest significance, of course, changes state on receipt of the cp alone (see Fig. 16.4).

The application of pulses in the parallel up-counter shown in Fig. 16.4 is as follows:

1. The cp is applied to flip-flops B_1, B_2, B_3, and B_4.
2. The output of B_1 is applied to B_2, B_3, and B_4.
3. The output of B_2 is applied to B_3 and B_4.
4. The output of B_3 is applied to B_4.

The Boolean equations for changing the states of the flip-flops in the parallel up-counter are:

1. $B_1 = cp$ **2.** $B_2 = cp \cdot B_1$

3. $B_3 = cp \cdot B_1 \cdot B_2$ **4.** $B_4 = cp \cdot B_1 \cdot B_2 \cdot B_3$

Each flip-flop in a parallel up-counter changes state only if all flip-flops of lower significance are in the ONE state. Assume that all flip-flops in the counter shown in Fig. 16.4 are reset to the ZERO state and contain an initial count of 0000. When cp_1 downclocks (see Fig. 16.2), flip-flop B_1 goes to the ONE state and the counter contains 0001. The output of B_1

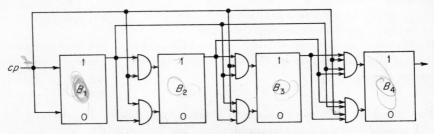

Fig. 16.4 Four-stage parallel up-counter.

is applied to the AND gate supplying an input to B_2. When the next clock pulse (cp_2) is received, it becomes the second input to the B_2 AND gate. The AND gate provides an output to both the ZERO side and the ONE side of B_2. Since B_2 is in the ZERO state, the downclock from the gate sets the flip-flop to the ONE state. The downclock of cp_2 also resets B_1 to the ZERO state so that the count in the counter is now 0010.

Pulse cp_3 switches flip-flop B_1. As B_1 changes state from ZERO to ONE, it does not produce a negative output; hence, the equation for the AND gate, $B_2 = cp \cdot B_1$, is not satisfied. Therefore, flip-flop B_2 does not change state, and the content of the counter is 0011.

At cp_4, the downclock again changes B_1 back to the ZERO state. This clock pulse is also applied simultaneously to the AND gates of B_2, B_3, and B_4. Since B_1 now produces a negative pulse from the ONE side, B_2 changes state. Flip-flop B_2 is in the ONE state when cp_4 is applied; thus, it produces a negative spike which changes the state of B_3. The resulting action of cp_3, then, is that B_1 and B_2 change to the ZERO state and B_3 changes to the ONE state. The count is now 0100.

The count progresses in the fashion described; the requirements of the Boolean equations must be met for the individual flip-flops to change state. At cp_7, the contents of the counter are 0111. When cp_8 arrives, B_1 changes to the ZERO state, supplying the gates to B_2, B_3, and B_4 with a downclock. The equations for changing the states of B_1, B_2, and B_3 are satisfied; thus the flip-flops change to the ZERO state. The output of these flip-flops also supplies the input required to satisfy the equation at B_4. Flip-flop B_4 is thus switched from the ZERO state to the ONE state. Except for a small transit time, all four flip-flops in the counter change state simultaneously on the application of cp_8.

At cp_{15}, the counter contains 1111, which is the maximum count for a four-stage counter. When cp_{16} is applied, the equations to change the states of all four flip-flops are satisfied, and each changes from the ONE state to the ZERO state. The count resulting from the application of cp_{16} is thus 0000. This count is the same configuration present before the downclock of cp_1. The counter has therefore been reset to its initial condition and is ready for recycling.

Down-counters

Serial down-counter. A down-counter is a counter which successively reduces by unit steps any count which is present in it. Except for one

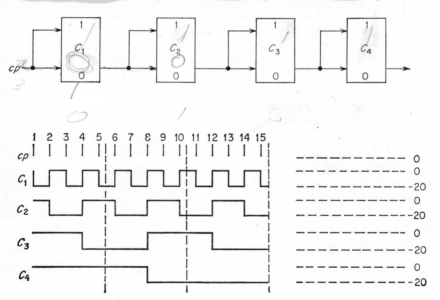

Fig. 16.5 Serial down-counter and timing diagram.

difference, a down-counter is similar in operation to an up-counter in that each successive downclock of a cp causes the least significant flip-flop to change state and each successive flip-flop is triggered by the downclock of the flip-flop preceding it. The difference between the up-counter and the down-counter is that in the down-counter, the ZERO-side outputs of the flip-flops are used to cause the next flip-flop to change state. The clock pulses applied result in the counter's continually reducing its count as follows: 1111, 1110, 1101, 1100, . . . , 0011, 0010, 0001, 0000, 1111, 1110, etc.

Assume that a maximum count of 1111 is contained in the four-stage serial down-counter shown in Fig. 16.5. On the downclock of cp_1, the state of flip-flop C_1 changes from ONE to ZERO. This change of state results in a count of 1110. Clock pulse cp_2 changes C_1 back to the ONE state, and the negative pulse from the ZERO side of C_1 applied to C_2 causes that flip-flop to change to the ZERO state. The operation of the down-counter is identical with that of the up-counter, except that the

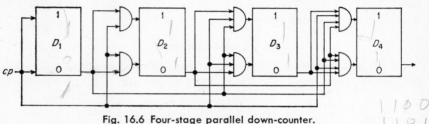

Fig. 16.6 Four-stage parallel down-counter.

negative pulses required to change the states of the flip-flops always come from the ZERO sides of the flip-flops of the next lower order. At cp_{15}, the count in the counter is 0000; and cp_{16} causes the count to go to 1111, the starting configuration of the counter.

Parallel down-counter. The serial down-counter presents the same problem as the serial up-counter: the possibility of loss of counts because of the ratio of the duration of clock pulses to the flip-flop switching time. Where a high rate of counting is required, the parallel down-counter can be used. In operation, the parallel down-counter is similar to the parallel up-counter, except that the downclock required to change the state of a flip-flop in the counting chain is taken from the ZERO side of the preceding flip-flop (see Fig. 16.6).

The application of pulses in the parallel down-counter is as follows:

1. The cp is applied to flip-flops D_1, D_2, D_3, and D_4.
2. The output of $\bar{D}_1$ is applied to D_2, D_3, and D_4.
3. The output of $\bar{D}_2$ is applied to D_3 and D_4.
4. The output $\bar{D}_3$ is applied to D_4.

The Boolean equations for changing the states of the flip-flops in the parallel down-counter are as follows:

1. $D_1 = cp$ **2.** $D_2 = cp \cdot \bar{D}_1$
3. $D_3 = cp \cdot \bar{D}_1 \cdot \bar{D}_2$ **4.** $D = cp \cdot \bar{D}_1 \cdot \bar{D}_2 \cdot \bar{D}_3$

Counter Variations

The maximum count of which a counter is capable is $2^n - 1$, where n equals the number of flip-flops in the circuit. Hence, a five-stage counter can have a maximum content of $2^5 - 1$, or 31 (11111). In certain computer operations it may be desired to count to a number less than the maximum capacity of the counter and then to recycle after this count. For instance, in order to count to 10, four flip-flops (having a maximum capacity of 15) are required. Consequently, the counter has to be modi-

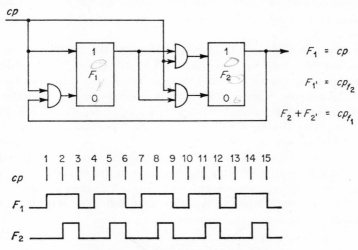

Fig. 16.7 Modulus 3 counter and timing diagram.

fied through the use of feedback and logical switching circuits to produce only one output pulse at the most significant flip-flop for every 10 pulses received at the least significant flip-flop. Such a counter is called a modulus 10 counter or, in briefer form, a mod 10 counter. The mod 3, mod 10, and mod 14 counters are described in the following paragraphs.

Mod 3 counter. Figure 16.7 is the logical diagram of a mod 3 counter. It is actually a modified parallel counter which uses feedback from flip-flop F_2 to inhibit flip-flop F_1 when F_2 is in the ONE state. The mod 3 counter counts as follows: 00 to 10 to 11 and then resets to cycle again.

The following equations apply in the operation of the mod 3 counter:

1. $F_1 = cp$ **2.** $\bar{F}_1 = cp \cdot F_2$ **3.** $F_2 + \bar{F}_2 = cp \cdot F_1$

The timing diagram of Fig. 16.7 shows that one complete pulse is produced by flip-flop F_2 only on receipt of a clock pulse having a designation which is a multiple of 3, that is, cp_3, cp_6, cp_9, cp_{12}, and so forth.

Flip-flops F_1 and F_2 are in the ZERO state at the beginning of a counting cycle. On receipt of cp_1, F_1 goes to the ONE state. Pulse cp_2 does not change F_1 back to the ZERO state because the conditions of the equation $\bar{F}_1 = F_2 \cdot cp$ are not met. Flip-flop F_2, however, changes from the ZERO state to the ONE state because its AND gate is primed by the proper voltage level of the pulse from the ONE side of F_1. Thus, the downclock of cp_2 changes the state of the flip-flop F_2 from ZERO to ONE. Both flip-flops are in the ONE state when cp_3 is applied to the circuit. Flip-flop F_1 now switches to the ZERO state when cp_3 is applied to the circuit because the equation $\bar{F}_1 = F_2 \cdot cp$ is satisfied. Flip-flop F_2 also goes to the ZERO state at the downclock of cp_3 because the conditions are identical with the switching caused by cp_2. The counter has now returned to its initial state of ZERO.

The count in the mod 3 counter is thus 00, 01, 11, 00, and so on. An unmodified two-stage counter counts 00, 01, 10, 11, 00. The mod 3 counter is therefore used when a count of three is desired for computer operation.

Mod 10 counter. Figure 16.8 shows a mod 10 counter. It is a modified parallel up-counter using feedback from $G_3' + G_4$ to inhibit flip-flops G_2 and G_3. The timing diagram of Fig. 16.7 indicates that a complete output pulse occurs on the tenth, twentieth, thirtieth, etc., input pulse. The logic of the counter is such that the flip-flops may switch to the ONE state at any time all preceding flip-flops are in the ONE state. Two of the flip-flops (G_2 and G_3), however, are inhibited. Flip-flops G_2 and G_3 can go to the ZERO state only when G_3 is in the ZERO state or G_4 is in the ONE state. The count progresses in the manner shown below:

cp	Count
1	0001
2	0010
3	0011
4	0100
5	0101
6	0110
7	0111
8	1110
9	1111
10	0000

The Boolean equations for the mod 10 counter are as follows:

$$G_1 + G_1' = cp$$
$$G_2 = cp \cdot G_1$$
$$G_2' = cp \cdot G_1 \cdot G_4 + cp \cdot G_1 \cdot G_3'$$
$$G_3 = cp \cdot G_1 \cdot G_2$$
$$G_3' = cp \cdot G_1 \cdot G_2(G_3 + G_4')$$
$$G_4 + G_4' = cp \cdot G_1 \cdot G_2 \cdot G_3$$

Mod 14 counter. A minor change in logic can convert the mod 10 counter into a mod 14 counter. Instead of the ZERO-side output of the third flip-flop and the ONE-side output of the fourth flip-flop, the ONE-side output of the third flip-flop and the ZERO-side output of the fourth flip-flop are used.

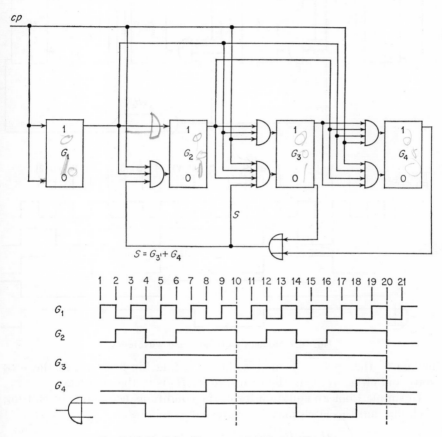

Fig. 16.8 Modulus 10 counter and timing diagram.

The logic diagram of a mod 14 counter is shown in Fig. 16.9. The mod 14 counter is also a modified parallel counter using feedback. Flip-flops H_2 and H_3 are inhibited by H_3 and H_4', which are fed into an OR circuit.

The timing diagram of Fig. 16.9 indicates that a complete output pulse occurs on the fourteenth cp and every fourteenth cp thereafter.

To switch H_4 to the ONE state, the sole requirement is that all preceding flip-flops be in the ONE state. Flip-flops H_2 and H_3, however, can-

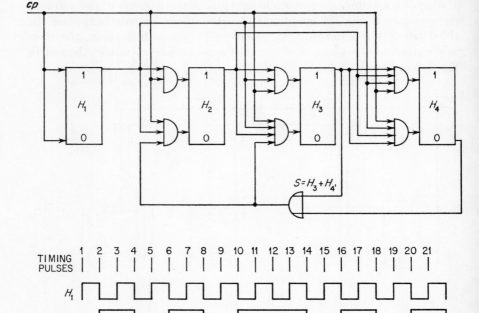

Fig. 16.9 Modulus 14 counter and waveforms.

not go to the ZERO state unless the preceding flip-flops are in the ONE state and either H_3 is in the ONE state or H_4 is in the ZERO state.

In simple Boolean equation form, the conditions necessary for causing each flip-flop to switch may be expressed as follows:

$$H_1 + H_1' = cp$$
$$H_2 = cp \cdot H_1$$
$$H_2' = cp \cdot H_1 \cdot H_3 + cp \cdot H_1 H_4'$$
$$H_3 = cp \cdot H_1 \cdot H_2$$
$$H_3' = cp \cdot H_1 \cdot H_2(H_3 + H_4')$$
$$H_4 + H_4' = cp \cdot H_1 \cdot H_2 \cdot H_3$$

Decoders

The information contained in the flip-flops or other bistable elements of a computer would be useless unless there were a way to convert the binary configuration into a usable signal that would initiate action in other parts of the computer. This function is performed by the decoder.

A decoder is a circuit consisting of one or more AND gates used to detect certain counts in a counter or register. These decoded outputs can be used to initiate specific actions in the computer or to indicate when certain operations have been completed. For example, assume that a down-counter is used to control two computer operations; that is, the computer is to add on the count of five and is to print out the results on the count of three. Two decoders, G_1 and G_2, would be connected to the down-counter as shown in Fig. 16.10.

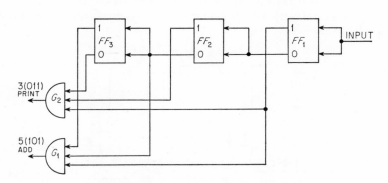

Fig. 16.10 Down-counter with decoder gates.

When the count is reduced to five, only G_1 will have an output to instruct the computer to add. On the count of three, only G_2 will have an output to instruct the computer to print out the results.

The inputs to G_1 are from the ONE side of FF_1, the ZERO side of FF_2, and the ONE side of FF_3. Hence, G_1 will produce a high output only on the count of five (101). The inputs to G_2 are from the ONE side of FF_1, the ONE side of FF_2, and the ZERO side of FF_3. G_2 will produce a high output only on the count of three (011). Note that although a counter or register is using the binary system, the count or number can be decoded in its decimal equivalent.

Regardless of the count to be decoded, there will always be a decoder input from each flip-flop in the counter or register. This is because an undecoded flip-flop may be in the ONE or the ZERO state, and thus the counter or register could have a count other than that to be decoded.

Detect and NOT detect nets. Figure 16.11 shows an application of the counters and decoding nets as they would be used to perform a computer subroutine during the execution of a command. The waveforms are shown in Fig. 16.12. The computer subroutine is the following:

1. Add, or accumulate, a series of binary digits ranging from 1 through 4.
2. Print out successive totals on paper tape.
3. Inhibit the print-out of any total over 59.
4. Store any total exceeding 59 in the memory unit.
5. Reset the counter to zero after each storage operation.
6. Continue steps 1 through 5 as long as add pulses occur.

Analysis. The circuit shown in Fig. 16.11 consists of the following three main blocks:

1. A control counter consisting of flip-flops A_1 through A_3
2. An accumulator counter consisting of flip-flops B_1 through B_6
3. A decoding network which generates print signals and memory store signals

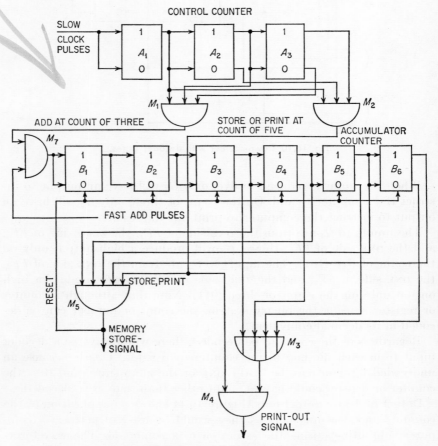

Fig. 16.11 Detect and NOT detect nets.

Slow clock pulses are applied to the control counter. Each time a count of 011 is contained in the counter, AND gate M_1 applies a signal to AND gate M_7. Gate M_7 is applied to the flip-flops in the accumulator counter. Depending on the frequency of the fast pulses in relation to that of the slow clock pulses, up to four add pulses will enter the accumulator counter

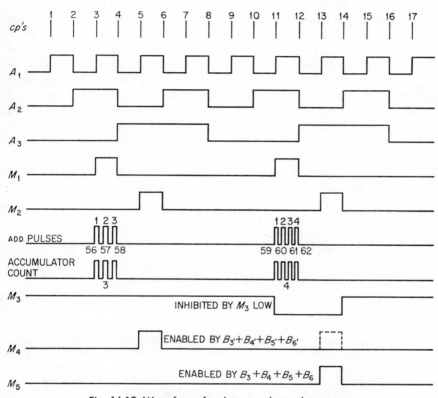

Fig. 16.12 Waveforms for detect and NOT detect nets.

before the pulses from M_1 is removed. Assume that a count of 55 (110111) is contained in the counter when gate M_7 is operative. The counter will count up to 58 (111010). This number is within the limits set by the problem; hence the pulses are accumulated. When the control counter reaches the count of five (101), gate M_2 applies a pulse to AND gates M_4 and M_5. Gate M_4 is enabled at this time because there is a high ZERO-side output from B_3 when a count of 58 is in the accumulator counter. (The program requires a count of 60 or greater to inhibit the print-out of the accumulated count. Since decimal 60 equals 111100, a high ZERO-side output from any one of the four most significant flip-flops, B_3 through B_6, satisfies the equation for a print-out operation. Conversely, when flip-flops B_3 through B_6 go to the ONE state, the count is 60 or more.) The binary contents of the accumulator counter are transferred to another circuit where they are made available for print-out. (The transfer circuits are not shown in Fig. 16.11, for purposes of simplification.)

When the control counter reaches the count of 011 on the second cycle, gate M_7 is again enabled by the output from gate M_1. At this time, four add pulses are accepted by the accumulator counter, which progresses to a total count of 62 (111110). There is no longer an output from the ZERO sides of flip-flops B_3 through B_6, and thus no pulse is passed through gate M_3. There are, however, ONE-side outputs from all four of these flip-flops applied to AND gate M_5. Therefore, when the control counter reaches a count of binary 101, the pulse from gate M_2, available at both M_4 and M_5, satisfies the conditions at M_5 only, and the memory store signal is generated. The signal commands the computer to store the contents of the counter and reset all the flip-flops in the counter to the ZERO state in preparation for the next cycle.

The equations which control the operation of this circuit are as follows:

1. $M_1 = A_1 \cdot A_2 \cdot \bar{A}_3$
2. $M_2 = A_1 \cdot \bar{A}_2 \cdot A_3$
3. $M_3 = \bar{B}_3 + \bar{B}_4 + \bar{B}_5 + \bar{B}_6$
4. $M_4 = M_2 \cdot M_3$
5. $M_5 = M_2 \cdot B_3 \cdot B_4 \cdot B_5 \cdot B_6$
6. $M_7 = M_1 \cdot$ add pulses

Summary

Binary counters and decoders play an important role in the control and synchronization of information in digital computers. The prime component of the counter is the flip-flop, which may be composed of transistors, vacuum tubes, or magnetic cores. Cascading the flip-flop stages enables the computer continually to monitor the number of pulses applied and provide a gating action according to a preprogrammed sequence.

Counters may be classified into two main categories: serial and parallel. In the parallel counter the input pulses are applied to both sides of each flip-flop in the counter; parallel operation shortens the transition time, allowing the counter to operate at a high pulse recurrence frequency. In the serial counter the input pulses are applied only to the least significant flip-flop, and the least significant flip-flops are connected to the flip-flops of the next higher significance. The advantage of the serial counter is simplicity.

Either parallel or serial counters can be further classified as up-counters, down-counters, combinations, and modified counters. Up-counters have the ONE-side output of one flip-flop connected to both inputs of the next flip-flop in the counting chain. Down-counters utilize the ZERO-side outputs of flip-flops as inputs to the following flip-flops in the counting chain.

Decoders or detect nets are used in conjunction with counters to control either the counter or other logical switching circuits. A decoder produces a high output for one particular counter configuration or combination of configurations. Sometimes the logical unit employed as the decoder is the OR gate, but more often the AND gate is used.

QUESTIONS

16.1 List at least three electronic devices that can be used as flip-flop elements.

16.2 How often will the most significant flip-flop in a five-flip-flop binary up-counter change states with respect to the input pulses?

16.3 What is the electrical difference between an up-counter and a down-counter?

16.4 Describe the difference between a serial counter and a parallel counter.

16.5 What limits the number of stages of a parallel counter?

16.6 How many flip-flops would be required in a mod 5 counter? Explain your answer.

16.7 What is the purpose of a decoder?

16.8 How long will the detected count of three be "high" from a decoder if the pulse repetition rate is 10 kc?

Chapter 17

Storage and Shift Registers

In many digital computers binary counters located in the arithmetic or control section must be time-shared; that is, the same group of flip-flops is used for different purposes. The flip-flops can be made to reset to a predetermined count, count up or down, or inhibit the count at a certain number with the proper control signals. Often the information in the counter must be removed before it is needed in the program. To accomplish this circulation and temporary storage of information, storage registers and shift registers are used.

Storage registers and shift registers must be able to perform the following three functions.

1. Receive information from another source
2. Preserve this information without alteration or loss of signal strength until it is needed
3. Deliver this information to another circuit of the computer when it is required by the program

Applications

Schematically, storage registers and shift registers are similar to the binary counter. They are composed of storage cells, such as flip-flops or magnetic cores (bimags), each of which is an elementary location capable of storing a single binary digit (bit). These elementary locations, also termed *memory cells*, are grouped to hold words. A word is, in a fixed-word-length binary computer, of finite length, depending upon the design criteria and the programming requirements. The number of bits in a word determines the size of the register.

Usually, a word which is to be stored has a predetermined function in the computer operation, and thus it will be always transferred to a specific storage register. Assume that a binary counter generates a series of counts which are to be used alternately as a multiplier and as a divisor. The setting of a control flip-flop to the ONE state every nth clock pulse causes the count in the counter to be placed in a register where it may be used in the program as a multiplier. On another predetermined clock pulse the flip-flop is reset to the ZERO state, and the contents of the counter may go into a register where they are used as a divisor. These registers are used exclusively for these purposes and thus can be designated as the MP (MultiPlier) register and the DV (DiVisor) register. These registers become addresses in the program. In programming symbology, then, a step in the operation of the computer may be "Divide X DV," which means: Divide the operand X (which is already in the arithmetic unit) by the operand which is found in the DV register. The programming step, of course, is written in binary form, which is the language of the computer.

An interesting possibility in computer design presents itself at this point. It is possible that the DV register at this step may contain all 0s. Since it is arithmetically impossible to divide by 0, a decoder would have to be incorporated into this register to detect a content of all 0s. Should all 0s be detected, this step would require modification. The detecting counter could command the computer to do a number of things, such as set an alarm, halt the computer, skip the step, substitute a predetermined divisor, and so forth, depending upon the programming requirement.

A register also requires a means by which it is possible to read in, or record, the information without alteration and in proper bit locations. It must also be possible, whenever the program calls for it, to sample either certain bits or an entire word in a register without destroying or removing the contents of this register.

Finally, there must be a means of reading out this information when it is needed and inserting it in another register or in the memory. After this information is removed, the register must be capable of having the previously stored information erased in anticipation of receiving new information. This process of erasing is called *clearing*, and it resets the register states to their normal state, usually ZERO.

Design Considerations

Size, power consumption, cost of components and of construction, and reliability are important factors in the design of registers, just as they are for all computer circuits. Three important features, however, that must be considered for these registers are mode of access, access time, and permanence of storage.

There are two basic modes of access or methods of depositing and withdrawing information: parallel and serial. Access time for a storage register is that time which is required for it to be addressed from the program and for the information to be transferred to another location. These two parts of access time are termed the *preparation period* and the *action period.* During the preparation period, the address contained in the program must be decoded and made available to the register as a control pulse or level. Access time also includes the interval required to couple the reading and writing circuits to the register.

The action period of access time is the interval actually required for reading or writing the contents of the memory. The action period may range from a time within the microsecond order for normal transit time from one electronic circuit to another up to a large number of milliseconds for electromechanical devices where print-out or writing on a rotating magnetic drum is required.

Access time also includes time for destructive read-out. Such bistable devices as bimag cores and magnetic drums usually destroy the contents when they are read out. If retention of the contents of the register is required for future use, the bits must be read back in and recorded at this time.

The permanence with which data is retained in a storage medium is another important factor to consider. Magnetic storage elements can retain information for long periods of time without external power. The electronic storage elements, such as vacuum-tube and transistor flip-flops, do require external power to retain the information; however, they retain the information as long as power is being applied.

Flip-flop Storage Registers

Three basic storage registers are those composed of magnetic cores, magnetic drums, and flip-flops. A combination storage and shift register composed of bimag cores was explained in Chap. 15, Ferromagnetic Cores. Magnetic drum storage is covered in Chap. 22, Computer Memory Systems. This chapter is limited to a discussion of the basic registers composed of flip-flops. (Refer to Chap. 22 for the theory of operation of memory devices in general.) Each flip-flop in a register is capable of storing a single data bit. The number of bits in a data word therefore determines the number of flip-flops in a storage register.

Analysis. Figure 17.1 shows a parallel storage register which requires AND circuits to receive information from its associated counter. The operation of the counter shown in Fig. 17.1 is identical with that of the serial counter described in Chap. 15. The ONE sides and the ZERO sides of flip-flops I_1 through I_4 of the counter are connected to the ONE sides and ZERO sides, respectively, of flip-flops J_1 through J_4 of the storage register via the external AND gates. Each side of flip-flops J_1 through J_4 is also connected to an input line which transmits read-in pulse rp, which enables the AND gates.

The conditions for operation of individual flip-flops in the storage register are as follows:

1. $J_n = I_n \cdot rp$ **2.** $\bar{J}_n = \bar{I}_n \cdot rp$

where n is the number of the flip-flop of the same significance.

Figure 17.2 is a timing diagram demonstrating the operation of the counter and storage register of Fig. 17.1. Counter I operates in a straightforward fashion, recording the number of input clock pulses (cp's) applied

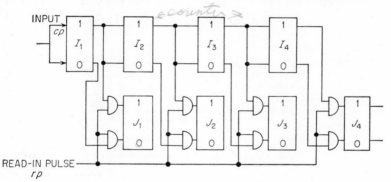

serial
Takes input
Bit by Bit
in sequence
of another

Parallel
takes in
By words

Fig. 17.1 Parallel storage register using external AND circuits.

to the flip-flops. Read-in pulses (rp's) are generated externally to the circuit shown in Fig. 17.1 at certain intervals. They are delayed slightly in relation to the input pulses to permit the switching of all flip-flops in counter I; otherwise, a garbled or incomplete count would be transferred to register J. At rp_1, cp_5 has just placed a binary count of 0101 in counter I. Read-in pulse rp_1 is applied to the AND gates connected to both sides of each flip-flop in register J. The equations for the transfer of information follow.

1. $J_1 = I_1 \cdot rp$ **2.** $\bar{J}_2 = \bar{I}_2 \cdot rp$
3. $J_3 = I_3 \cdot rp$ **4.** $\bar{J}_4 = \bar{I}_4 \cdot rp$

The first read-in pulse which occurs after the fifth input pulse sets flip-flops J_1 and J_3 to the ONE state and flip-flops J_2 and J_4 to the ZERO state. The count of 1010 in counter I is transferred without alteration into register J. The contents of register J can now be used according to the needs of the program.

The counter continues to record each cp, and at cp_{11} (delayed), read-in pulse rp_2 is produced. The binary contents of counter I (1101) are transferred into the register. The equations for the transfer of information are as follows:

1. $J_1 = I_1 \cdot rp$ **2.** $J_2 = I_2 \cdot rp$
3. $\bar{J}_3 = \bar{I}_3 \cdot rp$ **4.** $J_4 = I_4 \cdot rp$

Figure 17.3 shows another type of parallel storage register. External AND gates are used here to transfer the ONE-side outputs from the flip-

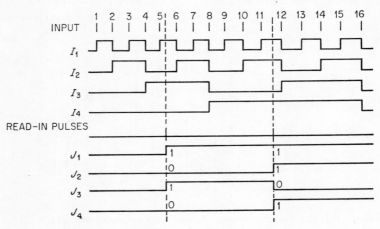

Fig. 17.2 Timing diagram for Fig. 17.1.

flops in counter K to the ONE-side inputs of the associated flip-flops in register L.

The following equations satisfy conditions for transfer of information to register L:

1. $L_n =$ clear pulse   **2.** $L_n = K_n \cdot rp$

where n is the number of the flip-flop of the same significance. Before a count in counter K is transferred to register L, a clear pulse resets flip-flops L_1 through L_4 to the ZERO state. The register is now clear, or reset to 0000, and can accept any contents from counter K when the read-in pulse is given. In this circuit the AND gates are connected only to the ONE sides of the flip-flops in register L. On the read-in pulse, only those flip-flops K_1 through K_4 which contain a binary 1 satisfy the equations to cause a switch input to flip-flops L_1 through L_4. If counter K contains a count of 0101, the equations controlling the insertion of information in the register are as follows:

1. $L_2 = K_2 \cdot rp$ **2.** $L_4 = K_4 \cdot rp$

Flip-flops L_1 and L_3 will remain in the ZERO state since there is no input to the ONE sides.

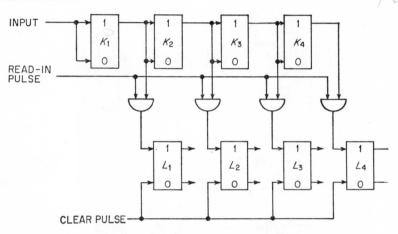

Fig. 17.3 Storage register using external AND gates and clear pulse.

The contents of register L would then be read out to another part of the computer on command, and the register reset to 0000 before the next read-in pulse is produced.

Shift Registers

The methods described thus far involve parallel transfer of data from one circuit to a register. It is obvious that each bit of data in such a transfer requires its own transfer path, complete with whatever gating circuits are needed to perform the task. Sometimes such parallel transmission of data is not feasible. A computer of 18 bits, for instance, would require a minimum of 18 lines.

Over long distances this type of transmission is not warranted because of the expensive hardware involved. If, for instance, a counter is in use to record occurrences remote from a data-processing center, a single line is far more practical. This calls for serial transmission of information. For this type of operation, information has to be lined up, in effect, and passed through the line one bit at a time. The serial transmission mode requires a shift register.

While a shift register can be composed of bimag, transistor, or vacuum-tube flip-flops, only the flip-flop circuits are described here.

Figure 17.4 shows a shift register (flip-flops Q_1 through Q_3) which receives the output of counter O through storage register P. Figure 17.5 is the timing diagram for this circuit.

Analysis. Counter O is a three-stage serial up-counter which performs according to the theory of operation given in Chap. 15. Storage register

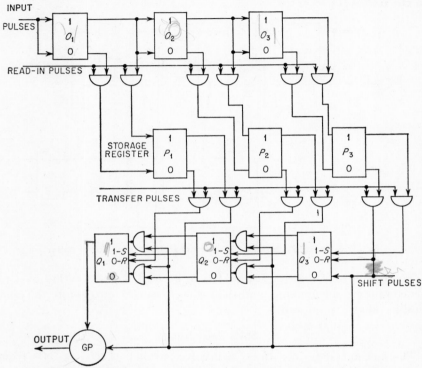

Fig. 17.4 Flip-flop shift register with associated counter and storage register.

P, in parallel with counter O, accepts the contents of flip-flops O_1 through O_3 on the downclock of the read-in pulse. After the read-in pulse is generated, a transfer pulse is generated which causes the contents of shift register Q to accept the contents of storage register P.

Following the transfer pulse, a series of shift pulses causes the binary contents of register Q to be passed one at a time through the flip-flops from the most significant bit to the least significant. As each shift pulse is generated, the contents of the least significant flip-flop (Q_1) are shifted out through a gate pulse amplifier (GP) which gates the pulse into the transmission line. The equation for producing a gated pulse on the transmission line is as follows:

$$\text{Transmitted pulse} = Q_1 \cdot \text{shift pulse}$$

The internal gating of flip-flops Q_1 through Q_3 is somewhat more complex than that of flip-flops previously described in Chaps. 15 and 16. Two input functions are required: The first is the transfer of information from the storage register; the second is the application of shift pulses. For this reason, the transfer inputs, which are generated as the output of AND gates between registers P and Q, are applied to the SET and RESET inputs. The output sides of the P flip-flops are connected through individual AND gates to the input sides of associated Q-register flip-flops. An output from the ONE side of P_1, for instance, goes to the SET input at the ONE side of Q_1 where it is designated 1-S (SET to the ONE state). Likewise, an output from the ZERO side of P_1 goes to the RESET input at the ZERO side of Q_1 where it is designated 0-R (RESET to the ZERO state).

To place the information on the output line, a second input circuit is required along with shift pulses for the flip flops in register Q. The distribution of the pulses required for operation of the registers is apparent in this diagram. Note that each read-in pulse follows a clock pulse, so that the flip-flops in the counter have had time to switch. The transfer pulse, which places the contents of the storage register in the shift register, must occur after the read-in pulse. The shift pulses, which cause the individual bits in the shift register to be placed on the transmission line, must occur after the transfer pulses.

It is also apparent from the timing diagram that the train of shift pulses must be generated in its entirety before the second read-in pulse occurs; otherwise, garbled information may result.

Assume that the counter composed of flip-flops O_1 through O_3 contains a binary count of 110 at cp_6. Between cp_6 and cp_7 the first read-in pulse is generated, and it transfers the count into the storage register. (The counter will continue to count until it is reset to 000 by cp_8, after which it will continue to count a second cycle.)

At a predetermined time after the first read-in pulse, the first transfer pulse is generated. This pulse transfers the contents of the storage register (110) in parallel into the shift register, composed of flip-flops Q_1 through Q_3, by resetting Q_1 to the ZERO state and setting Q_2 and Q_3 to the ONE state.

At cp_8, the first of a train of shift pulses is received and is applied simultaneously to the ZERO sides of Q_1 through Q_3 and the ONE sides of Q_1 and Q_2. The output on the ONE side of Q_3 and the shift pulse complete the equation $Q_2 = Q_3 \cdot$ shift pulse, and a SET input is applied to the ONE side of Q_2. Flip-flop Q_2, however, is already in the ONE state and therefore this input has no effect on the flip-flop. The shift pulse causes Q_3 to go to the ZERO state.

The shift pulse is applied to the ONE-side input of Q_1, satisfying the equation $Q_1 = Q_2 \cdot$ shift pulse, so that Q_1 goes to the ONE state.

The ONE side of Q_1 is connected to the gate pulse amplifier. The equation for the generation of a pulse on the transmission line through the gate pulse amplifier is $1 = Q_1 \cdot$ shift pulse. Since Q_1 is not in the ONE state when the first shift pulse is generated, the equation is not satisfied, and a 0 (no pulse) is placed on the line.

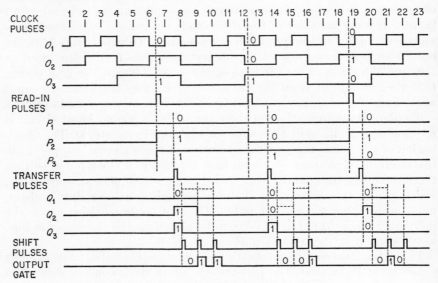

Fig. 17.5 Timing diagram for Fig. 17.4.

As a result of the first shift pulse, the following changes have occurred:

1. Flip-flop Q_3 has switched from the ONE state to the ZERO state.
2. Flip-flop Q_2 remains in the ONE state.
3. Flip-flop Q_1 has switched from the ZERO state to the ONE state.
4. A 0 has been shifted out of the shift register.

The second shift pulse again resets Q_3 to ZERO; but since it is already in the ZERO state, the pulse has no effect. Simultaneously, the shift pulse and the ZERO-side output of Q_3 cause Q_2 to go to the ZERO state. Flip-flop Q_2 is in the ONE state; thus its ONE-side output causes a setting action at the ONE-side input of Q_1. However, Q_1 is in the ONE state, so this SET input also has no effect. Flip-flop Q_1 is in the ONE state; the ONE-side output and the second shift pulse cause a 1 to be generated on the transmission line.

As a result of the second shift pulse, the following changes have occurred:

1. Flip-flop Q_3 remains in the ZERO state.
2. Flip-flop Q_2 has switched from the ONE state to the ZERO state.

3. Flip-flop Q_1 remains in the ONE state.

4. A 1 has been shifted out of the shift register.

Only flip-flop Q_1 now holds a 1. Although Q_1 originally held the least significant bit in the register, it now holds the most significant bit.

When the third shift pulse is generated, Q_3 and Q_2 are not affected, but the ZERO-side output of Q_2 causes Q_1 to go to the ZERO state. The ONE-side output from Q_1 satisfies the equation for generating a 1 on the transmission line, and a 1 is shifted out.

As a result of the third shift pulse, the following changes have occurred:

1. Flip-flops Q_3 and Q_2 remain in the ZERO state.

2. Flip-flop Q_1 has switched from the ONE state to the ZERO state.

3. A 1 has been shifted out of the shift register.

The register is now cleared to 000, and the contents inserted at the first transfer pulse are shifted out. The order of significance has been reversed during the process so that the original counter contents (110) are transmitted as 011. The most significant digit has become the least significant and vice versa. For operation in a computer at the other end of the transmission line, these bits can be either inserted in a machine designed to operate with operands in reverse order or reinverted by another shift register or a delay loop which holds each incoming digit for a specific time until placed in the usual order.

Tables 17.1 and 17.2 provide a pulse-by-pulse analysis of the operation just described and of the next two shift cycles shown in the timing diagram of Fig. 17.5.

Table 17.1

Pulse	Function	Time of operation
1. Clock	Operates counter (O_1, O_2, and O_3)	Independently generated
2. Read-in	Enables the storage register (P_1, P_2, and P_3) to sample a specific binary configuration in the counter	Between any two successive cp's of the counter
3. Transfer	Enables the shift register (Q_1, Q_2, and Q_3) to sample a specific binary configuration in the storage register	Between any two successive read-in pulses
4. Shift	Enables the shift register to release one binary bit to its output gate	A train of three such pulses must occur between any two successive transfer pulses

Table 17.2

Shift cycle	Number of shift pulse	Resulting count Q_1 Q_2 Q_3	Bit shifted out
First	0	0 1 1	0
	1	1 1 0	0
	2	1 0 0	1
	3	0 0 0	1
Second	0	0 0 1	0
	1	0 1 0	0
	2	1 0 0	0
	3	0 0 0	1
Third	0	0 1 0	0
	1	1 0 0	0
	2	0 0 0	1
	3	0 0 0	0

Shifting as an Arithmetic Function

When a binary number is shifted, the magnitude of the number is changed by a power of 2 equal to the number of shifts made. Thus when a binary number is shifted one place to the left, it is doubled; when it is shifted one place to the right, it is halved. Table 17.3 shows how a number is affected when it is shifted. In the table, the binary number 101000 (decimal 40) is shifted. (Note that 0s are filled in to the left of the most significant digit in the example to fill all positions of the 10-stage register.)

Table 17.3 Effect of Shift on Number

Number of shift	Shift-left operation	Shift-right operation
Original number	0000101000 (40)	0000101000 (40)
First shift	0001010000 (80)	0000010100 (20)
Second shift	0010100000 (160)	0000001010 (10)
Third shift	0101000000 (320)	0000000101 (5)
Fourth shift	1010000000 (640)	0000000010 (2)

The successive halving of the number in the shift-right operation causes the least significant bit of the number to be lost on the fourth shift. In some applications the decimal 2 which results is sufficiently accurate for computations. (In a 24-bit register, loss of the least significant bit as a result of shifting to the right results in a loss of accuracy of the full-length word of about 1 in 16 million if the least significant bit is lost on the first shift to the right.)

As a result of the fifth shift left of the original number the most significant digit is lost, and the number is drastically changed. When 1010000000 (640) is doubled on another shift, the most significant digit has no place in which to be inserted. It is lost, and the number becomes 0100000000 (256), which is completely incorrect. For this reason, shifting to the right or to the left in computer operations must be carefully planned; a limit must be set for the number of shifts according to the location of the most significant and least significant digits.

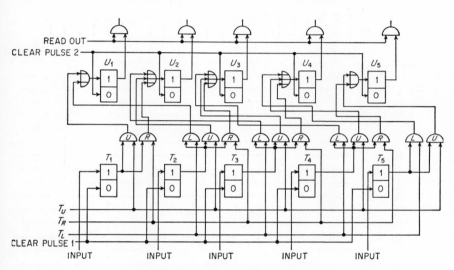

Fig. 17.6 Parallel shifting registers.

Figure 17.6 shows two parallel shifting registers capable of transferring the binary contents of register T to the left, to the right, or (without a positional shift) to register U. This configuration is similar to that found in arithmetic units of many computers. When a transfer pulse (TU, TL, or TR) is applied, the contents of flip-flops T_1 through T_5 are transferred to flip-flops U_1 through U_5. The contents of register U can be passed back to register T directly for a subsequent shift or they can be transferred to another part of the computer as an operand.

Analysis. The equations for the flip-flops in the register U (Fig. 17.6) are as follows:

1. $U_1 = T_1 \cdot TU + T_2 \cdot TL$
2. $\bar{U}_1 = $ clear pulse 2
3. $U_2 = T_2 \cdot TU + T_3 \cdot TL + T_1 \cdot TR$
4. $\bar{U}_2 = $ clear pulse 2
5. $U_3 = T_3 \cdot TU + T_4 \cdot TL + T_2 \cdot TR$

6. $\bar{U}_3$ = clear pulse 2

7. $U_4 = T_4 \cdot TU + T_5 \cdot TL + T_3 \cdot TR$

8. $\bar{U}_4$ = clear pulse 2

9. $U_5 = T_5 \cdot TU + T_4 \cdot TR$

10. $\bar{U}_5$ = clear pulse 2

Clear pulse 1 resets flip-flops T_1 through T_5 to the ZERO state. Clear pulse 2 then resets flip-flops U_1 through U_5. Both registers are cleared

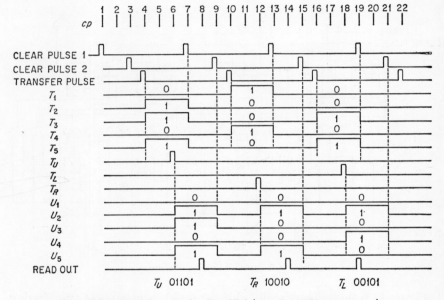

Fig. 17.7 Timing diagram for Fig. 17.6 (parallel shifting registers).

of their previous contents to ensure error-free operation during a cycle. A transfer pulse (not shown) changes flip-flops in register T to the ONE state in parallel with the register or counter containing the count to be shifted.

Figure 17.7 is the timing diagram for the circuit shown in Fig. 17.6. Assume that the first transfer pulse, at cp_4, causes the count of 01101 to be placed in T_1 through T_5. At cp_6, a gated pulse TU, which is originated according to program requirements, is applied to the gates marked U. The transfer-unshifted pulse TU and the ONE-side outputs of flip-flops T_2, T_3, and T_5 cause flip-flops U_2, U_3, and U_5 to go to the ONE state. The count 01101 is thus transferred directly to register U. Since the count is no longer needed in register T, flip-flops T_1 through T_5 are reset to ZERO at cp_7 by clear pulse 1. At cp_8, the read-out pulse transfers the contents of flip-flops U_1 through U_5; and at cp_9, clear pulse 2 resets the flip-flops to the ZERO state.

The second cycle in the timing diagram is different in this respect: the gated transfer pulse is a TR, causing each bit to be shifted one position to the right. This means that the original contents of flip-flops T_1 through T_5 (10010) becomes 01001 in flip-flops U_1 through U_5. Since U_1 has been reset by clear pulse 2 at cp_9 of the previous cycle, the flip-flop is unchanged by transfer-right pulse TR. For the transfer-right operation, the ONE-side output of T_5 is not connected to a transfer-right gate; therefore, if T_5 is in the ONE state, the 1 bit is lost when the bits shift to the right.

During the third cycle in the timing diagram, the binary contents 00101 are shifted left on the transfer. Thus at cp_{18}, a gated TL (transfer-left) pulse is generated by the computer. Each bit is transferred one place to the left, and the contents 00101 becomes 01010. The ONE-side output of T_1 is not connected through a transfer-left gate, and any 1 bit in T_1 is lost when the bits shift to the left. The equations describing the inputs to the T and U flip-flops are as follows:

1. $T_1 = \text{set } T_1 + U_1 \cdot \text{set } T \text{ register}$
2. $T_2 = \text{set } T_2 + U_2 \cdot \text{set } T \text{ register}$
3. $T_3 = \text{set } T_3 + U_3 \cdot \text{set } T \text{ register}$
4. $T_4 = \text{set } T_4 + U_4 \cdot \text{set } T \text{ register}$
5. $T_5 = \text{set } T_5 + U_5 \cdot \text{set } T \text{ register}$
6. $\bar{T}_1 = \text{clear pulse 1}$
7. $\bar{T}_2 = \text{clear pulse 1}$
8. $\bar{T}_3 = \text{clear pulse 1}$
9. $\bar{T}_4 = \text{clear pulse 1}$
10. $\bar{T}_5 = \text{clear pulse 1}$
11. $U_1 = T_1 \cdot TU + T_2 \cdot TL$
12. $U_2 = T_2 \cdot TU + T_1 \cdot TR + T_3 \cdot TL$
13. $U_3 = T_3 \cdot TU + T_2 \cdot TR + T_4 \cdot TL$
14. $U_4 = T_4 \cdot TU + T_3 \cdot TR + T_5 \cdot TL$
15. $U_5 = T_5 \cdot TU + T_4 \cdot TR$
16. $\bar{U}_1 = \text{clear pulse 2}$
17. $\bar{U}_2 = \text{clear pulse 2}$
18. $\bar{U}_3 = \text{clear pulse 2}$
19. $\bar{U}_4 = \text{clear pulse 2}$
20. $\bar{U}_5 = \text{clear pulse 2}$

Summary

Storage of processed data is one of the most important functions the digital computer data processor performs. Binary information must be sampled at regularly programmed intervals and retained until required for comparison with other information or for shifting into output devices. Storage registers must be versatile and have access times which will not interfere with the normal flow of data in the information stream. Flip-flop storage registers provide this basic function in that a read-in pulse will record the computer's count without disturbing the operation, and they will hold the information until ready for use in the output or receiving device.

Occasionally it becomes necessary for output information to be distributed in serial rather than parallel form. The shift register is capable of accomplishing this function by transferring stored data in a step-by-step process.

QUESTIONS

17.1 In which two units of a digital computer are counters and storage and shift registers used extensively?

17.2 Which type of electronic component would be most economical to operate in a storage register which holds information for a relatively long period of time?

17.3 Define access time.

17.4 Describe how a binary number can be halved by shifting the number in a register. How can a binary number be doubled?

17.5 Show a serial-to-parallel conversion unit for five bits using a storage register and a shift register.

Chapter 18

Diode and Transistor Matrices

The control function necessary in data-processing and arithmetic operations is implemented largely through the use of switching networks of various sizes. These switching networks, or *matrices*, are composed of AND or OR circuits producing a discrete output signal for each combination of input signals. The term matrix is used to describe these large switching arrangements because of their similarity to mathematical matrices, being neatly arranged in rows and columns. Three types of matrix are in general use: diode, transistor, and magnetic core. The diode matrix is used mainly in control functions, producing start-stop operations at certain counts of a control or instruction counter. The transistor and core matrices are used in the address- and instruction-selecting portions of the computer, the transistor being used as an element to provide amplification. This chapter discusses the general principles of diode and transistor matrices and shows typical applications. The core matrix is covered in Chap. 22, Computer Memory Systems.

Diode Matrices

Figure 18.1 is a logical diagram of a system composed of a counter, a detect net and a NOT detect net. Corresponding Boolean equations and timing diagrams are also shown in this figure. The diodes (two for each AND and OR gate) are not shown. This diagram would be complicated further if the counter contained three, five, or more flip-flops, because the gate inputs would be increased proportionately.

The detect net shown in Fig. 18.2 performs the same functions as that shown in Fig. 18.1; however, it is drawn schematically as the grid or matrix type of detect net. In this form there is a simple means for showing the flip-flop outputs and the diode voltage potentials (B+ for the AND gates, B− for the OR gates).

Note that the counter is drawn so that the least significant digit is on the right. Diodes CR_1 and CR_2 constitute the AND gate for detecting binary 01. When this number occurs in the counter, the B_1 and B_2' lines go positive, causing diodes CR_1 and CR_2 to cut off, producing a high out-

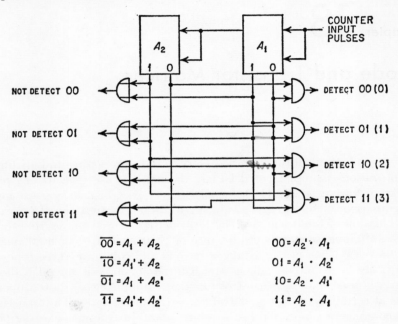

$$\overline{00} = A_1 + A_2 \qquad\qquad 00 = A_2' \cdot A_1$$
$$\overline{10} = A_1' + A_2 \qquad\qquad 01 = A_1 \cdot A_2'$$
$$\overline{01} = A_1 + A_2' \qquad\qquad 10 = A_2 \cdot A_1'$$
$$\overline{11} = A_1' + A_2' \qquad\qquad 11 = A_2 \cdot A_1$$

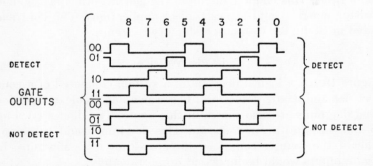

Fig. 18.1 Unmodified detect and NOT detect nets and timing diagram.

put on line 01. When the counter configuration changes from 01 to 10, the diode CR_1 conducts; a substantial voltage is dropped across R_1, and the output at X goes low, thus terminating the detected signal. The detected signal will not occur again until B_1 and B_2' outputs are again high; there is no other count configuration in the entire counting range where this can happen.

Diodes CR_5 and CR_6 constitute the OR gate for NOT detecting binary 10. When any configuration other than binary 10 is present in the counter, either diode CR_5 or diode CR_6, but not both, is conducting. While either

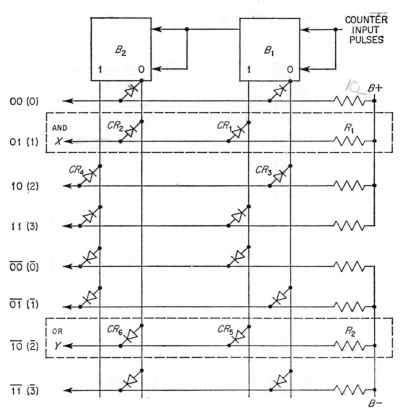

Fig. 18.2 Single-stage diode matrix.

diode CR_5 or diode CR_6 is conducting, there is substantial voltage drop across load resistor R_2, causing the output at point Y to remain high (positive in respect to the B— voltage). However, when the B_1 and B_2' lines are negative (binary 10), diodes CR_5 and CR_6 are cut off; hence, there can be no electron flow from the B— source through either diode. As a result, the output at Y drops from its previous high logic level to the low logic level. This low output remains until either diode CR_5 or diode CR_6 conducts. Thus, the Y output is high for all configurations except binary 10 (decimal 2).

The other AND and OR gates (two diodes connected to each horizontal line) function in the same manner but at different times.

Figure 18.3 illustrates a matrix which will detect the eight possible configurations of a three-flip-flop counter. Note the absence of NOT detect gates and associated circuitry. Flip-flops C_1, C_2, and C_3 will produce

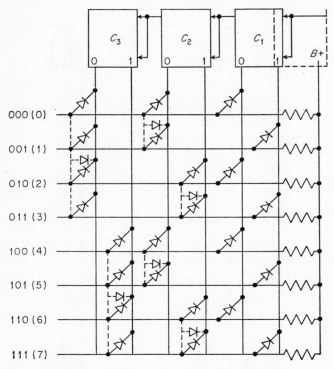

Fig. 18.3 One-stage diode matrix for three-stage counter.

count configurations of 2^3, or 8. Each of the eight counts requires three diodes for proper detection. Thus, a total of 8×3, or 24, diodes seems to be required. It follows then that a counter containing four flip-flops requires $2^4 \times 4$, or 64, diodes; a counter composed of five flip-flops requires $2^5 \times 5$, or 160, diodes. The general formula for the one-stage matrix is $n2^n$, with n representing the number of input variables.

It is apparent that the number of diodes required as the number of flip-flops increases becomes prohibitive if diode economy is a factor. There is a method of matrix arrangement, however, that reduces the number of diodes required to detect the larger binary configurations. This arrangement is called a *tree* or *pyramid* because of its branching appearance.

An example of treeing is shown in the two-stage matrix of Fig. 18.4. The economy of diodes is achieved by (1) dividing the counter into pairs of flip-flops, (2) ANDing each possible output combination from each pair, and (3) ANDing the output of the two ANDed pairs to yield the decoded

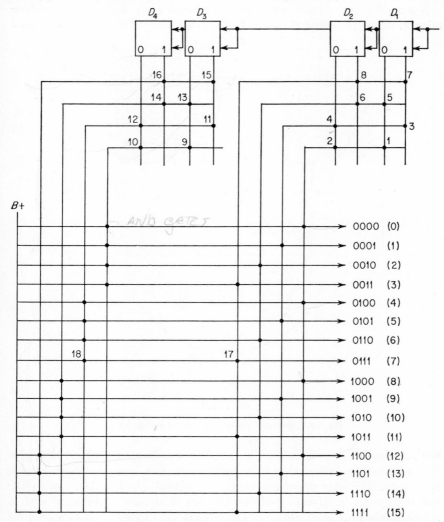

Fig. 18.4 Two-stage detect matrix. Each dot represents one diode in an AND gate.

binary number. Note that in Fig. 18.3, each diode is used only once. In Fig. 18.4, however, the diode pair 1 and 2 is used four different times; this pair is used in the detection of counts 0, 4, 8, and 12. Diode pair 3 and 4 is used in the detection of counts 1, 5, 9, and 13. Each pair of diodes is used in the detection of four numbers. This eliminates the need for 16 of the 64 diodes required if a one-stage matrix were used to detect all possible configurations of Fig. 18.3; hence, only 48 diodes are necessary. Figure 18.5 shows the detect-7 portion of the two-stage matrix.

A second matrix characteristic reveals another means to further economize in diode use. Observe in Fig. 18.3 that the outputs of C_2 are used

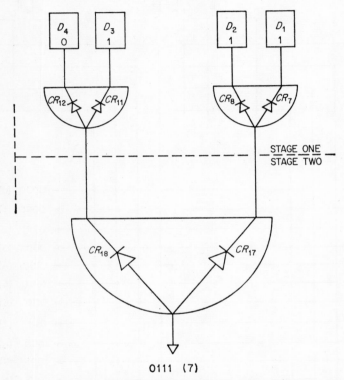

0111 (7)

Fig. 18.5 Detect-7 portion of matrix in Fig. 18.4.

during two consecutive configurations. These pairs and quartets of diodes are duplications since they are performing the same function simultaneously. The only difference is that their individual outputs go to different AND gates. If each pair or quartet of diodes is replaced with a single diode and each single-diode output is divided into two or four branches (depending on whether the replacement diode is for a pair or a quartet of diodes), it is possible to eliminate one of the diodes from the pairs and three of the diodes from quartets (see the dotted diode substitutions in Fig. 18.3). Thus it is possible to eliminate a total of 10 diodes.

Transistor Matrices

A transistor matrix consists of gating circuits which combine two coordinate input signals to produce a single output signal. The signal is then applied to current drivers which will initiate a memory read or write operation. Figure 18.6 illustrates a typical transistor matrix. This is the usual

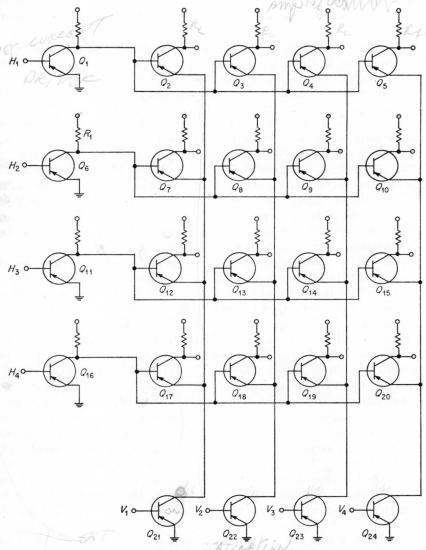

Fig. 18.6 Untreed transistor matrix.

maximum size of such a matrix, which is composed of four horizontal and four vertical lines. There is a transistor at each intersection (see Q_8, for example) with its base connected to a horizontal line and its emitter connected to a vertical line. Each transistor forms a gate which will produce an output when the vertical and horizontal input requirements are met. If a signal to one of the four vertical inputs and a second signal to one of the four horizontal inputs are applied simultaneously, a particular transistor in the matrix will turn on and produce a negative voltage output.

Transistors Q_1, Q_6, Q_{11}, and Q_{16} (Fig. 18.6) are the horizontal inputs, and transistors Q_{21}, Q_{22}, Q_{23}, and Q_{24} are the vertical inputs. The collector of each horizontal input transistor is tied to the bases of four horizontal transistors. When a horizontal input transistor is turned off, it will prime the inputs to the four gate transistors in its horizontal line. The collector of each vertical input transistor is tied to the emitter of four vertical transistors. When a vertical input transistor is turned on, it will prime the inputs to the four gate transistors in its vertical line.

The transistor matrix produces an output signal when a vertical input transistor is turned on by a negative logic-level input applied to its base, and a horizontal input transistor is turned off by a positive logic-level input to its base. Basic logic rules state that one vertical input and one horizontal input will be addressed at a time. Consequently, there will be but one output at a time from a given transistor matrix.

Using Fig. 18.6 as a reference, assume Q_{21} receives a negative pulse at V_1. This turns Q_{21} on and makes current available to the emitters of Q_{17}, Q_{12}, Q_7, and Q_2. If horizontal input transistor Q_6 receives a positive pulse, it turns off. Previously Q_6 was conducting because of the negative voltage applied to its base through H_2. When its conduction stops, there is no longer a voltage drop across resistor R_1. Thus, the voltage now applied to the base of Q_7 becomes more negative and causes Q_7 to conduct. This produces a desired high output at the collector of Q_7.

The height of a transistor matrix is limited by the maximum collector current rating of the vertical input transistors. As illustrated in Fig. 18.8 (a simplification of Fig. 18.7), vertical transistor Q_{21} must supply cutoff current (I'_{co}) to transistors Q_{17}, Q_{12}, and Q_2, as well as collector current (I_c) and base current (I_b) to Q_7. Worst-case design stipulates that with one transistor on, the additional I'_{co} of other OFF transistors on any vertical line could exceed the current rating of the vertical input transistor for that line. To prevent this from occurring, the matrix is limited to three OFF transistors and one ON transistor in any vertical line that is addressed.

The width of a transistor matrix is also limited. This is determined by the leakage current of the OFF vertical input transistors and the emitter-

Ico is your limiting factor

to-base current of the ON transistor. This is illustrated in Fig. 18.8 (an excerpt from Fig. 18.6). The dotted lines leading to R_1 of horizontal input transistor Q_6 indicate the composition and direction of current flow R_1. Q_6 has the emitter-to-base current of Q_7 plus the leakage currents

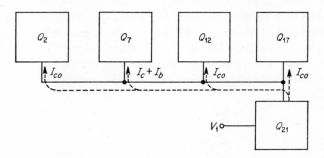

Fig. 18.7 Current limitations, vertical.

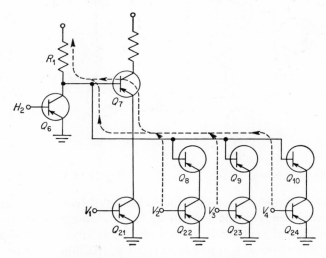

Fig. 18.8 Current limitations, horizontal.

through Q_{22}, Q_{23}, and Q_{24} via Q_8, Q_9, and Q_{10}. The logic levels in vacuum-tube computer circuitry cover ranges from 10 to 50 volts or more, while the logic levels in direct-coupled transistor circuitry vary only a few tenths of a volt between maximum and minimum signal output. If another vertical input transistor were added, the increase in leakage current to R_1 could cause the voltage drop across it to go below (go toward positive) the level necessary to hold Q_7 on. For this reason the width of the transistor matrix is limited to four transistors.

Transistor-Diode Matrices

It is often desirable to AND the signals of two gate transistors in two different transistor matrices through a specific diode in a diode matrix. Such a combination requires conditions which are now investigated.

Horizontal and vertical drivers. Gate transistor matrices do not ordinarily furnish sufficient current to drive a diode gate with its associated circuitry. Consequently, when transistor matrix signals are used to operate diodes in diode matrices, the drive current must be increased. This is accomplished through the use of transistor current-amplifying devices named *drivers*.

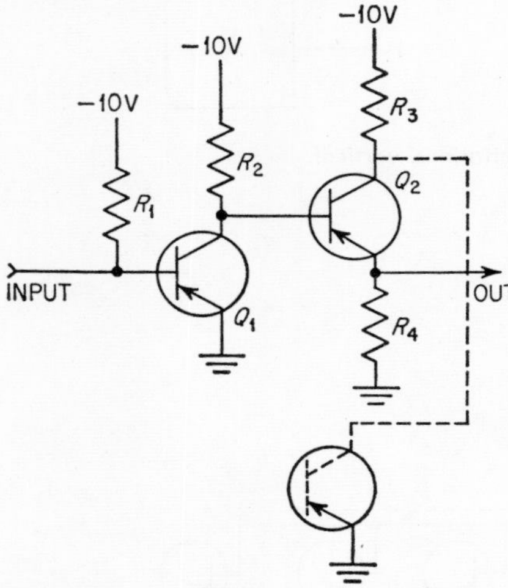

Fig. 18.9 Horizontal driver. 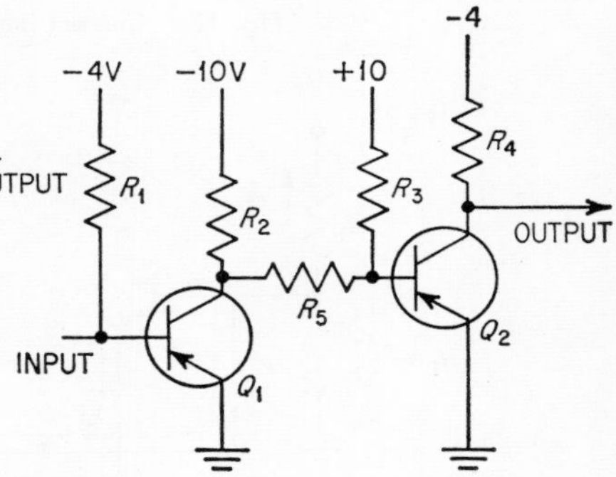   Fig. 18.10 Vertical driver.

Figure 18.9 shows an example of a horizontal driver. With buffer transistor Q_1 turned on, current flows in R_2, maintaining a positive signal on the base of Q_2 and keeping Q_2 turned off. A positive output signal from one of the collectors in a transistor matrix is fed into the base of Q_1 to turn Q_1 off. With no current flowing through R_2, the full -10 volts is felt at the base of Q_2, turning Q_2 on. Such an upper driver feeds current to one of the diode-matrix horizontal inputs.

Figure 18.10 shows an example of a vertical driver. With buffer transistor Q_1 turned on, R_2 and R_3 form a positive-bias network to ensure that Q_2 will be off. With the advent of a positive signal to the base of Q_1 from one of the collectors of a different transistor matrix, Q_1 turns off, the signal to the base of Q_2 goes more negative, and Q_2 turns on. Such a lower driver feeds current to one of the diode-matrix vertical inputs.

A horizontal driver and a vertical driver must be on to have current flow through one diode in a diode matrix.

Function of transistor-diode matrix. Figure 18.11 illustrates a simplified version of a core-diode matrix with its associated horizontal and vertical drivers. Only a representative group of the diodes contained in a matrix is shown. In order to cause current flow through the pulse transformer, a horizontal and a vertical driver must be on simultane-

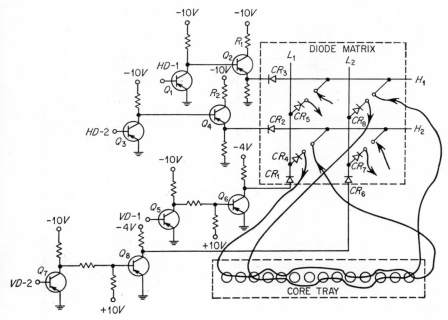

Fig. 18.11 Typical diode matrix.

ously. Assuming HD-2 and VD-1 are on, the horizontal line H_2 and the vertical line L_1 of the diode matrix will be selected. When Q_5 is cut off, current will flow through Q_6, through "sneak-path" diode CR_1, through intersecting diode CR_4, through certain of the pulse transformers in the core tray, through sneak-path diode CR_2, through transistor Q_4, and out R_2 to the -10-volt power supply. As a result of the transformer wiring and the above circuit action, a binary word of 11101000011001 is generated on the secondaries of the pulse transformers where a 1 is represented by an induced voltage.

As a second example, assume HD_1 and VD_2 are on. This will cause current flow through Q_8, CR_6, CR_8, pulse transformers, CR_3, Q_2, and R_1 to the -10-volt power supply. In this instance the binary word 00111001100111 is generated.

The sneak-path diodes contained in the diode matrix are used to reduce the shunt current caused by the low impedance of the parallel back
diodes which shunt the selected diode and core. Without the sneak-path
diodes, the leakage would result in marginal or false read-out.

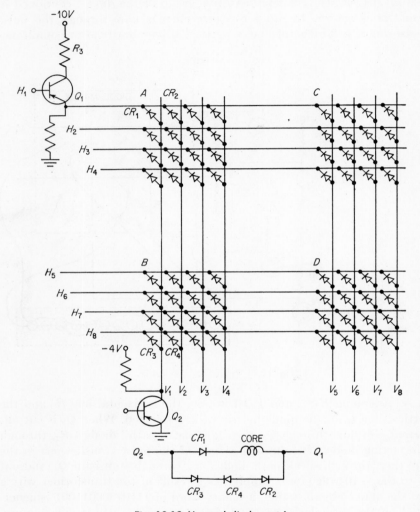

Fig. 18.12 Untreed diode matrix.

Untreed matrix. Figure 18.12 illustrates an untreed matrix consisting
of four units: A, B, C, and D. Assume an $H_1 V_1$ selection. When Q_1 and
Q_2 go into conduction, diode CR_1 is addressed and will pulse the desired
wires through the cores (see the core circuits for Fig. 18.11, diodes CR_4

and CR_8). Note, however, that an alternate path is provided from Q_2 through Q_1. This is a forward direction through CR_3, a backward direction through CR_4, and a forward direction through CR_2 to Q_1. The result is a shunting effect due to the parallel impedance of the back-diode

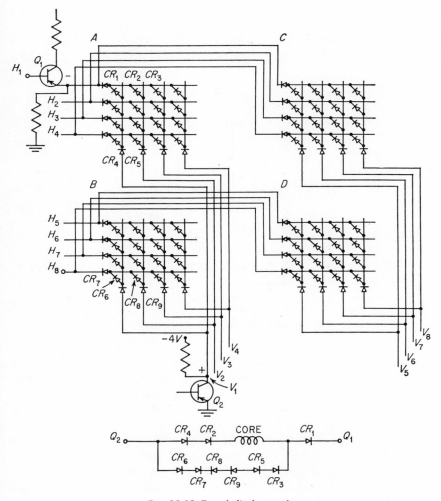

Fig. 18.13 Treed diode matrix.

leak paths (see insert at bottom of Fig. 18.12). If this shunting effect is sufficient, a marginal or uncertain read-out from the cores may occur; hence, the number of these leak paths determines the maximum size of an untreed diode matrix.

A back diode is a reverse-biased diode in the matrix that shunts the addressed diode and its associated core. A forward diode in the matrix is forward-biased and offers a low impedance. In the insert to Fig. 18.12, CR_3 and CR_2 are forward diodes and CR_4 is a back diode.

Besides the main current path which operates diode CR_1, more than 50 leak paths can be traced through units A, B, C, and D; each leak path contains at least one back diode and two forward diodes.

The forward series diodes also have a limiting effect on the maximum size of the untreed diode matrix since their cumulative effect will reduce

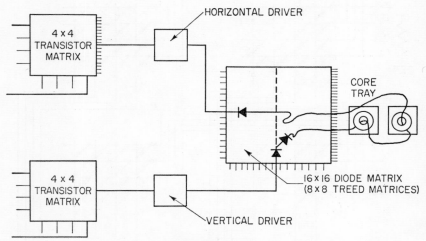

Fig. 18.14 Transistor-diode matrix.

the amplitude of the output signal. Practical design has resulted in the selection of an 8×8 matrix as the largest operational untreed matrix.

Treed matrix. To illustrate a treed diode matrix in a limited space, four 4×4 matrices are used to produce the 8×8 matrix shown in Fig. 18.13. Here each unit (A, B, C, or D) has four additional diodes at the horizontal inputs and four additional diodes at the vertical inputs. Again by using sneak-path diodes and connecting the units as shown, the shunting impedance can be greatly increased, thus preventing marginal read-out or false signal read-out. To demonstrate this, use Fig. 18.13 and refer to the same $V_1 H_1$ intersection that was used in the untreed matrix. By following this line it can be seen that a leakage current must now flow through two back diodes (CR_8 and CR_9) before reaching H_1 (see insert on Fig. 18.14). Each 4×4 has also been separated by sneak-path diodes, thus placing additional impedance between matrix units. Therefore, a leakage current passing from V_1 through units B and C to H_1 will encounter the impedance of three back diodes.

Summary

A matrix is any combination of the AND or OR gates, or both, normally required in computer detection operations so that greater economy in design and function is attained.

This economy can be approached through the use of the following:

1. Two-stage matrices
2. Dual and quadruple use of diodes
3. Diode-transistor combinations
4. Treeing

A transistor-diode matrix is composed of vertical and horizontal wires with a transistor at each intersection. When a vertical and a horizontal line are addressed simultaneously, the transistor at the point of intersection is turned on to yield an output from its collector. A transistor matrix will accept two coordinate input signals and, from them, produce a single DCTL output signal. Operational requirements are that a vertical input transistor be turned on with a negative level before a horizontal input transistor is turned off by a positive pulse. Turning on the vertical input transistor will complete the emitter-current path of the intersection transistor, and turning off the horizontal input transistor will supply the base voltage required to turn the intersecting transistor on.

The maximum size of an individual transistor matrix is limited to 4 × 4. However, several 4 × 4 matrices may be treed to meet the requirements of a larger matrix for particular applications.

Each output line from a transistor matrix is connected to either an upper or a lower driver of a diode matrix. Consequently, it is necessary to have two transistor matrices to operate a diode matrix.

The function of upper and lower drivers is to provide adequate current for addressing individual diodes in a diode matrix from DCTL levels.

A diode matrix is designed to accept two coordinate input signals and generate a current flow through the selected primary windings of pulse transformers.

Simultaneous addressing of two coordinates in a diode matrix results in current flowing through the lower driver transistor, the sneak-path diode, the intersecting coordinate diode, the pulse transformers, the upper driver transistor, and the collector resistor of the upper driver to the power supply.

The present maximum size of an individual untreed diode matrix in computer circuits is 8 × 8. By treeing several diode matrices, a matrix can be formed to meet specific circuit requirements.

QUESTIONS

18.1 What is a matrix?

18.2 List the functions of the matrices used in digital computers.

18.3 How does a core matrix differ from a diode matrix?

18.4 Explain the differences between a single-stage diode matrix and a two-stage diode matrix.

18.5 Design a diode matrix that will detect the counts from 10 to 20 from a five-flip-flop counter.

18.6 When is it possible to eliminate diodes from a detect matrix?

18.7 What are the characteristics of a NOT detect matrix?

18.8 What factors limit the height and width of a transistor matrix?

18.9 Define the term "sneak path."

18.10 What is the difference between a treed matrix and an untreed matrix?

Chapter 19

Adders and Subtracters

A computer usually performs all its arithmetic operations by addition or subtraction. Chapter 21, The Arithmetic Units, shows how multiplication is performed by addition and how division is performed primarily by subtraction. The adder and, in some instances, the subtracter are the heart of the arithmetic unit. All associated registers and counters are concerned with providing information to the adders and subtracters and controlling the number of additions and subtractions.

Because of the importance of adders and subtracters in arithmetic operations, this chapter explains the operation of these units. Some circuits used to implement the logic are illustrated.

Adders

The logical requirements of an adder can be determined by constructing a truth table for addition (Table 19.1).

Table 19.1 Truth Table for Adder

Augend	X	0	1	0	1
Addend	Y	0	0	1	1
Sum	S	0	1	1	0
Carry	C	0	0	0	1

Inputs — Augend, Addend
Output — Sum, Carry

The truth table considers a single order, and only two binary digits are added at one time. The truth table indicates which of the four possible combinations of X and Y will produce a sum and a carry. From the truth table it can be seen that a sum is produced when the augend X is 1 and the addend Y is 0, and vice versa. A carry is produced when both X and Y are 1. Logical equations may be written for the sum and the carry in terms of X and Y, as follows:

$$S = X\bar{Y} + \bar{X}Y$$
$$C = XY$$

The equation for the sum describes the exclusive-OR function. The exclusive-OR function provides a "true" output when one, but not both,

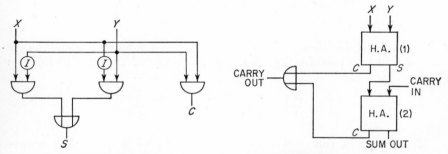

Fig. 19.1 Half-adder, logical diagram.   Fig. 19.2 Full adder, block diagram.

of the inputs is present. A logical diagram can be drawn from these equations (Fig. 19.1).

The truth table considered only two inputs. In practice, an adder must be able to accept a carry from a previous order and add it to the augend and addend bits in the order under consideration. Since the equation and diagram do not consider the possible carry from a previous order, the adder as developed to this point (Fig. 19.1) is termed a *half-adder*.

Full adder. A full adder handles the possible carry from a previous order. A full adder consists of two half-adders. One half-adder adds the augend and addend in a particular order. The other half-adder adds the resulting sum to a carry from a previous order. As a result of these two additions, a single sum and a single carry output are produced for that particular order. A block diagram of the full adder is given in Fig. 19.2.

Half-adders are represented by the blocks labeled $H.A.$ Half-adder 1 adds the X and Y inputs for that order. Half-adder 2 adds the sum output of half-adder 1 to the carry input developed in a lower order. As a result, a sum output for the order is developed. A carry may develop from either half-adder and hence is applied to the OR gate. It is seen from inspection that a carry output cannot exist at both outputs simultaneously.

HALF ADDER - CANNOT HANDLE THE possible CARRY From the previous ORDER

A truth table for the full adder (Table 19.2) indicates all possible combinations when three inputs are used.

Table 19.2 Full-adder Truth Table

Augend	X	0	1	0	1	0	1	0	1
Addend	Y	0	0	1	1	0	0	1	1
Carry	C_{in}	0	0	0	0	1	1	1	1
Sum	S	0	1	1	0	1	0	0	1
Carry	C_{out}	0	0	0	1	0	1	1	1

The truth table shows that there are four combinations that produce a sum and four combinations that produce a carry. They are as follows:

$$S = X\overline{YC} + \bar{X}Y\bar{C} + \overline{XY}C + XYC$$
$$C = XY\bar{C} + X\bar{Y}C + \bar{X}YC + XYC$$

Terms may be collected so that the operation of the full adder as previously discussed becomes more apparent:

$$S = C(\overline{XY} + XY) + \bar{C}(X\bar{Y} + \bar{X}Y)$$
$$C_{out} = C_{in}(X\bar{Y} + \bar{X}Y + XY) + \bar{C}XY$$

Parallel and Serial Adder Units

Half-adders and full adders using only the components necessary to execute the operations of a single order have been developed. It will now be shown how the adders are used to add binary numbers of several orders. Addition can be performed in parallel (each order added simultaneously) or in series (each order added sequentially). Both parallel and serial units are discussed.

Parallel operation. A computer operating in parallel requires an adder for each order; hence, a three-bit word requires three adders. The diagram in Fig. 19.3 illustrates an adder unit capable of adding two three-bit numbers.

The least significant order requires a half-adder since no carry input is involved. Each subsequent order uses a full adder. A complete full adder consists of two half-adders and an external OR circuit. A carry output from the most significant order becomes the most significant digit (MSD) of the sum.

A numerical example describes the operation of the adder unit more clearly. The following numbers are applied to the adders:

$$X = 111$$
$$Y = \underline{110}$$
$$1101$$

The first order is applied to the half-adder. A sum output, but no carry, is developed. In the second order both X_2 and Y_2 are 1s. The sum from the upper half-adder portion is 0, and a carry is generated. No carry

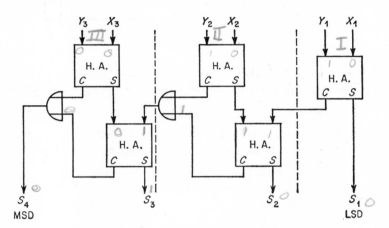

Fig. 19.3 Parallel-adder unit.

from the least significant digit (LSD) order was generated; hence, the sum from the lower half-adder of the second order is 0.

In the third order both X_3 and Y_3 are 1s. The sum from the upper half-adder portion is 0, and a carry is generated. The 0 sum output from the upper half-adder portion of the third order is added to the carry from the second order. The sum output of the third order is 1.

The carry developed from the third order becomes the MSD of the sum.

Serial adder. To perform serial addition, only one full adder is necessary. The orders are shifted into the adder sequentially with the LSD applied first. Any carry is delayed one bit time so that it may be added to the following order. Figure 19.4 shows a serial adder and the inputs that are contained in shift registers.

The serial-adder unit is composed of two half-adders, an OR circuit, and a delay device. The inputs to the first half-adder provide a sum and a possible carry. The sum output from the first half-adder is applied to the second half-adder. The delay time of the delay device is equal to the pulse repetition time (PRT) of the shift pulse so that the second half-adder adds the sum output of the order applied to the (serial-adder) unit to a carry from the previous order. The final sum output is generated one PRT after the final shift has occurred. Any carry that was propa-

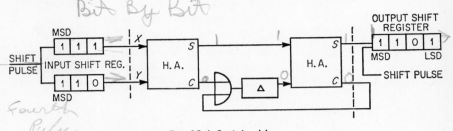

Fig. 19.4 Serial adder.

gated from the most significant order of the augend and addend travels through the delay line during this time and becomes a sum output.

Subtracters

A logical subtracter can also be developed by using truth tables. Table 19.3 is a half-subtracter truth table, from which it is seen that the

Table 19.3 Half-subtracter Truth Table

Minuend	X	0	1	0	1
Subtrahend	Y	0	0	1	1
Difference	D	0	1	1	0
Borrow	B	0	0	1	0

equations for the difference and the borrow are

$$D = X\bar{Y} + \bar{X}Y$$
$$B = \bar{X}Y$$

The equation for the difference is the same as the sum equation of the half-adder. The borrow output occurs when the minuend is 0 and the subtrahend is 1. The borrow output indicates that a 1 must be borrowed from a higher order.

The output of a 1 from the borrow is subtracted from the minuend of the next higher order just as in the decimal system.

It is now possible to draw a logical diagram from the equation. The only differences between the half-subtracter and the half-adder are the carry and borrow equations.

The truth table (Table 19.3) describes the function of a half-subtracter because no provision is made for a borrow from a previous order. A full subtracter provides for this borrow.

Full subtracter. Figure 19.5 shows a full subtracter, which consists of two half-subtracters and an external OR gate. Two subtractions are performed. First a borrow indication from a previous order is subtracted from the minuend X, and the subtrahend Y is subtracted from the dif-

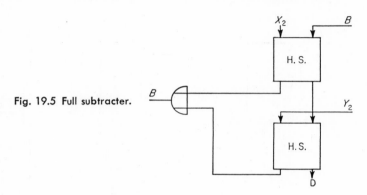

Fig. 19.5 Full subtracter.

ference. If necessity for a borrow arises from either half-subtracter, it is applied through the OR gate to the next higher order.

A truth table for the full subtracter (Table 19.4) shows that the equa-

Table 19.4 Full-subtracter Truth Table

Minuend	X	0	1	0	1	0	1	0	1
Subtrahend	Y	0	0	1	1	0	0	1	1
Borrow	B_{in}	0	0	0	0	1	1	1	1
Difference	D	0	1	1	0	1	0	0	1
Borrow	B_{out}	0	0	1	0	1	0	1	1

tions for the difference and the borrow are as follows:

$$D = X\bar{Y}\bar{B} + \bar{X}Y\bar{B} + \bar{X}\bar{Y}B + XYB$$
$$B = \bar{X}Y\bar{B} + \bar{X}\bar{Y}B + \bar{X}YB + XYB$$

Parallel and Serial Subtracter Units

Subtracters can be arranged to operate in parallel or in series. Both arrangements are illustrated.

Parallel operation. The parallel-subtracter unit (Fig. 19.6) has three orders. The first order is a half-subtracter, and the next two higher orders are full subtracters. The borrow output from a lower order is applied to the next higher order and subtracted from the minuend in the first half-subtracter. The subtrahend is subtracted from the difference in the second half-subtracter, and the correct difference for the particular order is obtained. The subtracter subtracts only when the minuend is larger than the subtrahend.

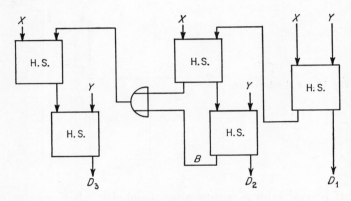

Fig. 19.6 Parallel subtracter.

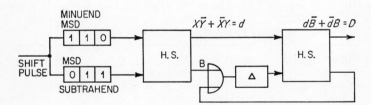

Fig. 19.7 Serial subtraction.

Serial subtracter. A serial subtracter and a serial adder are similar in logical operation. The only difference is the generation of the borrow. A serial subtracter is shown in Fig. 19.7.

Subtraction can also be accomplished if the subtrahend Y is first subtracted from the minuend and the borrow is subtracted from the difference. The delay time is one shift PRT, allowing any borrow to be subtracted from the next higher order.

Adder and Subtracter Circuits

An adder unit composed of diode gates and inverters can be constructed easily. Two adder configurations employing transistor gates are illustrated.

One is a DCTL configuration; the other is an RTL configuration. Subtracter circuits are not shown because of their similarity to adder circuits.

DCTL adders. Figure 19.8 shows a DCTL half-adder. The half-adder is constructed of three series AND gates for negative inputs: $Q_1 \cdot Q_2$, $Q_3 \cdot Q_4$, $Q_2 \cdot Q_5$ (see Chap. 7). Two of these gates are connected as an OR

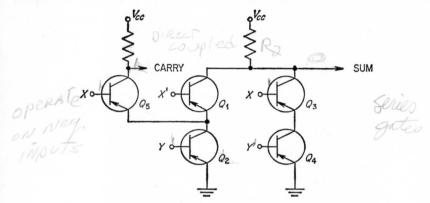

Fig. 19.8 DCTL half-adder.

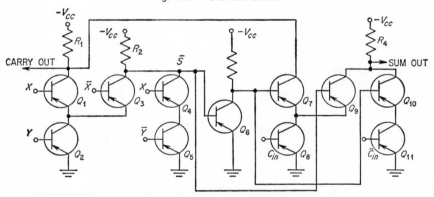

Fig. 19.9 DCTL full adder.

circuit through resistor R_2 to produce a sum. The remaining AND gate, $Q_2 \cdot Q_5$, produces the carry.

The full-adder configuration (Fig. 19.9) is constructed of two half-adder combinations and an inverter (Q_6). Resistor R_2 is the common load resistor for the two AND-OR combinations of $Q_2 \cdot Q_3$ and $Q_4 \cdot Q_5$. The carry gate for the first adder is $Q_1 \cdot Q_2$. The sum output ($+$) from the first half-adder is inverted through Q_6 and the proper negative level applied to Q_7, which is the upper transistor of a series AND gate that combines C_{in} and the sum. Resistor R_1 is also the collector resistor for AND gate $Q_7 \cdot Q_8$, thereby forming an OR gate for the two conditions required to generate a carry output. AND gate $Q_7 \cdot Q_8$ adds $C_{in} \cdot \bar{S}$; gate $Q_{10} \cdot Q_{11}$ is the AND gate that adds $S \cdot C_{in}$. Resistor R_4 is the common load resistor for both AND gates, thus forming the OR gate for the final sum output.

RTL (Kirchhoff) adder. Figure 19.10 shows an RTL full adder. The inputs are for negative levels. With no signals applied, both transistors are cut off. However, the components are chosen so that Q_2 is deeper in cutoff than Q_1. The bias conditions are such that one input is sufficient

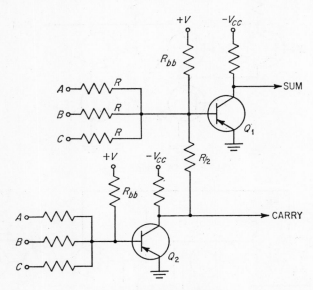

Fig. 19.10 RTL full adder.

to turn on Q_1, but two inputs are required to turn on Q_2. However, when two inputs are present at Q_2, the collector voltage of Q_2 that is applied to the base of Q_1 through resistor R_2 reverse-biases Q_1. When three inputs are present, the reverse bias on Q_1 is overcome, and both transistors are on.

The adder circuit provides the sum and carry output for negative "true" inputs. A carry input is produced at Q_2 when two inputs are present, but no sum is generated from Q_1 because of the reverse bias. When all three inputs are present, Q_1 and Q_2 are on, and a sum and a carry are generated.

Summary

The logical operation of binary adders and subtracters is similar. The exclusive-OR gate is the basic gate used to construct the units. The adder or subtracter units can be constructed to operate in parallel or in series. The parallel unit is the more expensive type. Although the serial units perform operations with fewer components, the operations generally require more time.

QUESTIONS

19.1 Write the logical equations for a half-adder using A and B as the input variables.

19.2 Draw the logical diagrams from the equations of Question 19.1.

19.3 Write the equations for developing a sum and a carry in a full adder using A, B, and C as the input variables.

19.4 What is the advantage of the serial adder over the parallel adder? What is the disadvantage?

19.5 What is the purpose of transistor Q_6 in Fig. 19.9?

Chapter **20**

Computer Control and Data Flow

Flow from INPUT to OU

Computer control and data flow are combined in this chapter because of their close interrelationship. The term "data flow" refers to the passage of information through a computer and the various forms that this information assumes. The term "computer control" refers to the control unit and the control circuits which are the means by which the computer implements data flow in accordance with the instructions it receives.

A knowledge of control circuits simplifies the computer to an ingenious but quite understandable system of logic. Furthermore, a familiarity with data flow and control circuits provides the proper foundation for the study of computer programming.

Overall View of Computer Data Flow

An overall view of data flow in a typical digital computer can be obtained from Fig. 20.1. The diagram indicates some fundamental aspects of the flow of data through a typical digital computer. Note that the flow of data is represented as moving from left to right by steps, or blocks.

The first step is the input device, which accepts raw unprocessed data (basic facts of the problem) from the external environment of the computer. Input forms include punched cards, punched tape, magnetic tape, and inputs inserted by manually operated keyboards. Input data in decimal form (such as decimal keyboard inputs) are converted to binary form before entering the memory or storage units. The binary mode of operation rather than decimal is used in nearly all high-speed computers because it allows the use of simpler circuits.

After the incoming data has been converted to binary form, it enters the memory, or storage unit. The memory works with the computation section in the processing of data. The input data is then stored in the memory until needed for computation. It is partially processed and then stored again in the memory until other related data can be processed. The data is then returned to the computation section for final processing. The final results are either transferred out or stored temporarily in the

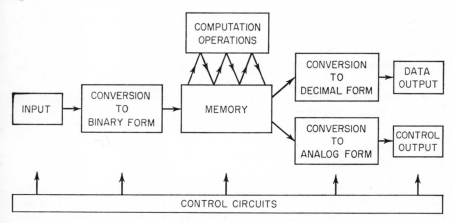

Fig. 20.1 Data flow in typical digital computer.

memory. The memory could then contain at the same time the following three different types of data:

1. Raw (unworked)
2. Partly processed
3. Fully processed

DATA CAN Be obTAINED

The final results undergo conversion after they leave the memory. If the computer is being used for conventional calculation operations, the processed results are usually reconverted to decimal form. On the other hand, if the computer is to be used to control physical actions, the digital data is converted to analog voltages which are sent to motor controls and relays.

The final step in data flow involves the output, of which there are, broadly speaking, two general types:

1. On-line equipment such as a visual indicator or a high-speed printer which uses the computer output as soon as it is produced
2. Off-line equipment such as a punched-card-to-magnetic-tape converter or a keyboard typewriter, both of which require buffering equipment

Data output units convert the final digital results, whether decimal or binary, into one of several forms according to the needs of the business or institution involved. Equipment used for this purpose includes tape punchers and printers, card punchers, magnetic-tape writers, and electric typewriters. Control output units amplify the control analog voltages for transmission to external control units. Analog control outputs are used in a wide variety of applications such as industrial automation and missile guidance.

Basic factors in understanding data flow. Since all the previously mentioned steps take place under the direction of control circuits, it is impractical to attempt to understand any of the details of computer data flow without some knowledge of the control circuits and the basic computer cycle.

The information appearing in the computer can be divided into the following three basic types:

1. Data
2. Instructions
3. Addresses (locations)

What is referred to as data is the material with which the computer works in various stages of processing from input to output. The actual composition of data would depend on the type of application of the computer. In the case of a computer working on payrolls, data would include hours worked, hourly rate, tax withheld, and net pay. If a computer were working on sales statistics, data could include gross sales, net sales performance in previous years, competitors' performance, and projected future sales. This data is fed into the machine as the problem. The computer manipulates this data according to instructions. The results are taken from the output section as answers. In the case of a control problem, data could consist of speed, distance, time, angles, weight, fuel, or other factors.

Instructions direct what is to be done with the data as it moves through the computer. Typical instructions would be *add, subtract, multiply, divide, shift* (data from one part of the computer to another), *write* (information into the memory), and *read* (information from the memory).

Addresses are the places in the memory where information is stored. The information stored at a particular memory address (location) could be either data or an instruction with possibly one or more addresses.

Basic Computer Cycle

Every computer operates in a basic three-phase cycle which is repeated over and over. The three phases are:

1. Instruction selection — *Take from memory*
2. Instruction evaluation (decoding)
3. Instruction execution

During the instruction-selection phase, the instruction that the computer will execute is selected. Instructions were previously stored at specific memory locations by the programmer. The selection of instructions in proper sequence is often accomplished by a program counter (see Fig. 20.2). In simplest form the program counter is a counter which advances one count each time it receives a signal indicating that the previous instruction has been completed. This signal is known as the *end instruction*.

In computer operation the program-counter output is decoded into a specific address. This location is the next instruction, complete with any addresses associated with it. The instruction is read from the memory into an instruction register, which consists of two parts, the operation register and the address register (Fig. 20.2). The operation register holds the part of the instruction that has to do with the operation the machine is to perform, and the address register holds the address of any data in the memory that will be required during the execution of the instruction.

During the instruction-evaluation phase, the operation and address parts of the instruction are both decoded. The address portion is decoded into two discrete outputs which will be referred to as X and Y. The operation portion is decoded into a single discrete output which signals to the appropriate circuits the particular operation which is to be performed. In Fig. 20.2 this signal is initiated when one of the four wires leaving the operation decoder goes high.

In the last phase of the basic computer operating cycle, the instruction-execution phase, the decoded instruction outputs are used to execute the instruction. From the point of view of the use that is made of the address portion, there are two types of instructions: those involving memory locations and those not involving memory locations. In the case of the former, the X and Y outputs are used to select the proper data-holding address. The data at this address is then processed in a manner controlled by the discrete operation level, that is, the high signal on one of the wires coming out of the operation decoder. Each wire corresponds to a particular instruction such as *add, subtract, transfer,* and *print out*. In practical computers there will be many more than four instructions listed.

If the instruction is of the type that does not involve data from a memory location, then the X and Y levels will not have the same function. Instead, they will indicate an "empty" address; or, by the inhibiting action of transfer gates, the memory will not be read at all. In either case, no data will be read from the memory. Such an operation could be a transfer of data from the input to the arithmetic unit or from the arithmetic unit to the output (see $GA3$ and $GA4$ in Fig. 20.2). In practice, transfers like these two examples would be infrequent since in most digital

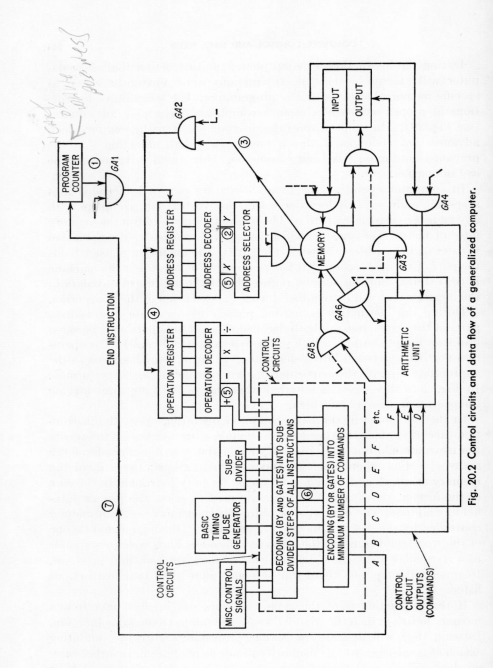

Fig. 20.2 Control circuits and data flow of a generalized computer.

352

computers the access to the computation unit (arithmetic unit) is through the memory. In such a case the data paths controlled by $GA3$ and $GA4$ in Fig. 20.2 would not exist. The following discussion is a step-by-step example of digital computer data flow based on Fig. 20.2.

Instruction-selection phase

1. The initial count in the program counter, corresponding to the address of the first instruction in coded form, is sent to the address register.
2. The input is decoded into actual address-selecting discrete outputs X and Y.
3. The address is read from the memory, and the contents of this address (an instruction) are sent to the instruction register through a gate.

Instruction-evaluation phase

4. The operation and address portions of the instruction are decoded.

Instruction-execution phase

5. The output of the operation decoder is coordinated with the sub-divider steps, basic timing pulses, and miscellaneous control signals into subdivided steps of all instructions. These steps are commands to perform the individual parts of an instruction, as the various additions and shifts needed to carry out a single multiply instruction or various transfers such as those enabled by $GA5$ and $GA6$.
6. Since many of the instruction steps referred to in step 5 are the same for different instructions, each of these identical steps is encoded by OR gates into a single control output wire. Each of these wires leads to the circuits to be actuated in executing the particular step (see control outputs labeled B, C, D, E, and F in Fig. 20.2). When all other steps of an instruction have been executed, the control circuits send out the last control output of the instruction (*end* instruction; see line A, Fig. 20.2). This instruction advances the program counter to the count corresponding to the next instruction.

Control-circuit Operation

Figure 20.2 gives a generalized view of the control circuits. Figure 20.3 shows a simplified control-circuit operation in more detail. In this discussion, numbers refer to circled reference numbers in Fig. 20.3. For example, note reference 1 located above the delay line (DL) near the upper right-hand corner of Fig. 20.3. The instruction register consists of two parts, an operation register on the left and an address register on the right. In the diagram, the address register and the operation register each contain two flip-flops. This number is shown because of space limitations. Actually each register contains eight flip-flops. This means that the address register can hold the indications of 256 addresses, 00000000 to 11111111, and the instruction register can hold 256 coded instructions.

Instruction-selection phase. The START input takes the place of the *end* instruction when computer operation begins (see Fig. 20.3). This

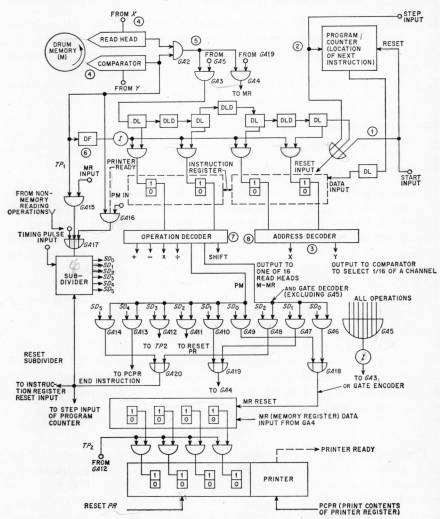

Fig. 20.3 Control circuits of a single-address computer.

input resets the program counter to a count corresponding to the coded first instruction location. At the same time, the instruction register is reset. A short time later the OR gate is enabled, and the contents of the program counter appear in the address portion of the instruction register. The purpose of the delay line (*DL*) is to prevent the contents of the program counter from being placed in the instruction register until after the counters have been fully reset. The input gating shown here is merely a representation; additional logic is required to handle all input situations. Nearly the same operations take place in the case of the *end* instruction input to the counter. However, the counter is stepped instead of reset. Reference 2 indicates the step input to the program counter.

The address-register contents are decoded into X and Y discrete outputs, which are used to select the proper instruction address on the memory drum (see 3 and 4). Since each flip-flop shown in Fig. 20.3 represents four flip-flops, the X input could select any one of 16 read heads, one for each data channel, and the Y input would select one-sixteenth of the selected channel on the basis of time through the comparator. The comparator gives a high output when two equal binary numbers are applied to it at the same time.

When the comparator indicates that the selected channel portion is about to come under the selected read head, it produces an output (5) which will accomplish two objectives. First, the output will prime $GA2$ so that the read-head output will be fed through $GA3$ into the delay-line shift register. Second, when the output drops, the downclock will trigger the differentiator-clipper (6), which will provide a spike enabling the data in the shift register to drop into the AND gates feeding the instruction register at the proper instant.

Instruction-evaluation phase. The operation and address portions of the instruction are decoded (7 and 8). Therefore, one of the wires leading out of the operation decoder will go high at the same time one of the 16 X wires will go high to select a drum data-channel read head. Concurrently, a four-digit binary channel-segment indicator will be fed on the four Y wires to the comparator (3, 4, and 5).

Instruction-execution phase. Previous sections have explained how a number in the program counter can be converted to a completely decoded instruction ready for execution by the computer. The following sections explain how two hypothetical instructions, M-MR and PM, are executed. As has been mentioned in the section Basic Computer Cycle, there are instructions which do not involve data from memory locations. However, the two instructions (M-MR and PM) used here both involve reading the memory. In computer terminology, instruction names are often arbitrary. In the case of this hypothetical computer, the following designations are used: M-MR means "memory-to-memory register transfer instruction or read instruction"; PM means "print the contents of a memory location instruction." The logic involved is as shown in Fig. 20.3.

Steps in Execution of M-MR

1. Assume that the complete instruction, M-MR, is in the instruction register. X and Y outputs from the address decoder (3) begin to select the data indicated by the address portion of the M-MR instruction. The operation of the read head and the comparator is the same as that described for the instruction-selection process. However, after the data leaves $GA2$, it is handled in a different way. During the instruction-selection phase, $GA5$ (in the control circuits), a detector of "no output from the operation decoder," was high; and as a result $GA3$ was enabled. This allowed the output of $GA2$ to be transferred to the delay-line shift register. During this phase an instruction is present; as a result, the output from $GA5$ will be low and data will not pass through $GA3$

2. A glance at the operation decoder shows that it has various outputs corresponding to various instructions. The M-MR output is routed to $GA6$ in the AND-gate decoder (see Fig. 20.2 for corresponding portion) and to $GA15$ in the subdivider input. The subdivider SD_0 output (which is present when $GA17$ is low) and M-MR enable $GA6$. This causes the output of encoding gate 18 to reset the memory register. Encoding gates are used to reduce the number of transfer paths to one for each command (see control circuits in Fig. 20.2 for corresponding portion).

3. As soon as the memory is ready to be read, the comparator output (5) will be high, enabling $GA15$ and $GA17$. The enabling of the gates causes the subdivider to step to SD_1 to enable $GA7$. The $GA7$ output applied through $GA19$ enables $GA4$, to allow the contents of the memory address to be read into the memory register (MR). The delay-line shift register which actually feeds MR is not shown.

4. This step completes the execution of the instruction. The next subdivider step (2) will enable $GA8$, which, through encoding gate 20, will cause the subdivider to be reset and the end instruction signal to be applied to the program counter step input (2).

Steps in Execution of PM

1. The first part of this instruction involves reading the memory and is therefore a repetition of instruction M-MR. The same operations will be performed as in steps 1, 2, and 3 in the immediately preceding paragraphs with the exception that $GA9$ and $GA10$ will perform the functions which were performed by $GA6$ and $GA7$. Note also that the subdivider input for PM is $GA16$ instead of $GA15$. $GA16$ has the additional condition that the printer (an output unit) be ready to accept data before data can be transferred to it.

2. When subdivider step 2 comes up during the PM instruction, $GA2$ resets the printer register (PR). When step 3 occurs, $GA12$ transfers data to PR. Step 4 causes the contents of PR to be printed out. This signal comes from $GA13$ and is labeled $PCPR$ (print contents of printer register).
3. When the data in PR has been printed, the execution of the PM instruction is complete. The next step (5) will produce an output from $GA14$. This output will reset the subdivider to SD_0 and provide the *end* instruction or step input to the program counter.

Summary

Data enters the computer at the input stage. It is usually converted to binary form before entering the memory. The memory and arithmetic unit work together in performing calculations. The arithmetic unit performs the actual calculations while the memory stores data before, between, and after calculations take place. After leaving the memory, data is converted either to another digital form or, in the case of control applications, to analog form.

Data, instructions, or addresses comprise the basic forms which digital information may take in the computer. The instructions and addresses are utilized in processing the data. Instructions tell what is to be done with the data, and the addresses are the locations of the instructions and data.

All computer data flow takes place under the direction of the control circuits. In general form, the control circuits have two parts. The first part is an AND-gate decoder, which coordinates the inputs from the operation decoder, the subdivider, and the basic timing pulses. The second part is an OR-gate encoder, which combines the decoder outputs into a minimum number of commands used to direct the operation of the computer.

QUESTIONS

20.1 In which form is data when it enters the memory and arithmetic section? Why?
20.2 Define "on-line equipment" and "off-line equipment."
20.3 Into what parts is the input information divided?
20.4 What is the purpose of the program counter?
20.5 What is the purpose of the instruction register? How long does it hold the data it receives?
20.6 Briefly describe the three-phase cycle executed by computers.

Exam tue = (5 - 19)

Chapter **21**

The Arithmetic Unit

The arithmetic unit performs all the mathematical operations in the computer. The arithmetic unit in most machines is capable of performing addition, subtraction, multplication, and division. More difficult operations such as extracting square roots, differentiating, integrating, and finding values of trigonometric functions can also be performed. Arithmetic units also perform other operations not usually thought of as arithmetic, such as comparing numbers, shifting right, and shifting left.

It is possible to design a separate adder, subtracter, multiplier, or divider. This is done in special-purpose machines where one or two specific operations are to be performed. A single unit that performs all operations is desirable in a general-purpose computer. Arithmetic units can be constructed that perform all operations by a modification of the addition process. In Chap. 3 it was shown how subtraction can be performed by a process of complementing and adding. Multiplication can be performed by successive additions, and division can be performed by successive subtractions.

This chapter describes the basic requirements of an arithmetic unit and shows how it can perform the four basic operations of addition, subtraction, multiplication, and division. The exact logical operation involved in performing these operations, however, varies from machine to machine. The sample arithmetic unit described in this chapter performs all its operations by addition.

Sample Arithmetic Unit

In order to describe the requirements of an arithmetic unit, a sample arithmetic unit is used. The components of the sample unit are found in most general-purpose computers.

The sample arithmetic unit is a parallel unit having a capacity of

358

four bits. It is capable of adding, subtracting, and multiplying. A block diagram of the sample unit is shown in Fig. 21.1, and a logical diagram is shown in Fig. 21.2. Division is not performed in the sample machine; the number of additional elements required make showing the divide operation impractical. However, after the requirements for division have been discussed, it will not be difficult to visualize the additional components necessary to perform the divide operation.

Block diagram. The block diagram of the sample unit is shown in Fig. 21.1. The block diagram shows a four-bit parallel adder, five registers,

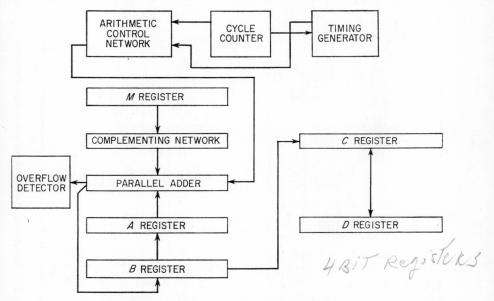

Fig. 21.1 Sample arithmetic unit, block diagram.

a complementing network, an overflow detector, a cycle counter, a timing generator, and a control network. The units shown in the block diagram are the basic ones found in most arithmetic units. The timing generator is not always considered a part of the arithmetic unit but generally is included with the control unit. It is discussed here to aid in illustrating how a sequence of steps required to perform an arithmetic operation is controlled. The purpose of each block is discussed.

Adders. The adders in this sample unit are full adders of the type discussed in Chap. 19. Each adder is capable of accepting the addend, the augend, and a carry from the previous order and producing a sum and a carry output.

Registers. The registers contain all information to be used in an arithmetic operation and the result of the operation. Five registers are

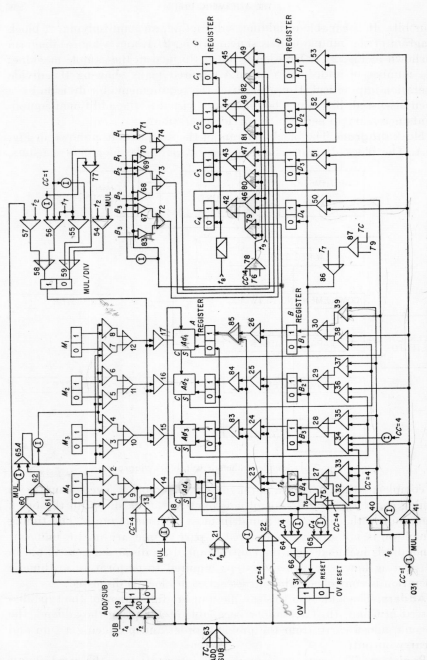

Fig. 21.2 Sample parallel arithmetic unit, logical diagram.

used in this unit. They are the M, A, B, C, and D registers. The M register is the main register. All information taken from the memory passes through the M register. The M, A, and B registers are used for the add and subtract operations. All registers are used for the multiply operation. The gates used to transfer information from one register to another are not shown on the diagram.

Complementing network. A number is applied to the adder in its true or in its complemented form, depending upon the arithmetic operation being performed. A logical diagram of a complementer is shown in Fig. 21.3. The circuit consists of two AND gates and an OR gate. The true

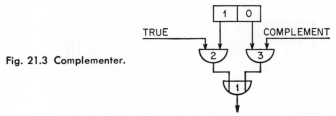

Fig. 21.3 Complementer.

and complement inputs determine whether or not the information bit contained in the M register flip-flop will be complemented. A true input applied to $GA2$ will produce a true output of 1 from the complementer if the flip-flop is in the ONE state. If the complement input is present, there is no output from the complementer when the flip-flop is in the ONE state. If the flip-flop is in the ZERO state when the complement input is present, there will again be a true output from the complementer. A complementing network such as the one discussed here is required for each order in a parallel system. The conditions for a true or a complement input are determined by the control gates for the operation being performed.

Overflow detector. The overflow detector provides an indication when the result of an arithmetic operation exceeds the word length the unit is capable of handling. The word length of the sample machine is four bits. If two numbers are added, it is possible that the number of bits in the sum may exceed four; if this occurs, the overflow detector will provide an output. The output may be used to trigger an alarm, or it may be used by the programmer as a part of the program to stop one sequence of operations and initiate a new sequence. The logical operation of the overflow detector is covered later in the discussion of addition and subtraction as performed by the sample unit.

Cycle counter. It was stated that multiplication and division can be accomplished by a sequence of additions and subtractions. The cycle counter keeps a record of the number of additions and subtractions performed. In this unit, the cycle counter is a down-counter. At the beginning of the multiply operation, the cycle counter is set to the number of add cycles required to complete an operation. At the completion of each add cycle, the count in the counter is reduced by 1. Outputs are taken from the counter, decoded, and applied to control gates so that a completed operation will be indicated. Other gates are also controlled by the cycle counter during the multiply operation, to effect the proper sequence of events.

Timing-pulse generator. The timing for the arithmetic unit is synchronized with the basic timing of the computer. The timing pulses for

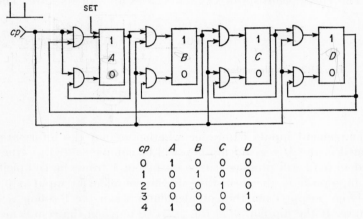

cp	A	B	C	D
0	1	0	0	0
1	0	1	0	0
2	0	0	1	0
3	0	0	0	1
4	1	0	0	0

Fig. 21.4 Four-stage ring counter and timing chart.

the arithmetic unit can be generated by a separate counter, usually a ring counter. The purpose of the counter is to initiate the transfer, clear, shift, and other necessary commands in a definite order so that the desired arithmetic operation can be performed. A ring counter is useful because only one high output is present at any given time from its stages. Each output can be used to initiate a separate operation. A four-stage ring counter is illustrated in Fig. 21.4.

The timing chart in Fig. 21.4 shows that flip-flops A, B, C, and D are set to the ONE state sequentially.

Initially flip-flop A is set to the ONE state, while flip-flops B, C, and D are in the ZERO state. The output from the ONE side of flip-flop A is applied to the ZERO input gate of A and the ONE input of B. The first clock pulse through these gates will set B to the ONE state and reset A to the ZERO state. The second clock pulse sets C to the ONE state and resets B. The third clock pulse sets D to the ONE state and resets C. The ONE output of D is applied to the ONE input gate of A so that the fourth input pulse sets A and resets D.

The actual counter used in the sample arithmetic unit is shown in

Fig. 21.5. It is a 10-stage ring counter used to generate nine pulses numbered t_1 through t_9. The output of the first stage is not used. It may be necessary to use a complete sequence (t_1 through t_9) or only a portion of the sequence (t_6 through t_9). The complete cycle is referred to as a *major cycle* and the abbreviated count is referred to as a *minor cycle*.

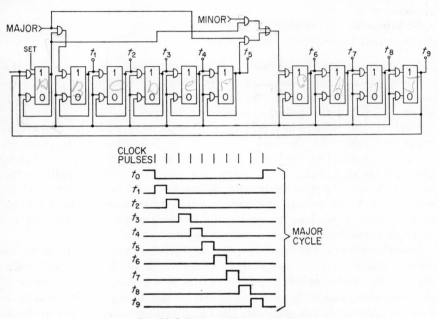

Fig. 21.5 Timing-pulse generator.

The gates controlling the major and minor cycles are shown in Fig. 21.5. The output of A is applied to either B or G, depending upon whether a major-cycle or a minor-cycle control pulse is present. If the output of A is applied to B, the complete count will be generated. If the output of A is applied to G, the partial count will be generated. Minor cycles are used for each successive addition or subtraction in multiply and divide operations where the complete add or subtract sequence of operation does not have to be performed.

Methods of representing positive and negative numbers. Some computers have arrangements for indicating both positive and negative numbers. One popular method of distinguishing between the two is the sign-magnitude notation. In such a notation, the MSD is the sign bit; the remaining digits are the magnitude bits. If the number is positive, the sign bit is a 0. If the number is negative, the sign bit is a 1. For example, $+7$ is written as 0111; -7 is written as 1111. This notation is used in the sample unit. It will be shown that positive and negative numbers are handled differently.

Instructions

The sample arithmetic unit has the following four instructions:

1. Transfer-clear
2. Add
3. Subtract
4. Multiply

Each instruction is generated by the control unit. It is assumed the computer is a single-address computer where the instruction word consists of the command and the memory location of one number upon which an arithmetic operation is to be performed.

Each of the instructions will be explained, first with the block diagram and then with the logical diagram. It is impractical to show all the gates required for each operation, but the essential gates are shown. Once an instruction has been given, it is executed automatically in the arithmetic unit by the arithmetic timing pulses. The number of steps required to carry out an instruction varies from machine to machine. Some of the steps done automatically in the sample machine may require an extra instruction in another machine.

Transfer-clear. The purpose of the transfer-clear operation is to extract a number from the memory and place it in the arithmetic unit. Specifically, the number is placed in the B register. If the number is positive, the magnitude bits are placed in the B register in their true form. If the number is negative, the magnitude bits are placed in the B register in their complemented form.

The reason for placing the operand in the B register can be seen by referring to Fig. 21.1. The two inputs to the adder are the contents of the A register applied directly and the contents of the M register applied through the complementing network. The transfer-clear instruction places the first number in the B register. When an add, subtract, or multiply instruction is generated, the second number is extracted from the memory and placed in the M register. All operations are done by additions. The contents of the B register are transferred to the A register to become an adder input. The B register is cleared, and the result of the operation (sum or difference) is placed back into the B register. If successive additions or subtractions are required, the transfer from the B register to the A register and the placing of the adder results in the B register can be repeated as many times as required.

Operational Steps. The transfer-clear instruction is essentially an add operation. No other number is present in the arithmetic unit at this time; hence the number extracted from the memory is added to 0000 and the sum is placed in the B register. The sequence of steps with respect to the timing pulses follows (refer to the logical diagram in Fig. 21.2).

1. At t_1 time, the transfer-clear level is generated. The level is generated by the control unit, and t_1 senses for its presence. This portion of the operation is not shown. Any instruction level is a pulse that remains present for the entire operational sequence. The pulse is applied to the appropriate gates in the arithmetic unit. These gates are pointed out as the explanation continues.

2. At t_2 time, the add/subtract flip-flop is set to the ZERO state. The transfer-clear level is an input to OR gate 63. The output of $GA63$ is applied to $GA20$. When t_2 occurs, the flip-flop will be set to the ZERO state. The t_2 pulse is also applied to the ZERO-side reset of all the flip-flops in the M register to clear the M register.

3. At t_3 time, the number is extracted from a memory location and placed in the M register. The logic for this operation is not shown. The address of the number to be extracted is a part of the instruction word generated by the control unit. The address portion of the word is sensed and decoded at this time, and the number is extracted.

   When the number is extracted and placed in the M register, the sign bit is sampled to determine whether the number is positive or negative. If the number is negative, the magnitude bits must be complemented. The sign bit is contained in M_4, the most significant flip-flop. Assume that the number is 0011 ($+3$); the bit in M_4 is a 0. The ONE-side output of M_4 is applied to $GA2$ of complementing unit CM_4, and the ZERO-side output is applied to $GA1$. Flip-flop M_4 is in the ZERO state, but there is no output from $GA1$ because the add/subtract flip-flop was reset to the ZERO state by the t_2 pulse. Consequently, there is no output from $GA9$. The output of $GA9$ is applied to the complement control network which consists of $GA60$, $GA61$, and $GA62$. If the number were negative, an output would be generated from $GA62$. Since no output is present from CM_4, no outputs are present at $GA60$ and $GA61$. The output of $GA62$ is applied through $GA65$ and an inverter to CM_3, CM_2, and CM_1. This true level is generated whenever there is no output from the complement control network. The outputs from CM_3, CM_2, and CM_1 are 0, 1, and 1, respectively. The outputs from the complementers are applied to the adders through $GA15$, $GA16$, and $GA17$, which are multiply control gates enabled by the multiply control flip-flop. Pulse t_2 sets this flip-flop to the ONE state. The flip-flop remains in the ONE state during the add and subtract operations.

4. Pulse t_4 is not used during this instruction.

5. Pulse t_5 is not used during this instruction.

6. At t_6 time, the sign and magnitude bits from the B register are both transferred to the A register. The t_6 pulse is applied to $GA23$ through $GA26$. The transfer-clear level is applied to $GA23$ through OR gate 22. If any flip-flop in the B register contained a 1, t_6 would be able to go through the transfer gate and set its associated A flip-flop. $CC = 4$ is a decoded output from the cycle counter that is present when the cycle counter has a count of four. However, the cycle counter is reset to zero during the transfer-clear operation.

Although there is no information present in the B register, the add process is still performed. The contents of the M register are added to all zeros. The sum outputs of Ad_4 through Ad_1 are 0, 0, 1, and 1, respectively.

7. At t_7 time, the B register is cleared.

8. At t_8 time, the sum outputs of the adders are transferred into the B register. The transfer gates from the adders to the B register used during this operation are gates 33, 35, 37, and 39. The sum outputs of Ad_4, Ad_3, Ad_2, and Ad_1 are applied to these gates, respectively. The presence of the transfer-clear level at $GA40$ allows transfer pulse t_8 to set the proper flip-flops. For example, output of Ad_2 is a binary 1; hence, pulse t_8 passes through $GA37$ to set B_2 to the ONE state. The count in the B register is 0011.

9. At t_9 time, the A register is cleared. The operation is complete.

Addition. The operation of the sample unit during the add instruction is essentially the same as during the transfer-clear operation. The description of the add instruction is as follows: Extract the number from its storage location and place it in the M register. Add this number to the number in the B register. Store the sum in the B register. If the sum is positive, store the sum with its magnitude bits complemented.

The operational sequence is the same as the transfer-clear sequence with the exception that the add level is generated at t_1. The control gates that were actuated by the transfer-clear level are actuated by the add level.

Addition of Negative Numbers. Assume that -1 (1001) is to be added to -2 (1010). The number -2 has been placed in the B register, and -1 is to be extracted from the memory. The magnitude bits of the number in the B register are complemented so that -2 is represented as 101. The number -1 will be taken from the memory in its true form (1001) and placed in the M register. The sign bit is sensed and is found to be a negative number. The magnitude bits of the number will be complemented before passing to the adder. When the B-register contents are transferred to the A register, the adder inputs and output are as follows:

M register	1001	
M register complemented	1110	-1
A register	1101	-2
	1, 1011	
	$\rightarrow 1$	end-around carry
Adder output	1100	-3 (magnitude bits complemented)

The sum as a result of adding two negative numbers is a negative number. Observe that the magnitude bits of the sum are complemented.

An end-around-carry operation is shown in the example. Provisions for end-around operation are incorporated in the sample unit. In Fig. 21.2 the carry output from Ad_4 is gated through $GA18$ and applied as a carry input to the LSD adder, Ad_1. $GA18$ is actuated for all except the multiply operation. The presence of a multiply level will inhibit the gate. During addition a carry is generated only if both numbers are negative. The MSD will not change signs as a result of the carry, and the sum will be correct if the word length is not exceeded. If the word length is exceeded, an overflow indication will occur. Overflow is discussed later in the chapter.

Addition of a Positive Number to a Negative Number. It is possible to add a positive number to a negative number. For example, add $+4$ to -3. The adder inputs are as follows:

M register	0100	$+4$
Complementer	0100	
A register	1100	-3
End-around carry	1, 0000	
	$\rightarrow 1$	
Adder	0001	$+1$

Overflow. An overflow condition exists if the sum of two numbers is greater than the maximum number that can be held in the register. In the sample unit the maximum number that can be stored in the machine is ± 7 since only three bits are used for magnitude bits. The possibility of an overflow exists if two positive or two negative numbers are added. An overflow exists if the sign of the sum is different from the sign of the two numbers that are added. Consider the following examples of addition:

1.	$+2$	0010		2.	-2	1101	
	$+3$	0011			-3	1100	
	$+5$	0101	sign does not change		-5	1, 1001	sign does not
						$\rightarrow 1$	change
						1010	
3.	$+4$	0100		4.	-4	1011	
	$+5$	0101			-5	1010	
	$+9$	1001	sign changes, overflow		-9	0101	sign changes, overflow

The equation for an overflow condition is $X_s Y_s \bar{S}_s + \bar{X}_s \bar{Y}_s S_s = OVF$, where X_s and Y_s are the sign bits of the augend and addend and S_s is the sign bit of the sum.

An overflow flip-flop is shown in Fig. 21.2. If one of the conditions described by the equation exists, the flip-flop is set to the ONE state. The overflow-detector network is also used to detect an overflow during subtraction. When subtraction is discussed, it will be seen that the conditions for overflow are the same as for addition.

Subtraction. The subtract instruction is as follows: Extract a number from the memory and place it in the M register. Subtract this number from the number located in the B register.

The same sign notation is used in the subtract operation as in the transfer-clear and add operations. The logical operation of the complementer during the subtract instruction is different from the logical operation during the add instruction.

Subtraction is performed by the complement-and-add method. To illustrate complementing requirements, two problems will be presented. First, $+5$ will be subtracted from 0, and then -5 will be subtracted from 0 as follows:

0	0000	Complement sign and magnitude of	0000
$-(+)5$	0101	subtrahend and add	1010
-5			1010

In the preceding problem both the sign and the magnitude of the subtrahend were complemented so that the result in signed magnitude notation is -5 (1010). Consider the following example:

0	0000	Complement	0000
$-(-)5$	1101	Sign	0101
$+5$			0101

In this problem, only the sign bit is complemented to indicate $+5$. The basic rules for subtraction are:

1. The minuend is placed in the B register as the result of a transfer-clear instruction or a previous operation.
2. The subtrahend is extracted from the memory and applied to the adder by way of the M register and the complementer.
3. If the subtrahend is a positive number, both sign and magnitude bits are complemented.
4. If the subtrahend is a negative number, only the sign bit is complemented.

The subtract sequence with reference to timing pulses is as follows:

1. At t_1 time, the subtract level is generated and applied to the proper gates.

2. At t_2 time, the add/subtract flip-flop is set to the ZERO state. The M register is cleared.
3. At t_3 time, the subtrahend from the memory is entered into the M register.
4. At t_4 time, the add/subtract flip-flop is set to the ONE state. The ONE-side output of the flip-flop is applied to the ZERO input gate of the sign complementer, thereby complementing the sign bit of the number in the M register. Assume that the number in the M register is -4 (1100). According to subtraction rule 4, only the sign bit is complemented. There is no output from the complementer at this time, indicating a binary 0. Since there is no output from the magnitude complementer, there is no output from complement control gate 62, and the magnitude bits remain in their true form.
5. At t_5 time, no operation occurs.
6. At t_6 time, the sign and magnitude bits are transferred from the B register to the A register.
7. At t_7 time, the B register is cleared and overflow is sensed. (The overflow condition is discussed later.)
8. At t_8 time, the contents of the adder are transferred to the B register through $GA35$, $GA37$, and $GA39$.
9. At t_9 time, the A register is cleared.

Overflow. Overflow may occur during subtraction when positive and negative numbers are involved. Consider the following examples:

1.	$+6$	0110	A register
	$(-)-5$	0101	output of complementer
	11	1011	only the sign is complemented
2.	-6	1001	A register (magnitude bits complemented)
	$-(+)5$	1010	output of complementer (both sign and magnitude
	-11	1 0011	complemented)
		→1	
		0100	

In both examples the sign bit of the difference is the opposite of the sign bits of the minuend and subtrahend. The overflow conditions that apply to adders also apply to subtracters. The conditions are again $X_s Y_s \bar{A}_s + \bar{X}_s \bar{Y}_s A_s$, where X_s and Y_s are the sign bits of subtrahend and minuend, respectively, and A_s is the sign-bit output of the adder.

Multiplication. Binary multiplication with paper and pencil must be discussed before the operation of the arithmetic unit is described.

Binary multiplication rules using 1s and 0s are almost too simple to warrant mention. The rules are as follows:

$$0 \times 0 = 0 \quad 1 \times 0 = 0 \quad 1 \times 1 = 1$$

Binary numbers may be multiplied as in decimal notation. For example, multiply 3 × 3 as follows:

$$
\begin{array}{l}
011 \\
011 \\
\hline
011 \quad \text{first partial product} \\
011 \quad \text{second partial product} \\
\hline
1001
\end{array}
$$

Although this operation is simple to perform with paper and pencil, it is difficult to mechanize in a computer. A number involving three or more digits involves adding three numbers. The adder is capable of adding only two numbers at a time. Another difficulty is that two or more carries may be generated in an order.

A crude, but nevertheless correct, method is to add the multiplicand to itself the number of times specified by the multiplier. For example, if 115 were to be multiplied by 23, the number 115 could be successively added 23 times. A shorter method is to add 115 three times as indicated by the units digit of the multiplier. The tens digit of the multiplier indicates that 20 more additions are to be performed; however, the multiplicand digit may be shifted left one place with respect to the accumulated sum before being added to itself. Shifting the multiplicand digit to the left is equivalent to multiplication by 10. Hence, 115 must be added only twice and shifted left to satisfy the required 20 additions. This is, of course, the reason for shifting while doing multiplication in longhand. The problem is illustrated in tabular form. The partial product (the sum of the first three additions) is shifted to the right instead of the multiplicand being shifted to the left, as follows:

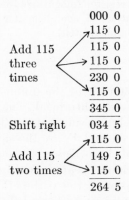

$$
\begin{array}{ll}
 & 000\ 0 \\
 & 115\ 0 \\
\text{Add 115} & 115\ 0 \\
\text{three} & 115\ 0 \\
\text{times} & 230\ 0 \\
 & 115\ 0 \\
\hline
 & 345\ 0 \\
\text{Shift right} & 034\ 5 \\
 & 115\ 0 \\
\text{Add 115} & 149\ 5 \\
\text{two times} & 115\ 0 \\
\hline
 & 264\ 5
\end{array}
$$

The computer multiplies in much the same manner. When binary multiplication is performed, the multiplicand is added if the multiplier digit is a 1. If the multiplier digit is a 0, no addition is performed. The accumulated sum is shifted right once for each order of the multiplier. This method of multiplication is termed the *accumulator method*. The product is formed as a result of repeated additions. An accumulator consists of an adder unit and a register. In the sample arithmetic unit, the B and C registers are the accumulator registers for the multiply operation.

Assume that 0110 is to be multiplied by 0101. The multiplicand 0110 is contained in the M register, and the multiplier is contained in the C register. It will be shown that the multiplier bits are shifted out of the C register and the product that is the result of accumulated additions is held in the B and C registers. Table 21.1 shows the contents of the B and C registers (the M register is not shown).

Table 21.1

	B	C	
Initial	0000	0101	
Add 0110	0110	0101	
Shift	0011	0010	
Add 0000	0011	0010	
Shift	0001	1001	
Add 0110	0111	1001	
Shift	0011	1100	
Add 0000	0011	1100	
Shift	0001	1110	correct product

Initially the B register is reset to zero, and the multiplier is contained in the C register. The least significant bit (LSB) of the multiplier is sensed to determine whether addition should occur. After each sense-and-add sequence, the contents of the B and C registers are shifted right one place. The LSD in the C register is lost at each shift. This is of no consequence since this bit has been used. After the last bit of the multiplier has been sensed and the shift operation performed, the product is contained in the B and C registers.

The data flow can be followed in Fig. 21.2. The bits in the MSD position of the two numbers are the sign bits. In this example both numbers are positive. It is necessary to determine whether the product is a positive or a negative number. To do this, the sign bits alone are added and the result is stored in the MSD position of the B register. After this initial addition, the most significant position of the B register is no longer used. Only the magnitude bits accumulated in the B register are added. If two negative numbers had been added, the sum placed in the B register would have been 0, which indicates a positive product.

The steps involved in the multiply process are as follows:

1. Transfer the contents from the memory to the M register.
2. Transfer both sign and magnitude of the B register to the C register. Transfer the sign bit of the B register to the A register and clear the B register. At this time the contents of the registers are as follows:

$$
\begin{array}{llll}
M & 0110 & & \\
A & 0000 & C & 0101 \\
B & 0000 & D & 0000
\end{array}
$$

3. Add the sign bit of the M register to the sign bit of the B register. Store the sum in the most significant bit (MSB) position of the B register.
4. Sense the LSB of the C register; if it is a 1, add the magnitude bits of the M register to the magnitude bits of the B register. Since the LSB is a 1, the add sequence is performed. The contents of the adders are transferred to the B register shifted right one place: Ad_4 is placed in B_3, Ad_3 is placed in B_2, etc. The LSB of the adder (Ad_1) is placed in D_4. The contents of the C register are shifted by transferring the contents of the C register shifted right one place into the D register and then transferring the contents of the D register back to the C register.
5. The LSB of the C register is again sensed. This time it is a 0. The mechanics for addition are carried out each time. However, when the multiplier bit is a 0, the contents of the M register are prevented from being applied to the adder; hence, the magnitude bits in the B register are added to 0000. The shift-and-add sequence is repeated until all multiplier bits have been sensed. The MSB of the C register is a sign bit. If the bit were a 1, it would be treated as a 0 so that no extra addition occurs. The shift is performed.

Sequence 1. The multiply operation is now discussed with reference to the logical diagram (Fig. 21.2). The operational sequence is done with reference to the timing pulses.

1. At t_1 time, the multiply level is generated.
2. At t_2 time, the multiply control flip-flop is set to the ZERO state. The cycle counter is set to 4. The cycle counter is a down-counter used to keep track of the number of add sequences the computer must perform. The multiplier has four digits; therefore, four add sequences must be performed. At the completion of each add sequence the cycle counter is stepped, and the count is reduced by 1.
3. At t_3 time, the number is transferred from the memory to the M register.
4. At t_4 time, no operation occurs.

5. At t_5 time, no operation occurs.
6. At t_6 time, the sign bit is transferred from the B register to the A register. Both sign and magnitude bits are transferred to the C register. The count of four is decoded from the cycle counter and is applied to $GA22$ in the B-to-A transfer network (input $CC = 4$). The inverted signal is applied to $GA24, GA25, GA26$. When t_6 occurs, the sign bit in B_4 is tranferred to A_4 and C_4; the magnitude bits are transferred to the C register. $GA24, GA25,$ and $GA26$ in the B-to-A transfer network are inhibited; hence, no transfer may occur. The t_2 pulse resets the add/subtract flip-flop to the ZERO state, thus preventing the magnitude bits of the M register from being applied to the adder. The presence of $CC = 4$ allows only the MSD of the M register to be applied to the adder. If both sign bits were 1, the end-around carry to the LSD adder would be prevented by the presence of the multiply instruction at $GA18$.
7. At t_7 time, the B and D registers are cleared. The LSB in the C register is sensed. This is the first multiplier digit. If LSB is a 1, the magnitude bits of the M register are to be applied to the adder. If the LSD is a 0, the magnitude bits will continue to be inhibited. The multiplier bit is a 1; hence, $GA56$ is enabled to allow t_7 to set the multiply control flip-flop to the ONE state. The magnitude bits of the multiplicand are applied to the adder. The adder inputs and output are as follows:

M	0110
A	0000
Adder output	0110

The sign bits have been added, and the initial sensing and adding of the multiplicand has occurred.

8. At t_8 time, the sign bit from the adder is transferred into B_4. The sum magnitude bits are transferred into the B register shifted one place to the right.

The multiply level at $GA41$ in the adder-to-B-register transfer network allows transfer pulse t_8 to pass. The output of Ad_4 is applied to $GA32, GA33,$ and $GA34$. The count of four in the cycle counter enables $GA32$ if the sign bit is a 1. The cycle-counter output inhibits $GA34$. Thus, for the first operation the sign bit is applied only to B_4. B_3 receives no output at all from the adder during the first transfer.

The output of Ad_3 is applied to B_2 through $GA36$. Ad_2 is applied to B_1 through $GA38$, and Ad_4 is applied to D_4 through $GA50$. The information is transferred from the adder shifted right one place, and the LSB of the adder is placed in the MSD position of the D register. The C_4 output of the C register is applied to D_3, and each subsequent output is shifted right.

9. At t_{8d} time, a delayed t_8 pulse clears the C register.
10. At t_9 time, the contents of the D register are transferred unshifted into the C register. The A register is cleared. The cycle counter is stepped from a count of four to a count of three. The first add-and-shift sequence has now been completed.

Sequence 2. Only a portion of the sequence needs to be repeated to sense the next multiplier digit. The ring counter will start counting at t_6 instead of t_1. This operation was discussed previously. Although not shown, the minor-cycle level is controlled by the cycle counter. The ring counter counts a minor cycle as long as the cycle counter does not contain a count of four or zero. The minor-cycle operation is as follows:

1. At t_6 time, the magnitude bits of the B register are transferred to the A register. The absence of $CC = 4$ allows the transfer of the magnitude bits from the B register to the A register but prevents the transfer of the bits from the B register to the C register.
2. At t_7 time, C_1 is sensed. The 0 in C_1 resets the multiply flip-flop. The magnitude bits in the M register are removed from the adder input since $GA15$, $GA16$, and $GA17$ are no longer enabled. The sign bit M_4 is also prevented from entering the register. Since the cycle counter no longer has a count of four, $GA14$ is inhibited.

The adder inputs and output are as follows:

M	0000
A	0011
Adder output	0011

3. At t_8 time, the transfer-shift operation is repeated as described. Since the cycle counter does not have a count of four, the sum output of Ad_4 cannot be transferred to B_4. The output can be transferred to B_3 through $GA34$. The other adder outputs are shifted right as previously described. The contents of the C register are transferred and shifted right into D.
4. At t_{8d} time, the delayed t_8 pulse clears the C register.
5. At t_9 time, the contents of the D register are transferred to the C register. The cycle counter is stepped to 2.

The second sequence is completed. The contents of the B and C registers are as follows:

B	C
0001	1001

Sequence 3. The sequence is repeated for the third multiplier digit. C_1 contains a 1; hence, the magnitude bits of the M register are added to the contents in the B register, and a shift is performed. The adder inputs and output are as follows:

$$
\begin{array}{ll}
M & 0110 \\
A & 0001 \\
\hline
\text{Sum} & 0111
\end{array}
$$

At the end of the transfer-shift sequence, the contents of the B and C registers are as follows:

$$
\begin{array}{cc}
B & C \\
0011 & 1100
\end{array}
$$

The cycle counter is set to 1.

Sequence 4. The three magnitude bits of the multiplier have been sensed and shifted. The 0 contained in C_1 is the sign bit of the multiplier that was originally placed in C_4. The sign bit of the multiplier should not be considered as a multiplier bit. The $CC = 1$ output of the cycle counter is applied, through an inverter, to the ONE input gate of the multiply control flip-flop. The $CC = 1$ input then allows the flip-flop to be set to the ZERO state.

The contents of the B and C registers at the end of the sequence are as follows:

$$
\begin{array}{cc}
B & C \\
0011 & 1110 \\
\text{Sign} & \text{Magnitude}
\end{array}
$$

Multiplication of Negative Numbers. The logical diagram does not show all the gates necessary to multiply by a negative number. If the multiplier originally contained in the B register were a negative number, the magnitude bits would be complemented. The magnitude bits will have to be changed to their true form before being sent to the C register.

Roundoff. The word length of the product usually exceeds the capability of the machine. Usually a roundoff procedure is used, and only the bits in the B register are used since they are the MSBs. Usually if the number in the C register is 1000 or more, a 1 is added to the LSB in the B registers. Some computers add the 1 regardless of the contents of the B register. It must be remembered, of course, that a practical computer has a word length much longer than four bits; hence, the bits lost during roundoff do not have so much significance as the bits in the sample machine.

Division. The division process involves more details than the multiply operation. An examination of the division process shows the requirements of the arithmetic unit. The pencil-and-paper method of binary addition is discussed, and then it will be shown how this process is mechanized in a computer.

Binary division can be done by the longhand method in the same manner as decimal division. For example, divide 15 by 5 as follows:

$$
\begin{array}{r} 3 \\ 5\overline{)15} \end{array}
\qquad
\begin{array}{r} 11 \\ 101\overline{)1111} \\ \underline{101} \\ 101 \\ \underline{101} \end{array}
$$

Division can also be performed by successive subtraction. For example, 15 may be divided by 5 by subtracting 5 from 15 and successively subtracting 5 from the differences until 0 or a negative remainder is reached. The quotient is equal to the number of subtractions performed. The process is shown as follows in decimal and binary systems:

15		1111	
5	first subtraction	101	first subtraction
10		1010	
5	second subtraction	101	second subtraction
5		101	
5	third subtraction	101	third subtraction
0		000	

There is no apparent way, except by visual inspection, of indicating in binary the number of subtractions performed. The computer can obtain its quotient in binary by using the following rules:

1. Each time a subtraction leaves a positive remainder, a 1 is placed in the quotient.
2. Each time a subtraction leaves a negative remainder, a 0 is placed in the quotient.
3. The remainder is shifted left one place with respect to the divisor after each subtraction.

With these rules, the sample problem will again be solved, as follows:

Dividend	1111	*Quotient*
Divisor	1010	1
Remainder	0101	
Shift remainder left	1010	
	1010	
	0000	1

If this method of subtraction is compared closely with the longhand method, it will be seen that the relative positions of the divisor and the dividend are the same in both examples. In the longhand method, 101 is first divided into 111 (the three MSBs in the dividend). In the successive-subtraction method, 101 is subtracted first from the three MSDs since they are divisible by 101.

Since the divisor is smaller in value than the first three digits, the first quotient bit is a 1.

In the longhand method the remainder as a result of the first subtraction is 10, and the next dividend digit is brought down so that the remainder is 101. The divisor is divided into this remainder, and the result is, of course, 1. In the successive-subtraction method, the same relative position of the divisor and the remainder must be maintained. Hence, the remainder is shifted left one place before the next subtraction is performed. Since the divisor is not larger than the remainder, the quotient bit is again 1.

Handling of Negative Remainders. In the previous example, no 0 was generated in the quotient. The following examples will illustrate what steps must be taken when a 0 is generated. Divide 45 by 9 as follows:

$$
\begin{array}{r}
101 \\
1001\overline{)101101} \\
1001 \\
\hline
1001 \\
1001 \\
\hline
\end{array}
$$

It is seen by inspection that bringing down the next digit will result in a remainder smaller than the divisor; hence, a 0 is placed in the quotient. When the next digit is brought down, the remainder is not smaller than the divisor.

The successive-subtraction method is now illustrated as follows:

		Quotient
	101101	
Subtract	100100	
	001001	1
Shift	010010	
	100100	
	101110	0
Restore-add	100100	
	010010	
Shift	100100	
	100100	1

The result of the first subtraction is a positive number. This remainder is shifted left but is still smaller than the divisor. If subtraction were performed, a negative number would result. A computer has no way of knowing that the divisor is smaller than the remainder until subtraction has been performed. One indication is that the highest order will require a borrow. This excess borrow is termed an *overdraw*.

When an improper subtraction is performed, it is necessary to restore the remainder to its original value before the next dividend is used. To accomplish this, the divisor is added to the remainder before the next shift occurs.

Mechanization of the Division Process. The division process is a series of subtractions, shift-left operations, and (when necessary) additions. Some difficulties arise in the division process that did not arise in the multiply process. These difficulties and the means of solving them are now discussed.

Start of Division Process. The initial problem is to determine the correct position of the divisor with respect to the dividend. If a binary 25 were divided by a binary 5, the relative positions would be as follows:

$$11001$$
$$10100$$

However, if the divisor were a binary 7, the positions would have to be shown as in the following example:

$$11001$$
$$01110$$

One method of solving this problem is to align the MSBs of the dividend and the divisor and then subtract. If an overdraw occurs in this initial subtraction, the relative positions are incorrect, and an additional order of the dividend must be used.

To obtain the proper order, a restore-add operation is performed, and the divisor is shifted one place to the right. Subtraction is repeated. If no overdraw occurs, the order is correct.

Detection of Overdraw. Another problem is to determine when an overdraw occurs. The detection may be done with a bistable device. If logical subtracters are used in the arithmetic unit, a borrow indication from the MSD order could set the binary device to a chosen state to indicate that an overdraw has occurred.

Subtraction is usually done by complementing and adding as described earlier in the chapter. Whenever the subtrahend is smaller than the minuend, an end-around carry will be developed when the subtrahend is complemented and added to the minuend. No carry will be developed if the minuend is larger than the subtrahend. The absence of a carry indicates that an overdraw has occurred.

In Fig. 21.6 a carry allows an overdraw control flip-flop to be set to the ONE state when a sample pulse occurs. The absence of a carry will allow the flip-flop to be reset to the ZERO state. The state of the flip-flop determines whether the following sequence is to be a subtract sequence or a restore-add sequence.

Storing of Quotients. When a successful subtraction is performed, a 1 must be placed in the quotient. When an unsuccessful subtraction is encountered, a 0 must be placed in the quotient. The quotient bits may be stored in a shift register whose input is controlled by the overdraw detect circuit as shown in Fig. 21.7.

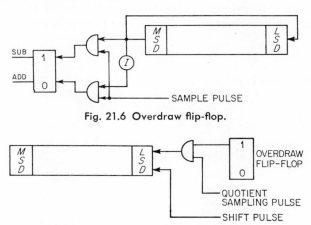

Fig. 21.6 Overdraw flip-flop.

Fig. 21.7 Quotient register and controls.

A quotient sampling pulse will allow a 1 to be placed in the least significant position of the shift register if the overdraw flip-flop is in the ONE state as a result of a previous successful subtraction. A subsequent shift pulse will shift the bit into the next position. The sequence is repeated after each subtract sequence.

Final Remainder. In the previous examples the final remainder was 0. Of course, this is not always the case. Consider the following example in which 22 is divided by 5:

$$
\begin{array}{r}
100.011 = 4\tfrac{3}{8} \\
101\overline{)10110\ 000} \\
\underline{101} \\
10\ 00 \\
\underline{01\ 01} \\
110 \\
\underline{101}
\end{array}
$$

The digits to the right of the decimal point have values of 2^{-1}, 2^{-2}, 2^{-3}, etc. The remainder here is equal to $2^{-2} + 2^{-3} = \tfrac{1}{4} + \tfrac{1}{8} = \tfrac{3}{8}$. The division process may be repeated as many times as necessary to produce the desired accuracy.

Scaling. To be versatile, a computer must be able to handle a wide range of numbers. One method of handling numbers is known as *scaling*. In this method all numbers in a computer are treated in a manner similar to the power-of-10 notation; that is, $2 \times 10^2 = 200$, $1.5 \times 10^3 = 1,500$, etc. It is customary to place numbers in a computer with decimal points to the extreme left of the magnitude bits and then assign the appropriate power. Some of the digits in the number may be used to indicate the power of the number. In a binary machine the power of 2, rather than the power of 10, is used. A binary 25 may be written as 0.11001×2^5. The number is now a fraction ($^{25}/_{32}$) to be multiplied by

$$2^5 : {}^{25}/_{32} \times 32 = 25.$$

When a problem is programmed, the exponents have to be accounted for just as a person would keep track of them when using a slide rule. The exponents have to be the same before addition and subtraction may be done. The exponents have to be added during multiplication and subtracted during division. Computers that use scaling have provisions for shifting right and shifting left.

Summary

This chapter has shown the principles of operation of arithmetic units by utilizing a sample machine as a pattern. The basic blocks that comprise an arithmetic unit are adders, registers, complementers, and transfer networks. The cycle counter, ring counter, and control gates may be considered as part of the control unit rather than the arithmetic unit. They were discussed here to show how they are used with arithmetic units.

The specific details of the timing sequence and the number of steps vary widely from machine to machine. However, the requirements are the same.

Arithmetic units may operate in series as well as in parallel. The serial-type unit operates upon each bit sequentially. Serial units were not discussed here. However, it is not difficult to visualize how serial operations may be mechanized. An explanation of the serial adder is given in Chap. 20.

QUESTIONS

21.1 What is the basic arithmetic operation of the arithmetic unit?

21.2 Which registers are used by the sample arithmetic unit in the multiply operation?

21.3 What would be the appearance of -5 stored in the memory?

21.4 When is the complementing network used?

21.5 For which arithmetic operations does the timing-pulse generator produce minor cycles?

21.6 Describe the general operation of the arithmetic unit at time intervals t_1 through t_9 when -4 is added to $+3$.

21.7 Describe the sequence of events when -4 is multiplied by $+3$ in the arithmetic unit.

22

Computer Memory Systems

The purpose of the memory system in a digital computer is twofold: (1) to provide adequate storage for all data and instructions necessary for the solution of a given problem and (2) to make this information available when needed by the data-processing units. To accomplish this, the memory system must include at least two basic elements: a storage unit, or memory, to hold the data to be processed and a selection mechanism to gain access to each memory location within the storage unit. Memory systems differ chiefly in the number and type of basic elements used.

The most important characteristics of any memory system are access speed and storage capacity. These characteristics are governed primarily by the type of storage unit employed in the system. The ideal storage unit would have a large storage capacity, adequate, for example, to store the complete accounting records of a large business organization. In addition, the unit would permit access to any one of its storage locations within a time interval measured in microseconds. A high access speed is necessary if maximum advantage is to be taken of the high-speed components located in other parts of the computer. Unfortunately, no single memory unit available today offers optimum characteristics with regard to both storage capacity and access speed. In general, a storage unit with a large capacity has an inherently long access time. For this reason, memory systems in most modern computers include several different types of storage units arranged in a system to facilitate maximum computing speed. Generally, a low-speed, high-capacity external memory is combined with a medium-speed, medium-capacity buffer memory and a high-speed, low-capacity main memory.

Optimum Memory System

One possible arrangement that could be used to achieve maximum computing speed when large quantities of data must be handled is shown in Fig. 22.1. In the system shown, a magnetic-tape unit is used for bulk storage of reference data. While this unit has a large storage

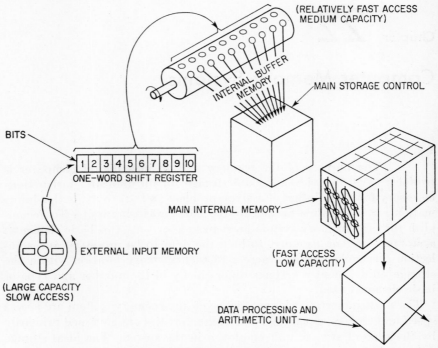

Fig. 22.1 Typical memory system.

capacity, it is difficult to design tape transport mechanisms to provide rapid access to specific memory locations; for this reason, such units are seldom used as the main internal memory of the computer. In the system shown in Fig. 22.1, the main memory is a magnetic-core storage device characterized by its exceptionally high access speed. The memory unit allows the arithmetic unit in the computer to gain rapid access to any desired word in its storage locations whenever the data is needed for computation. The magnetic-core memory, however, has a relatively low storage capacity and must be supplemented or "backed up" by a medium-speed, medium-capacity buffer memory. The buffer memory shown in the illustration is a rotating magnetic drum. The system operates as described in the following paragraphs.

All data and instructions necessary for the solution of a given problem are prerecorded on the tape as a series of coded words 10 digits in length. The information is stored on the tape in digit-serial, word-serial form (see Fig. 22.2a). For illustration purposes, assume that 1 million 10-digit words are stored on the tape. (This is well within the storage capacity of a 2,400-ft reel.) Assume further that the storage capacity of the main

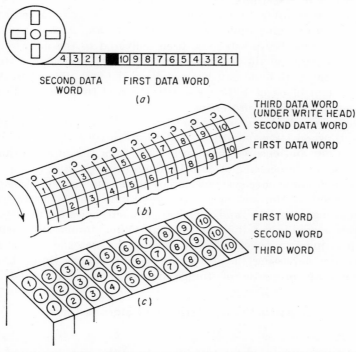

SECOND DATA WORD   FIRST DATA WORD

(a)

THIRD DATA WORD
(UNDER WRITE HEAD)
SECOND DATA WORD
FIRST DATA WORD

(b)

FIRST WORD
SECOND WORD
THIRD WORD

(c)

Fig. 22.2 Modes of storage. (a) Tape storage: digit-serial, word-serial. (b) Drum storage: digit-parallel, word-serial. (c) Magnetic-core storage: digit-parallel, word-serial.

core memory is 100 words and the capacity of the magnetic drum is 1,000 words.

Before computation can begin, the main memory must contain 100 words. These words are delivered from the tape to the main memory by way of the one-word shift register and the rotating drum or buffer memory.

The digits of each data word are shifted into the shift register from the tape unit in serial form (one digit at a time). When one complete word is contained in the shift register, it is transferred in parallel to the first memory location on the rotating drum (Fig. 22.2b). Words are continually transferred in this manner until all the data on the tape has been processed. Although the drum rotates at a faster speed than the tape, timing pulses from the computer's control circuits ensure that words from the tape are transferred to sequential locations on the drum.

When the 101st word is transferred to the drum, the first word previously transferred to the drum is delivered from the drum to the main memory. In the system shown, the words are delivered to the main memory in blocks of 100 words. The transfer in this case is at a much faster rate than the transfer from the tape to the drum, and the information is transferred in digit-parallel, word-serial form (Fig. 22.2c).

When the first 100 words have been delivered to the main memory, inhibiting circuits in the storage control unit prevent further transfers until after the arithmetic unit has processed the first 100 words. At that time a second block of 100 words is transferred from the drum to the main memory cores for processing.

A system employing a buffer memory greatly increases the speed of processing when large quantities of data are involved. The buffer acts as a reservoir and ensures that words flow from the tape continuously even during the processing of data by the arithmetic unit.

Most modern memory systems employ some combination of magnetic-tape, magnetic-drum, and magnetic-core storage units. For this reason the operating principles and physical characteristics of these storage units are covered in detail in this chapter. Other storage units using different principles are covered briefly to show the states of the art in this field. Before discussing the details of specific storage units, however, some important properties of storage units in general are discussed.

Important Characteristics of Storage Units

The capacity of a storage unit can be expressed in terms of the maximum number of bits, characters, or words that may be stored within the medium.

Storage units of small capacity, such as flip-flop storage registers, are usually rated according to their bit capacity. For example, a storage register with 36 flip-flops is capable of storing 36 single binary digits and is, therefore, said to have a capacity of 36 bits.

When the storage capacity of larger memory devices such as magnetic tapes and drums is described, the character or word capacity, rather than the bit capacity, is given. In such cases the number of bits in a character or the number of bits in a word must be stated if an intelligent comparison is to be made between storage media of different types.

Typical storage characteristics of commonly used storage units are listed in Table 22.1. The storage capacity of each unit is stated in characters. To determine the bit capacity, multiply the figures given by 6.

Modes of access. The bits of information stored in a memory unit are combined to form words of a specific bit length. Each word contains the same number of bits and is assigned a location number within the storage unit which is known as its address. The mode of access refers to the method used in the memory system to gain access to these storage locations, or addresses. The mode of access of the memory system is determined by the address-selection mechanism employed with the memory unit. The mode of access may be either random or sequential.

Random access refers to the ability of the memory system to provide immediate access to any memory location without regard to its physical position relative to other locations in the storage unit. In the random-access mode of operation, any memory location can be addressed in the same amount of time as any other location. Magnetic-core memories are usually operated in the random-access mode.

Sequential access indicates a one-after-the-other process. Memory locations on magnetic-tape units are usually addressed in this manner. This is the way it works: Each memory location passes the read and write heads in turn, but information is read out only when the proper address has been reached in the progression. This can be a relatively short period of time if the information required is near the previous address, but can be extremely long if the next location addressed is at the other end of a 3,600-ft reel of magnetic tape.

Sequential-access systems can be further classified into two groups: cyclic and progressive.

The cyclic mode of access is a sequential mode in which each memory location is available for selection at periodic intervals. Examples of this type of access include magnetic drums, tape loops, and delay lines.

The progressive mode of access, like the cyclic mode, is sequential in nature. But, where the cyclic system implies constant movement in one direction to get the periodic return of a piece of information, the progressive system is usually associated with stops and starts and is thus a bidirectional device. Examples of progressive access are magnetic tape (in reels), punched cards, and punched tape.

Table 22.1 shows the differences between the various memory media.

Access time. A discussion of the modes of access naturally leads to the determination of access time. Access time is defined as the time interval between the instant information is requested and the instant it becomes available. It is this time interval which scientists are constantly trying to decrease to speed up the memory systems.

In memory systems using the random-access method, the time interval will be the same for the addressing of any location of the memory medium.

Sequential-access systems, however, will have a different access time

Table 22.1 Characteristics of Typical Memory Media

Storage device	Typical capacity, characters	Access time, μsec	Modes of access	Volatile	Permanence	Use
Magnetic cores	10–100,000	1–10	Random	No	Erasable	High-speed internal storage
Magnetic drums	20–2,000,000	10–100	Sequential and cyclic	No	Erasable	Medium-speed internal storage
Magnetic-tape reels	2–20,000,000*	1–100‡	Sequential and progressive	No	Erasable	Slow-speed external storage
Delay lines	5–10,000	1–10	Sequential and cyclic	Yes	Erasable	Medium-speed internal storage
Electrostatic tubes	5–50,000	1–20	Random	Yes	Erasable	High-speed internal storage
Punched cards	80–90†	50–150	Sequential and progressive	No	Nonerasable	Low-speed external storage

* Per reel.
† Per card.
‡ Seconds.

for each piece of information from any given starting point. It is in this system that access time is given in maximum, minimum, and average times. The maximum access time is the longest amount of time required to obtain an item of information. As an example, in the magnetic drum the maximum access time is associated with that memory location which has just passed by the read heads and must make a complete revolution before again coming under the read heads. Minimum access time would be the shortest possible time needed to obtain the information. This can be seen in the magnetic drum as the next piece of information to pass under the read head. The average access time is the mean between the minimum and the maximum.

Permanence. This characteristic specifies whether or not information in storage may be erased. A magnetic memory is erasable since any word can be changed or deleted without altering the memory medium. In a nonerasable memory the information cannot be altered without replacing the component used as a memory medium. Examples of nonerasable memories are punched cards and punched tape.

Volatility. If information in the memory system is lost when power is removed, the memory system is said to be volatile. A delay line is a volatile medium, and in order to retain the information it must be periodically rewritten. If a power loss should occur, the information would be lost. Any magnitized memory system is a nonvolatile memory in that it does not lose its information except by being demagnetized.

Cost. A very important factor to any consumer is the cost of a computer. The memory system and its associated circuitry is the most expensive part of a computer. When costs of memory systems are being compared, the point of reference is the cost per character of information. Vacuum tubes are considered the most expensive storage medium, costing approximately $60 per character. Magnetic tapes are generally the least expensive, costing less than 1 cent per character stored.

Physical considerations. Many physical characteristics are involved in choosing a memory system. Depending on the point of view, some may be very important while others will make no particular difference in the final selection. The physical considerations include bulk, air-conditioning requirements, and power consumption.

Magnetic-drum Storage

Physical characteristics. A magnetic drum consists of a nonmagnetic-base cylinder, usually manufactured of aluminum because of its paramagnetic characteristics and good heat dissipation. This cylinder is precision-milled to exactly specified dimensions. The diameters of drums vary from 2 in. to 4 ft, and their length varies from $\frac{1}{4}$ in. to 3 ft. Presently there are three commercial methods of applying the magnetic surface to the aluminum base. One method is to dip or spray the aluminum surface with red or black iron oxide (Fe_2O_3 or Fe_3O_4). Red oxide is preferred because of its lower coercive force. Another method is to wrap the drum surface closely with ferromagnetic wire and then mill the surface flat. This method is the easiest way of obtaining certain other magnetic properties not present in the iron oxides. The third method of magnetic-surface preparation is to electroplate the surface with a ferromagnetic alloy. This method has the widest use because of the slightly better magnetic properties produced by electroplating.

The drum is usually formed directly on a shaft, and the shaft is turned to produce the drum rotation. This shaft can be directly connected to the rotor of a drive motor, or it can be belt-driven by an adjacent motor. The drum read and write heads are located close to the drum surface.

Displacement of read and write heads. The direct contact of heads with the drum surface would produce the largest output and hence the least chance for error. However, this situation would cause great friction and the drum would have only a short life. Therefore, the heads are placed approximately 0.001 to 0.002 in. from the drum surface. Care must be taken in the placement of the heads to ensure that drum expansion due to heat will not fill this space and cause lacerations of the magnetic coating. For this reason the heads are usually placed in position after the drum has reached its operating temperature. Sufficient time, therefore, should be allowed for the drum to reach its operating temperature before operations ensue.

The space between the drum surface and the heads is a major factor in determining the area occupied by the 1s and 0s on the surface.

In general it can be stated that the capacity of a drum depends on the surface area, but an important factor to be taken into consideration is the head separation. In moving the heads slightly away from the drum surface, tightly spaced bits are caused to interact with each other, and the interaction produces erroneous information read-outs.

The bit density around the circumference of the drum ranges from 50 to 120 bits to the inch per channel. A channel is a ring around the drum controlled by at least one read-write head.

The number of channels a drum is capable of handling depends on several factors to be considered at the design point. Some compromise must be reached between the storage capacity, the signal amplitude, and the reliability of the system to determine the channel spacing. Normally, this spacing is from 15 to 30 channels per inch. Figure 22.3 illustrates the writing technique used to place information on a magnetic surface.

Construction of read and write heads. Read and write heads have similiar construction. In fact, in many applications one head performs both functions, with external switching circuits controlling the input and output. Figure 22.4 illustrates the operation of a typical read-write head. At specific intervals this head is pulsed in one direction or the other, and a binary 1 or 0 is written.

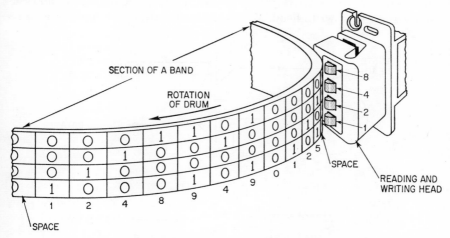

Fig. 22.3 Drum memory—reading and writing.

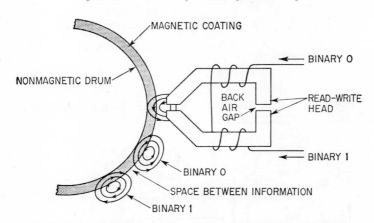

Fig. 22.4 Typical drum recording channel with a read-write head.

The head itself is constructed with an air gap in both the front end and the back end to reduce hysteresis loss. Read and write heads have very low retentivity. Some manufacturers place a paramagnetic shim between the outer poles in write heads to increase the outward deflection of the flux lines which would in turn induce a higher flux density on the drum surface.

Placement of heads. The read and write heads can be placed in varying positions over the drum. The spacing between read and write heads determines the delay or storage time of the drum. Figure 22.5a shows a 90° displacement between the write head and the read head. This system would have a relatively short storage time. Figure 22.5b shows a combination read-write head. With this combination, the minimum stor-

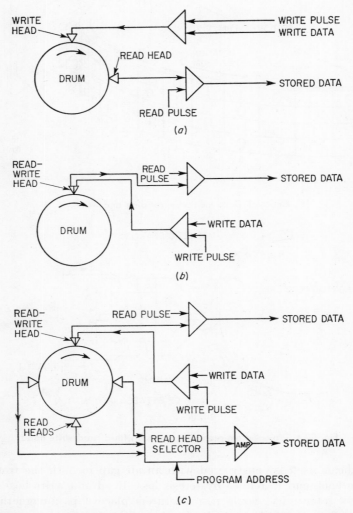

Fig. 22.5 Some variations of head placement in magnetic-drum storage techniques. (a) 90° displacement between read and write head. (b) Combination read-write head. (c) Single combination read-write head and three read heads.

age time extends to one revolution. Figure 22.5c shows a single writing device and four reading devices on one channel. A selection system is used to address a read head so that varying storage times may be obtained. The minimum read-out time will be the time it takes for the drum to turn one-quarter revolution.

Only minimum times have been given in the preceding examples. The maximum time can also vary, but the description of the process is too

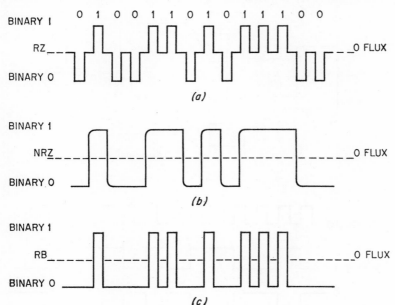

Fig. 22.6 Recordings on a magnetic surface. (a) Return-to-zero. (b) Non-return-to-zero. (c) Return-to-bias.

lengthy to be discussed here. Once a bit is written on a magnetic surface it becomes relatively permanent; hence, a loss of power will not erase the information on a drum. The one-head-per-channel system is quite common in magnetic-drum memories. In some drum memories, however, more than one head per channel is used.

Methods of recording on magnetic surfaces. There are many methods of placing information on magnetic surfaces, some of which were used for specific applications and some of which were meant for general systems. In this section the three main types of recording techniques commonly used are discussed. Figure 22.6 gives a pictorial representation of the three techniques.

The return-to-zero method (Fig. 22.6a) utilizes a pulse for each digit being recorded. The drum surface is magnetized in one direction for a 1 and in the opposite direction for a 0. The application of these pulses is controlled by the master timing section of the computer. There is a no-flux area between bits of information in the drum channel.

The non-return-to-zero technique (Fig. 22.6b) utilizes a constant magnetization in one direction for 1 or a series of 1s and then a direct rever-

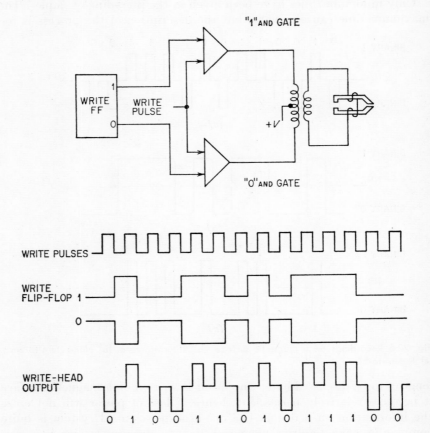

Fig. 22.7 Block diagram of return-to-zero recording method.

sal to the opposite flux for a 0 or a group of 0s. It is a two-level system, and there is no distinct spacing between bits in any one channel. Timing the read-outs then becomes very important in keeping the proper synchronization in the memory.

This technique (Fig. 22.6c) is similiar to the return-to-zero method in that it has a pulse for each binary 1, but it has only two levels present. This is usually accomplished by passing the complete drum surface under a write head or erase bar which will produce only binary 0s on the drum.

Thus for each 1 to be written, a pulse is applied to make one particular area opposite in magnetism from the surrounding area.

The block diagram in Fig. 22.7 illustrates a typical return-to-zero method. The write flip-flop is controlled by the chain of information to be recorded on the drum. If a 1 is to be recorded, the flip-flop goes to the ONE state; if a 0 is to be recorded, the flip-flop goes to the ZERO state. Whichever side is high will enable one of the AND gates. The AND-gate output is clocked by the write pulses and feeds the primary of a center-tapped transformer inducing currents of the opposite polarity in the secondary and setting up the polarity of the write head itself. This produces the waveform designated "write-head output," which is identical to the output shown for the return-to-zero recording method (Fig. 22.6a).

Addressing the drum memory. One of the basic requirements of a computer is to know where all the information is in its memory system and to be able to address that information. To obtain a particular bit of information on a drum, two things must be known about it: its channel number and its angular position. The channel numbers are evident and easy to determine, but the angular position is not. Angular position may be ascertained in several ways.

One method would be to write a 1 in every bit place of one channel. The bits are then sensed in a counter. When a 0 position is indicated, every space thereafter will have a specific number until the counter reaches maximum. After the maximum count, the next pulse returns the counter to 0 exactly 360° after the first 0. The output of the counter is then sent to a decoding matrix.

An address register, usually found in the control section, is fed a certain address for selecting the angular location. This address is then compared with the output of the angular-position counter; when they match, an output is fed to drum controls allowing either reading or writing to take place. Figure 22.8a illustrates how this is accomplished.

Another method is to allocate a specific number of channels to be used as bit address channels and to write the address of each angular position directly on the drum itself. These channels would then replace the angular-position counter, and their output would be fed directly to the detect matrix. An example of this method is shown in Fig. 22.8b. Since each angular position on the drum is assigned a binary number from 0 to 2,047, eleven address channels would be required to provide 2,048 bit addresses around the circumference of the drum.

Parity checks. To provide a parity check on a magnetic-drum memory, one additional channel is required; or, depending on the desired reliability, a complete duplicate drum system can be used. Most business computers need only one channel to determine whether the word being read is the same as the word that was written. This method of checking for parity is executed by adding an extra channel to the needed word length. If the word being stored has an odd number of binary 1s present, a 1 is recorded in the parity channel. If the word has an even number of binary 1s, a 0 is recorded in the channel. The method just described is known as an even parity check, since the parity bit is included with each

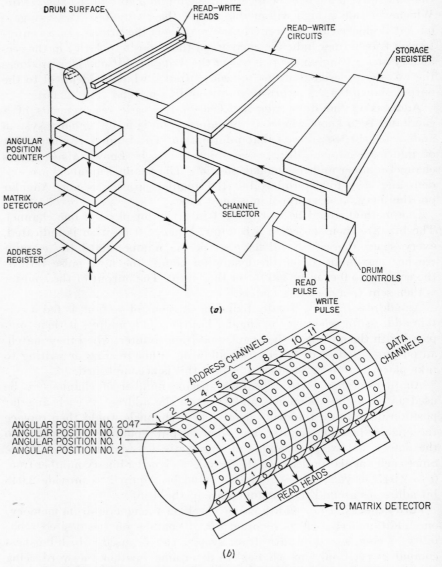

Fig. 22.8 (a) Typical drum memory circuits. (b) Typical drum channels.

word. Each time a word is read from the drum, the number of 1s is sensed and compared with the parity bit. If they are alike, the computer continues to operate. If they are unlike, the computer indicates this error by an alarm.

In the case where two duplicate systems are used for parity, both memories are addressed simultaneously and the complete outputs are compared. If there is a difference in outputs, an error is shown by the computer.

Access time. The access time is measured as maximum, minimum, or average. The average access time is the primary method of comparison between drum memory systems. It was stated previously that the access time depends on the speed of the drum and the special relationship of the read and write heads. Speeds range from 700 to 12,500 rpm, resulting in access times from 43 to 2.4 msec. These speeds require control pulse repetition rates from 50 to 150 kc, depending on the parameters set up for a particular drum.

Interlace. Another feature incorporated into magnetic memories, especially the magnetic drum, is the programming of the recorded material in a fashion known as interlace. This is a method devised to save time by placing consecutive addresses several bit distances apart on the drum. Many of the computer operations utilize consecutive address positions on the drums, but each word at these addresses must be processed by the computer before the next word can be taken. Hence, by properly spacing the addresses or interlacing the addresses, the next consecutive address can be under the read heads when the computer is ready for it. This process impairs drum capacity because of the necessity for more channels to form the address. Each word must carry its own address with it, and therefore less space is left for the words themselves.

Table 22.2 illustrates several of the points discussed. It shows an interlaced address system, numbered in binary from 0 to 14. These addresses contain consecutive numbers starting with 61 and progressing to 75, and each address is read out in parallel. It can be seen that four address locations are skipped to get to the next consecutive address. It is during this time that the computer will process one address and be ready for the next address when it arrives.

Also, note the parity-check channel shown on the right with a 1 for an odd number of 1s and a 0 for an even number of 1s (even parity).

Reliability and cost. A carefully designed magnetic-drum memory system has reliability. The major cause of trouble is the vacuum-tube circuitry associated with the drum. Periodic preventive maintenance can keep these problems to a minimum.

Because of the relative simplicity of the circuitry and of the physical components themselves, a drum memory will cost about 10 cents per character or less than 1 cent per bit.

Table 22.2 Drum Channels—Interlaced Address System

Address channels	Word-storage channels	Even-parity-check channel
0000	000111101	1
0011	001000000	1
0110	001000011	1
1001	001000110	1
1100	001001001	1
0001	000111110	1
0100	001000001	0
0111	001000100	0
1010	001000111	0
1101	001001010	1
0010	000111111	0
0101	001000010	0
1000	001000101	1
1011	001001000	0
1110	001001011	0

Magnetic-tape Storage

Magnetic tape is another commonly used memory storage medium in computer systems. A ferromagnetic material is applied to the surface of a long, flexible piece of base material. This ferromagnetic material is usually red oxide of iron which has been deposited by spraying or dipping the plastic or metallic base tape. These tapes are similar to those used for audio sound recording; however, more care is necessary in the production of computer tape to prevent blemishes or lack of uniformity.

As in the drum, the storage capacity of the tape is directly related to the surface area of the tape. But where the drum is wide and has a relatively short circumference, the tape is narrow (from $\frac{1}{4}$ to 2 in.) and extremely long (2,400 to 3,600 ft). This length implies a long access time.

Tapes are usually mechanized to run either forward or backward and hence are associated with a stop-and-start motion. This is a relatively time-consuming process. Time is saved by using tape loops on either side of the reading and writing devices so a tape driver wheel can move the tape before the servomotors move the reel. This process is explained in more detail in Chap. 23, Input-Output Equipment.

Another consideration is the time required for the tape to reach operating speed before there is enough relative motion between the tape and the heads to produce an output. For this reason information is usually recorded on magnetic tape in a series of data blocks with spaces or gaps between each block of information (see Fig. 22.9). When the tape is at rest, the read-write head is positioned at the center of a gap. With the proper gap length, no information is written or removed from the tape during the start-and-stop intervals.

In some applications the spacing between blocks is prearranged so that data blocks will arrive at the read heads exactly when needed by the processing units. In these cases, stops and starts are unnecessary, and much valuable time is saved.

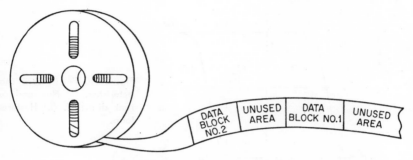

Fig. 22.9 Magnetic-tape recording.

Some of the disadvantages of magnetic-tape storage units are as follows:

1. Access to items on the tape is sequential, and consequently the access time associated with magnetic-tape units is relatively long.
2. To make changes or additions to data already recorded on the tape is a relatively complex and time-consuming process.
3. Simple mechanisms to provide parity and error checks on the stored information are difficult to design.
4. The tape is in constant contact with the friction driver roller and some wear is inevitable. As a result the tape becomes scarred or damaged with constant use.

Because of these disadvantages, magnetic-tape storage devices are seldom used as internal memories. They are more frequently used as external memory units for bulk storage of reference data.

Ferrite-core Storage Systems

Storage in magnetic cores appears to have emerged as the outstanding memory device of present-day computers. Using random-access ferrite storage, memory systems have the capability of a 1- to 10-μsec access time. Several thousand words can be stored in a single magnetic-core storage assembly, and by applying a multiplicity of such assemblies quite large capacities can be obtained in a practical manner. This storage, however, can in no way compete with the large volume which can be stored in a magnetic-tape memory.

Operating principles of the ferrite core. The fundamentals of ferrite cores have been discussed in Chap. 15. However, a brief review of the most important principles is given in the following paragraphs.

Figure 22.10a shows a ferrite core threaded by a single conductor. Assume that a pulse of current is sent through the conductor in the direc-

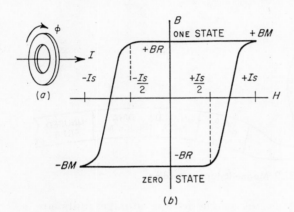

Fig. 22.10 Ferrite-core characteristics. (a) Flux and current direction. (b) Hysteresis loop.

tion shown and that the magnitude of this current is sufficient to saturate the core. Under these conditions, flux lines within the core assume the direction shown in the illustration. When the pulse of current is removed, the core retains most of its magnetism, and the direction of the flux lines remains unchanged. This condition of core magnetization is called the "positive state of residual magnetism" and is given the symbol $+BR$.

When a pulse of current of sufficient magnitude is applied in the direction opposite to that shown in Fig. 22.10a, the flux lines reverse their direction and again remain unchanged when the current is removed. This alternate magnetic state is called the "negative state of residual magnetism" and is assigned the symbol $-BR$.

The positive state of residual magnetism $(+BR)$ is generally referred to as the ONE state, and the negative state of residual magnetism is called the ZERO state.

The two magnetic states of a ferrite core may be illustrated graphically with the aid of a $B\text{-}H$ curve, or hysteresis loop. The curve of a typical ferrite core is shown in Fig. 22.10b. As shown in the figure, a current of a direction and magnitude equal to $+I_s$ produces a flux density of $+BM$ and switches the core to the ONE state. Although the magnetizing force is reduced to zero when the current pulse is removed, the core remains in the ONE state because of the residual magnetism $(+BR)$.

The curve of Fig. 22.10b also indicates that a current applied in the opposite direction, equal in magnitude to $-I_s$, switches the core to the ZERO state. Again, the core remains in the ZERO state when the pulse of current is removed, because of the residual magnetism $(+BR)$.

One important characteristic of the ferrite core is its ability to discriminate against small switching currents or random noise pulses. This characteristic is the result of the high squareness ratio BR/BM of its hysteresis loop (see Fig. 22.10b). Once the core is in one of its stable states, a current as large as 50 per cent of I_s, applied in the direction to switch the state of the core, has no effect. To switch the core to the opposite state, a relatively large current (in excess of $I_s/2$) must be applied. This characteristic is used to advantage in coincident-current core memories.

Coincident-current Core Memories

A coincident-current memory system consists of several core matrices, called *memory planes*, arranged one behind the other. A small section of one memory plane is illustrated in Fig. 22.11a. As shown in the figure, each memory plane consists of an array of ferrite cores arranged in rows and columns and threaded with four conductors. A typical memory plane might contain 1,000 cores. Each core is designed to store one bit of information; hence to store one thousand 36-bit words, 36 memory planes would be required.

The four conductors that thread each core in the memory plane are positioned as shown in Fig. 22.11b. As shown in the figure, each core is threaded with an X address wire, a Y address wire, an inhibit wire, and a sensing, or output, wire.

The X and Y address wires provide a means for gaining access to a single selected core within the array of cores for the purpose of inserting or removing data. The inhibit wire is used to prevent the storage of information in the selected core under certain conditions. The sensing or output wire provides an indication of the core contents during read-out.

Address selection in a ferrite-core memory relies on the principle of *coincident-current switching*. To understand this principle, recall from a statement previously made that a current of the magnitude $I_s/2$ is insufficient to accomplish a change in the state of a ferrite core (see Fig. 22.10). A current of this magnitude $(I_s/2)$ is called a half-select current. In this system, half-select currents may be applied to the X and Y address wires either individually or simultaneously.

As an example of coincident-current switching, assume the core shown in Fig. 22.11a is in the ZERO state and that a half-select current is applied to only one of the two address wires. Assume further that the current pulse is applied in the correct direction to switch the core. Under these conditions, no effect is produced in the core since a half-select current does not produce sufficient magnetomotive force to accomplish switching. The core, therefore, remains in the ZERO state.

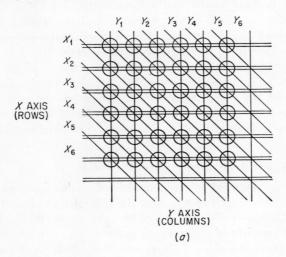

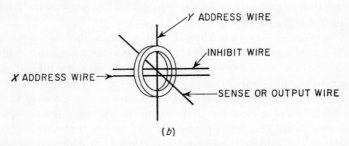

Fig. 22.11 Coincident-current memory section. (a) Simple section of a core memory plane. (b) Single core.

Assume now that two half-select currents are applied simultaneously, one each to the X and Y address wires. In this case, the magnetomotive force produced by the two currents is additive and results in switching the core to the ONE state.

Writing. By using the principles of coincident-current switching, information may be stored in any desired core of a memory plane without affecting the other cores. To see how this is accomplished, consider the small section of a memory plane illustrated in Fig. 22.11a.

As shown in the figure, 36 cores are arranged in six rows and six columns. The rows are labeled X_1 through X_6, and the columns are labeled Y_1 through Y_6. For the purpose of explanation, only the first three cores in rows X_1, X_2, and X_3 will be considered. These nine cores, together with the X and Y address wires that thread them, are redrawn in Fig. 22.12. The inhibit and sense wires have been omitted for clarity.

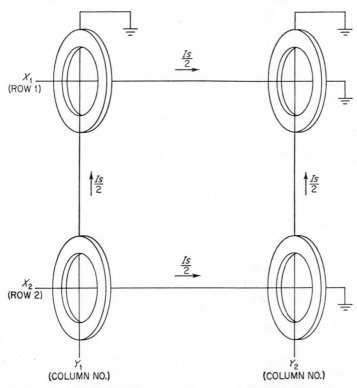

Fig. 22.12 Basic two-coordinate coincident-current memory plane.

Assume that all cores shown in Fig. 22.12 are in the zero state and that a binary 1 is to be written in the second core of row No. 2 without affecting the other cores. This is accomplished by applying two half-select currents simultaneously, one each to address wires X_2 and Y_2 in the correct direction to switch the core. The exciting currents are shown by arrows in Fig. 22.12. As shown in the figure, all cores in row No. 2 and column No. 2 are excited by half-select currents. Only the selected core, however, switches to the one state since it is the only one that receives the additive effect of two half-select currents. All other cores remain in the zero state.

By using the address-selection method just described, a binary 1 may be written in any desired core in the memory plane.

As previously mentioned, most ferrite-core memory systems contain several memory planes arranged one behind the other. The usual method of connection is to connect the address wires of corresponding rows and columns in each adjacent plane in series. The arrangement of memory

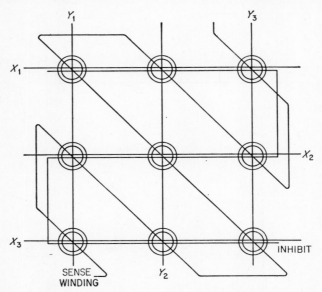

Fig. 22.13 Winding of a nine-bit single-plane core array.

planes and connection of address wires is illustrated in Fig. 22.14. The connection of only one pair of X and Y address wires is shown.

In this method of connection one write driver is used for each address line. Accordingly, in the simplified example of Fig. 22.13 six drivers, three X and three Y, would be provided. Because of the series connection, each address driver supplies current for all corresponding address wires in each plane. This means that when a binary 1 is written in a selected core of a single plane by actuating the proper X and Y drivers, this same binary 1 is also written in those cores in adjacent planes that occupy the same physical position. This effect, of course, is undesirable. Corresponding cores in each memory plane represent single bits in a binary word. For this reason, some way must be provided for preventing the storage of a binary 1 in those planes where a 0 is desired. This is provided through the use of a third wire, termed the *inhibit wire*.

The inhibit wire threads each core in the memory plane. When a current is applied to this wire, no core in that plane can be switched to the

ONE state. Figure 22.13 shows how the inhibit wire is threaded. The inhibit wire is excited with a current supplied by a single inhibit driver. There is one inhibit driver for each adjacent memory plane. During the writing phase, if a 0 is to be stored in any particular plane, the inhibit driver associated with that plane is triggered and a half-select current is applied to its inhibit wire.

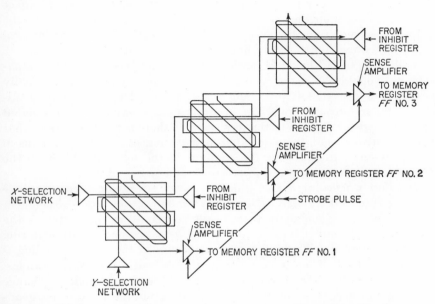

Fig. 22.14 Two-dimensional diagram of a three-plane coincident-current ferrite-core memory system.

As shown in Fig. 22.13, the direction of the inhibit current is opposite to that of the X address current and cancels its effect. As a result no core in that plane can switch to the ONE state.

Read-out. To read out a word stored in a ferrite-core memory, a 0 is written into each core associated with the bits of the selected word. As was true during the write cycle, one core for each memory plane is addressed during read-out. This type of read-out is accomplished by applying a half-select current to the X and Y address wires associated with the row and column in which the selected cores are located. Writing a binary 0 is similar to writing a binary 1 except that the half-select current is applied to the X and Y address wires in the opposite direction.

During the read-out phase, all cores previously in the ONE state are switched to the ZERO state, and the resultant change in magnetic flux is sensed by an output winding that threads each core. If the selected core is already in the ZERO state at this time, no output is produced. Figure 22.13 shows how each core in the memory plane is threaded by the sense winding.

The sense winding for each plane is connected to a separate sense amplifier, as illustrated in Fig. 22.14. An output on the sense winding of a given memory plane is amplified and ANDed with a strobe pulse in the sense amplifier. The purpose of the strobe pulse is to minimize the effect of noise voltages on the sense line. Through the use of a narrow strobe pulse, an output from the sense amplifier occurs only during the interval when the voltage on the sense line is at its maximum amplitude.

As illustrated in Fig. 22.14, each sense amplifier is connected to a separate flip-flop in the memory register. The memory register is usually cleared to 0 immediately preceding read-out time. Then, during the read-out cycle, an output from a core in a given plane switches its associated memory-register flip-flop to the ONE state. If there is no output from that plane at strobe time, the associated memory-register flip-flop remains in the ZERO state. In this way, the contents of the selected address in the ferrite-core memory are transferred to the memory register.

Winding particulars. The windings of a ferrite-core memory plane must be threaded through each core in a manner that reduces the effect of noise voltages generated in the windings. Noise in the output is the chief cause of trouble since it can result in an erroneous output during the read-out phase. The major source of noise in the output winding is caused by the half-select currents in the X and Y address windings. Although a half-select current is not of sufficient amplitude to change the state of the core, a small voltage is produced in the sense wire threading the core. Since many cores receive half-select currents during the read-out cycle and since each core is threaded by the same sense winding, the noise voltages can become additive and result in an erroneous output indication. This effect can be reduced to a minimum by threading the output winding through half of the cores in one direction and through the remaining cores in the other direction. When this is done, half the induced noise voltages are of one polarity while the other half are of the opposite polarity. The algebraic sum of all the induced noise voltage is therefore 0. The threading arrangement of the sense winding shown in Fig. 22.13 is a way to accomplish this result.

Noise is also produced by undesirable electromagnetic coupling between windings. This coupling can exist between wires in a single plane or between wires in adjacent planes. A wiring arrangement must be chosen that minimizes the effects of both types of coupling.

The most satisfactory wiring arrangement is one that ensures that currents in adjacent wires throughout the system flow in opposite directions. With this wiring arrangement, the magnetic field produced by current in one wire is effectively canceled by a magnetic field of opposite polarity created in the adjacent wire. The wiring arrangement shown in Fig. 22.13 utilizes this principle to reduce undesirable coupling to a minimum.

As an example of the effectiveness of this type of wiring arrangement, assume that one of the cores in the memory plane shown in Fig. 22.13 is interrogated during the read-out cycle. Assume further that the selected core contains a binary 1. Under these conditions, the core switches from the ONE to the ZERO state and produces a pulse of output current in the sense winding. Because the wires in adjacent memory planes are close to the excited sense winding, undesirable voltages may be induced in them because of the changing flux set up by the sense current. This effect is minimized, however, because current in adjacent wires of the sense winding flows in opposite directions to set up canceling magnetic fields.

As a second example, assume that column Y_1 in Fig. 22.13 is addressed and that current flows downward as shown. Because of the proximity of winding Y_1 and Y_2, the magnetic field surrounding Y_1 could induce a noise voltage in address wire Y_2. This effect is minimized, however, since the current that flows downward in Y_1 flows upward in the Y_1 winding of the adjacent plane. The two currents produce magnetic fields of opposite polarity which effectively cancel.

Electromagnetic coupling between X and Y address wires of the same core is prevented by placing the two wires at right angles to each other.

Operation of a Typical Coincident-current Ferrite-core Memory System

As explained in Chap. 20, Computer Control and Data Flow, a computer performs its functions by following instructions contained in an instruction register. Each instruction in the register takes the form of a binary-coded word of a given bit length. In a single-address machine, the instruction word is divided into two parts. The first part of the word is the operation code, and the second part is the address code. The operation code of a memory instruction directs the logic circuits associated with the ferrite-core memory whether to write data into the ferrite cores or to remove data from them. The address code of the memory instruction specifies the location in the ferrite-core memory at which storage or removal is to be accomplished.

A simplified block diagram of a ferrite-core coincident-current memory system is illustrated in Fig. 22.15. All the major logic blocks normally included in a typical system are shown in the diagram.

The input to the memory system is the binary-coded word in the instruction register. This word is interpreted or decoded by the X and Y address networks shown in the left portion of the diagram. As shown in the figure, the X address network consists of the read and write flip-flops,

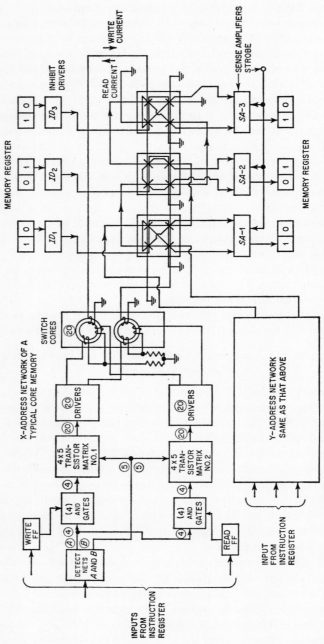

Fig. 22.15 Typical block diagram of a ferrite-core coincident-current memory system.

detect nets A and B, and two sets of AND gates, transistor matrices, output drivers, and switching cores. The circled numbers associated with the blocks in this section indicate either the number of wires connecting two blocks or the number of individual elements comprising the block. The Y address network shown in the lower left portion of the diagram is an exact duplicate of the X address network and for this reason is not shown in detail on the diagram.

The X and Y decoding networks supply half-select currents to those X and Y lines of the memory plane specified by the address portion of the instruction word. The read and write flip-flops in this section are controlled by the operation portion of the word. These flip-flops command the decoding networks to supply current in one direction for a write operation and in the opposite direction for a read operation.

The X and Y address networks shown are designed to supply a ferrite-core memory array containing 400 cores in each plane which are arranged in 20 rows and 20 columns. To simplify the drawing, only four bits in each plane are shown in the figure. For further simplification, a three-bit word has been assumed so that only three memory planes are needed in the array.

Data to be stored in the memory is supplied by the memory register shown in the upper right-hand portion of the figure. The memory register receives data from two sources. Initially, during loading, the memory register receives data from the input equipment associated with the computer. The memory register also receives data from the ferrite-core memory itself during the read-out cycle. Information received by the memory register during the read-out phase can then be conveniently rewritten into the memory if desired. Although only one memory register is employed, two are shown in the diagram to aid in the explanation of typical operation which follows.

Operation of the X and Y address networks. The purpose of the X and Y address networks of Fig. 22.15 is twofold: (1) to interpret the binary configuration contained in the address portion of the instruction register and (2) to supply current to the proper X and Y address lines of the memory array. To see how this is accomplished, consider first the general method of detection employed in this system.

The address portion of the instruction register is shown in the upper part of Fig. 22.16. As shown in the figure, this portion of the register consists of 10 flip-flops divided into two groups of five each. The binary configuration in the first five flip-flops specifies the row of the memory plane in which the selected cores are located. The binary configuration in the second group of five flip-flops specifies the column location.

A two-stage detect matrix is used at the output of the row flip-flops to detect 20 different binary configurations corresponding to the 20 rows in the ferrite-core memory plane. An identical two-stage matrix is provided at the output of the column flip-flops to detect the binary configurations corresponding to the 20 columns of the plane. Two-stage detect matrices were discussed in Chap. 18. The important principles, however, are reviewed in the following paragraphs. Since row and column detection are identical, only the detect matrices at the output of the row flip-flops are discussed.

Detection of the binary configuration in the row flip-flops is accomplished in two stages. The ONE-side and ZERO-side outputs of the first

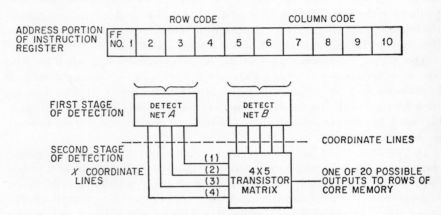

Fig. 22.16 Two-stage detection of address code.

two flip-flops are applied in various combinations to AND gates in detect matrix A. This matrix produces a single output on one of its output lines for each of the four possible binary configurations that may be present in the first two flip-flops. A signal will be present on output line No. 1, for example, for the configuration 00. Similarly, output line No. 2 will go high for the configuration 01.

Flip-flops 3 through 5 of the row group are detected in a similar way by detect matrix B. Although eight configurations are possible in five flip-flops, only five are employed in this part of the row code. When one of these five configurations is present, detect matrix B produces a single output on one of its five output lines. The outputs from detect matrices A and B become the X- and Y-coordinate inputs to the second stage of the two-stage matrix. This second stage is a 4×5 transistor detect matrix containing 20 transistor two-input AND gates. The output of each transistor AND gate is connected to one of the 20 rows in the ferrite-core memory plane. For a given binary configuration in the five row flip-flops, a signal is produced on one pair of X- and Y-coordinate input lines to the transistor matrix. In this way, one of the 20 transistor AND gates is actuated, and one row in the memory plane is selected. Selection of a single column in the ferrite-core memory plane is accomplished through a similar two-stage detection process. The method of detection just described is employed in the X and Y address networks shown in Fig. 22.15, except that the first stage of the detection system (detect nets A and B) feeds two identical second-stage matrices in parallel instead of one. Transistor matrix No. 1 is used to actuate a specific row in the core memory during the write cycle and matrix No. 2 performs the same function during the read cycle. Which of the two transistor matrices produces an output depends on the AND gates inserted in the X-coordinate input lines (input line A on the diagram). When the operation portion of the instruction word indicates that data is to be written into the memory, the write flip-flop is actuated and opens the upper set of AND gates. This enables transistor matrix No. 1 to produce an output. During the read cycle, the read flip-flop is actuated, the lower set of AND gates are opened, and transistor matrix No. 2 is enabled. Thus, one of the 20 outputs from either, but not both, of the selected transistor matrices causes one of the 20 drivers following that matrix to develop a voltage drop across the primary of a metallic-ribbon switch core. When this occurs, a half-select current is produced in the selected row of the memory plane.

There are 20 switch cores in this system, one for each row in the memory plane. The switch cores function as pulse transformers and also provide a convenient means for developing the opposite currents required during the read and write cycles. As shown in the diagram (Fig. 22.15), two primary windings are wound on each switch core. The primary winding actuated by a write driver is wound in the direction opposite from that winding associated with the read driver. As a result, the output current from the selected switch core flows in one direction during the write phase and in the opposite direction during the read cycle. This permits the writing of a binary 1 during storage of data and a binary 0 during read-out.

Consider now the operation of the complete memory system of Fig. 22.15 during first the write, and then the read, cycle. As an example of a typical write operation, assume that the binary word 101 is to be stored in memory location row No. 1, column No. 1. In this case, the binary code in the operation portion of the instruction word causes the write flip-flop to go to the ONE state. As a result, the upper set of AND gates open, and detection of the binary code in the address portion of the instruction word is accomplished by detect matrices A and B and transistor matrix No. 1. During the detection process, one X-coordinate input line and one Y-coordinate input line associated with transistor matrix No. 1 are pulsed simultaneously. As a result, one of the 20 transistor AND gates of matrix No. 1 is enabled, and the driver and core associated with row No. 1 of the memory planes are pulsed. Hence, a half-select current pulse appears in the X address winding of row No. 1 of the memory planes. Since a similar detection process occurs in the Y address-selection network, a half-select current pulse appears simultaneously in the Y address winding of column No. 1. When this occurs, the ferrite cores at the intersection of row No. 1, column No. 1 in each of the three memory planes tend to switch to the ONE state. Only the selected cores in memory planes No. 1 and No. 3 will switch, however, since the word in the memory register is 101. With this configuration in the memory register, the inhibit driver associated with memory-register flip-flop No. 2 supplies a half-select current to the inhibit wire of plane No. 2. For this reason, the selected core in this plane remains in the ZERO state. In this manner, the configuration 101 is written in row No. 1, column No. 1 of the ferrite-core memory. Since no limit is placed on the amount of time a ferrite memory can hold the stored information, the stored data becomes a permanent part of the memory and remains in storage until the read-out cycle.

When read-out is desired, the proper binary code is placed in the operations section of the instruction register. As a result of this code, the read flip-flop is set to the ONE state, and the lower set of AND gates are opened. Accordingly, detection of the binary code in the address portion of the instruction word is accomplished by detect matrices A and B and transistor matrix No. 2. The drivers associated with transistor matrix No. 2 in both the X and Y detection networks pulse the selected switch cores in a direction opposite to that produced previously by the write drivers. As a result, the selected core in row No. 1, column No. 1 of each plane (if in the ONE state) switches to the ZERO state. In the example, the binary configuration in storage is 101, and for this reason output pulses are induced only in the sense windings associated with planes No. 1 and No. 3. No output pulse is developed in the sense winding of plane No. 2 because the selected core in this plane is already in the ZERO state.

Output pulses on the sense lines are amplified in sense amplifiers and ANDed with a strobe pulse generated in coincidence with the read pulse. In the example under consideration, the outputs produced from sense amplifiers 1 and 3 set the corresponding memory-register flip-flops to the ONE state. In this way, the data present at memory location row No. 1, column No. 1 is transferred to the flip-flops of the memory register.

In many memory systems of this type, read-out automatically triggers a rewrite cycle while the word is still in the memory register. This is usually done while the computer is operating on the word itself. In this case information is written back into the same memory location from which it was withdrawn.

Other Storage Devices

This portion of this chapter deals with storage units which have found limited use in the computer industry. Some are outdated, having been replaced by newer ideas and methods, and others are found only in special applications.

Electrostatic storage systems. Electrostatic storage systems employ cathode-ray tubes for the storage of binary information. These systems feature fast random access to stored data and for this reason have been used as the main memory in many high-speed digital computers. Although seldom used in new design, they have played an important role in computer development; they are briefly discussed in the following paragraphs.

The most prominent system of electrostatic storage was developed by an Englishman, F. C. Williams, and named for him. The original Williams storage tube was a cathode-ray tube of conventional design. The only modification was a metal pickup plate attached to the outside face of the cathode-ray tube. This arrangement is shown in Fig. 22.17.

A single data bit is stored on the phosphorescent screen by deflecting the electron stream toward any one of approximately 1,000 storage loca-

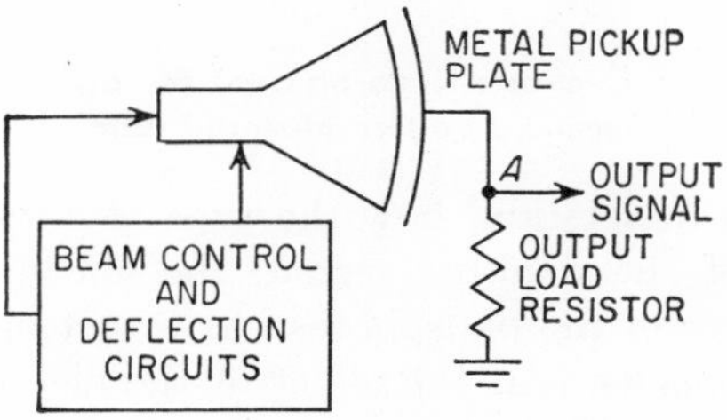

Fig. 22.17 Williams storage tube.

tions. The area assigned to each storage location on the phosphorescent screen has a width equal to approximately twice the electron-beam diameter. To write a binary 0, deflection voltages are applied to the deflection electrodes to position the beam to the desired storage location. The beam is then turned on or "unblanked" for approximately 1 μsec. During this interval the electron stream actuates approximately half the area of the storage location, and an illuminated spot is produced, as illustrated in Fig. 22.18a. To write a binary 1 in any desired location, the above procedure is repeated, except that the beam is unblanked for approximately 2 μsec and is deflected slightly along the horizontal axis. As a result of this horizontal motion, an illuminated dash appears on the phosphorescent screen (see Fig. 22.18b). The luminous pattern of data that appears on the screen after five bits of information are stored is shown in Fig. 22.18c.

To read the data stored on the phosphorescent screen, some electrostatic storage systems employ photoelectric devices that sense the difference between the illumination presented by a dot and that produced by the dash. The Williams system, however, does not rely on photoelectric emission for read-out. In this system a metal pickup plate senses changes in charge distribution on the phosphorescent screen rather than changes in light intensity.

To read the information present at any given storage location, a 0 is written in that position by reexciting the phosphorescent tube as previously explained (see Fig. 22.18a). If a 0 is already in storage at that location, a negative voltage is produced across the output load resistor because of capacitive coupling between the phosphorescent screen and the external pickup plate (see Fig. 22.17). Conversely, if a 1 is in storage at that location, a positive voltage is produced at the output.

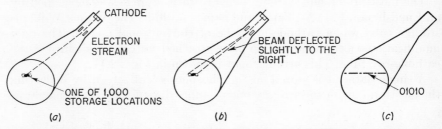

Fig. 22.18 Electrostatic storage. (a) Storage of binary 0 (dot). (b) Storage of binary 1 (dash). (c) Luminous pattern of stored data.

To understand how the type of data in storage determines the polarity of the read-out signal, the effect of electron bombardment at the surface of the phosphorescent target must be investigated.

Consider first the effect of the electron beam during the storage of a binary 0. Electrons in the stream bombard the phosphorescent screen at a high velocity, and the bombardment results in secondary emission at the target surface. This process is illustrated in Fig. 22.19a. As shown in the figure, for each electron that strikes the screen, several are released from its surface. Most of the emitted electrons are attracted by the positive potentials on the tube electrodes and are removed from the target area. Some electrons, however, fall back on the surface of the screen and accumulate in the vicinity of the bombarded area.

Figure 22.19b shows the charge distribution on and around the excited area after a binary 0 has been stored. As shown in the figure, the area subjected to direct bombardment is charged positively since it has lost electrons. The surrounding area, however, is charged negatively since it has gained electrons because of secondary electrons falling back on the screen.

Consider now the effects produced during the read-out cycle. To read out the binary 0 in storage, the beam is again turned on for 1 μsec and directed toward the same area (see Fig. 22.18*a*). Since this region has a deficiency of electrons because of previous bombardment, very little secondary emission takes place, and the charge distribution shown in Fig. 22.19*b* does not change appreciably. The electron beam does have an effect on the output circuit, however, because of the capacitance that exists between the phosphorescent screen and the metallic pickup plate.

Because of the repulsion of unlike charges, electrons in the pickup plate move away from the area of the electron beam. Electrons flow

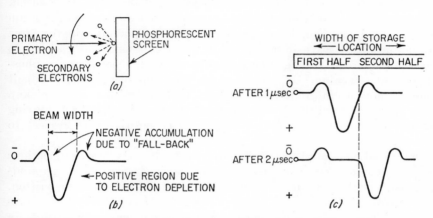

Fig. 22.19 Electrostatic screen bombardment. (*a*) Secondary emission due to electron bombardment. (*b*) Charge distribution on phosphorescent screen after storage of binary 0. (*c*) Charge distribution after storage of binary 1.

toward ground through the output load resistor and produce a negative potential with respect to ground at point *A* (Fig. 22.17).

To understand how a positive potential is produced during the read-out of a binary 1, again consider the charge distribution on the surface of the storage area during the storage phase.

During the storage of a binary 1, the beam is unblanked and deflected slightly along the horizontal axis as previously explained (Fig. 22.18*b*). During this 2-μsec interval, both halves of a given storage area are bombarded by the electron stream. Figure 22.19*c* illustrates the charge distribution produced in the first half of the storage area during the first microsecond. As shown in the figure, this distribution is identical with that produced when a binary 0 is stored. The area under direct bombardment becomes an electron depletion area and assumes a positive charge while the area surrounding this region becomes negatively charged because of secondary electrons which fall back to the surface. A similar process occurs during the bombardment of the second half of the storage area. Secondary emission produced in this region, however, effects the charge distribution of the first half of the storage area. Secondary electrons falling back to the surface enter the depletion area of the first region and neutralize its positive charge. Figure 22.19c shows the charge distribution in the first and second half of the storage location after the binary 1 is stored and the beam is turned off. Consider now the effect produced at the output (Fig. 22.17) during the read-out of this binary 1.

During read-out, the beam is directed toward the first half of the storage location only, since no horizontal deflection of the beam is produced. Since the region under direct bombardment is not an electron depletion region, secondary emission is produced and the potential in this area swings in the positive direction. This positive potential is coupled to the output circuit through the capacitance existing between the phosphorescent screen and the pickup plate. Electrons in the output circuit tend to move from ground up through the load resistor to the pickup plate and on toward the area of the positive potential. Electrons moving in this direction make point A of Fig. 22.17 positive with respect to ground.

One disadvantage of the Williams tube is that the storage locations on the phosphorescent screen tend to lose their charge to the surrounding area. For this reason, the stored data must be periodically rewritten.

The arrangement of cathode-ray tubes in an electrostatic storage system is similar to the arrangement of memory planes in a ferrite-core memory array. The deflection system for each tube is arranged in parallel, and each tube holds one bit of a word. In a 36-bit-per-word system, 36 tubes would be required. Since each tube contains approximately 1,000 memory locations, the capacity of such a system would be one thousand 36-bit words or six thousand 6-bit characters.

Delay lines. One of the first devices used as a memory system was the acoustic delay line. This type of delay line consists of a column of mercury with a piezoelectric crystal at each end of the column. Figure 22.20 is a block diagram showing how a delay-line memory system operates. The data to be stored is gated into the memory cycle by the read-in pulse. This read-in pulse must be controlled by the computer to prevent the reading in of new information over information to be rewritten.

A delay-line storage system is a volatile memory. If the data is not rewritten, it is lost.

Each piece of information is properly spaced by using a clock pulse. If a 1 is to be written, an output is sent to the driver which, in turn, operates the transmitting transducer. The transducer changes the electric pulse into a mechanical vibration which is transmitted through the delay medium and reconverted into an electric pulse by the receiving transducer. The output of the transducer is delivered to an amplifier and a reshaping circuit. If the information is then needed by the computer, a rewrite pulse gates it around to the input of the delay line, and the delay cycle is repeated.

The delay medium can be made of many types of materials, but mercury and quartz are most frequently used.

A sequential or cyclic mode of access is used in delay-line memories. Usually the length of the delay medium determines the amount of storage time. Addressing is performed through timing pulses. This brings up

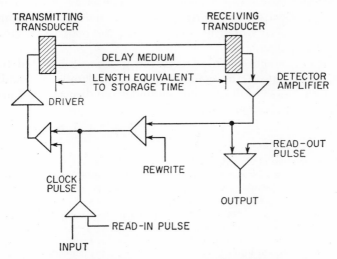

Fig. 22.20 Basic block diagram for a delay-line memory system.

the main disadvantage. Most delay media are sensitive to temperature, shocks, and various other stresses. All these tend to change the amount of storage time and hence disturb the overall timing.

The principles of magnetostriction have also been used in the design of delay lines for computer memory systems. In a magnetostrictive delay line, coils are wrapped around the ends of a metallic bar made of ferrous material. A pulse applied to the input coil creates a magnetic field. This field develops a stress on the bar because of magnetostriction. The stress is transmitted to the receiving end of the bar as a shock wave and generates a change in the magnetic field at that point. The change is sensed by a coil of wire, and a pulse is generated at the output.

Electric delay lines using lumped capacitance and inductance to form an artificial transmission line can also be used as the storage elements in computer memory systems.

Delay-line memories are relatively inexpensive, but are not so reliable as other memory systems.

Punched-card memory systems. Punched-card storage devices, like magnetic-tape units, are used chiefly for bulk storage of reference data and for this reason may be considered as part of the external memory of a computer.

Information is stored in devices of this nature by punching holes in predetermined locations on the card. Hole positions, or memory cells, are usually arranged on the card in rows and columns. Alphabetic and numeric symbols can then be represented by a code that depends on the number and position of punched holes. The IBM card, for example, contains 80 vertical columns with 12 hole positions to a column. Since one character can be stored in each column, the card has a storage capacity of 80 characters.

In operation, punched cards are placed in a stack and fed to a card reader at the input to the computer. Further details concerning processing of punched-card data are given under the discussion of input and output equipment (Chap. 23).

Summary

The memory system of a modern computer must be capable of storing vast quantities of reference data. In addition, to facilitate maximum computing speed, rapid access to each item of stored information is desirable. To meet these requirements, most memory systems employ two or more different types of storage units. Usually, a low-speed, high-capacity storage device is used as an external memory for bulk storage, and one or more high-speed, low-capacity memories are located internally to provide rapid access to stored information during data processing.

Many types of storage units using several different principles of storage are employed in modern computers. Devices utilizing magnetic principles, however, are most frequently found in new designs. Included in this category are magnetic-tape units, magnetic drums, and coincident-current magnetic-core arrays. Of these magnetic devices, tape units have the largest storage capacity but also have the longest access time. For this reason tape units are best suited for use as external memories in cases where vast quantities of reference data are required. High-speed internal memory systems usually employ magnetic drums and ferrite-core arrays, used singly or in combination. These devices have a smaller storage capacity than tape units but provide much faster access to stored information.

Some of the factors that must be considered when selecting a storage unit for a given memory application are reviewed in the following list:

Storage capacity The storage capacity is usually expressed in terms of the maximum number of characters or words that may be stored within the storage medium.
Mode of access The mode of access refers to the method used to gain access to the storage locations or addresses of the storage unit. The mode of access may be either random or sequential.
Access time Access time is the time interval between the instant information is requested and the instant it becomes available.
Permanence Permanence specifies whether or not information in storage may be erased.

Volatility Volatility specifies whether or not information is lost when power is removed.

Cost Cost is usually expressed in terms of cost per character of stored information.

Physical considerations Physical aspects to be considered are bulk, air-conditioning requirements, and power consumption.

QUESTIONS

22.1 What are the two most important characteristics considered in the selection of a memory system?

22.2 What type of information is normally stored in the external memory of a computer? What type of information is stored in the internal memory?

22.3 Why do computers usually have an auxiliary memory?

22.4 How is storage capacity expressed?

22.5 List the different modes of access.

22.6 Which is the fastest mode of access to storage locations?

22.7 What factors determine the storage time of a magnetic drum?

22.8 How are drum storage locations determined?

22.9 Which type of memory medium has the longest access time?

22.10 Which type of memory medium has the shortest access time?

22.11 In a ferrite-core memory system, how is a 1 which is written into a selected core prevented from being written in the cores of adjacent planes in the same physical location?

22.12 How are noise voltages canceled in a ferrite-core memory system?

22.13 What is the disadvantage of electrostatic storage?

Chapter **23**

Input-Output Equipment

The purpose of input equipment associated with a computer is to translate the various forms of input data into a form suitable for high-speed computations. After the computer manipulates the data in the prescribed fashion, the results are then retranslated by the output equipment into a form that can be either interpreted by a human operator (printed documents) or recorded on punched cards or various computer tapes as a permanent record that can be reused at a later time.

In bringing data from normal sources outside the machine into the memory of the computer, at least three distinct data forms and two distinct conversions are usually involved. This chapter describes some of the equipment used for input-output purposes and the conversion processes involved.

Direct and Indirect Input

Input data in its original form is termed *external data* and is usually in a form which can be read and utilized by human beings rather than machines. In commercial applications this would include sales slips, conventional time cards, accounting records, and business reports. Since none of these forms can be fed directly into a computer, some form of conversion is necessary. The most obvious method is direct conversion. In such a case, the computer operator, using an input device similar to a teletypewriter transmitter, reads data directly from normal business forms and types it into the memory of the computer. This procedure, however, generally has decided disadvantages from the point of view of cost and time. Rental time for a full-scale digital computer can easily cost $50 (or several times that amount) per hour. This includes capital costs and maintenance or rental as well as housing and specialized personnel. To illustrate the significance of this cost factor, consider a hypothetical example. If a concern utilizing such a computer had 3,000 employees and 1 min were required to feed in the payroll data on each employee, 5 hr would be required to process the entire payroll. At $50 an hour this would represent a $250 expenditure for computer time.

Now consider the effects of utilizing an indirect input system. If a card reader with a speed of 150 cards per minute were employed as an input buffer, the whole data-loading operation would take only 20 min. This would require an expenditure of only $17 for computer time. If the firm has a payroll each week, the yearly saving in computer time would be about $11,000. Since the annual cost of owning and operating such a card reader is much less than this amount, savings are effected by employing double data conversion. First the data from the time-keeper and from the permanent files is assembled as before. But instead of being fed directly into the machine, this data is punched onto cards. This activity represents an extra step involving some costs, but the additional costs are less than the cost of the computer time. Thus, it will be apparent that when computer time costs are high, money can be saved by investing in various input buffers such as high-speed punched-card readers. The employment of this type of equipment as opposed to feeding data directly into the computer may be termed indirect input.

Conversion of Data Forms

It is well to keep in mind the distinctions between the three forms of data involved in a typical indirect-input condition. At first, the data is on office forms and records of various sizes. Because of time factors involved, this data is converted to another form, the input form. In the example given, the input form was punched cards. The advantage of having data in the input form is that it can be fed quickly into the computer. The card punch used to convert data from external form to input form is not necessarily considered to be input equipment in the strictest sense. This is because the card punch is operated independently of the computer and at a different data-processing rate. Instead, this card punch could be termed input preparation equipment or pre-input equipment. In a large installation it could be quite appropriate, practical, and efficient to have three card-punch operators working several hours to prepare thousands of punched cards which will later be run through the computer in a few minutes.

The function of input equipment is to accept data in input form and convert it to electric impulses as quickly as possible (see Fig. 23.1). The highest practical input-equipment speed would be limited by the data-processing rate of the computer. This is, however, normally not a consideration since the computer's data-processing rate is almost invariably equal to or faster than that of the input equipment. The electric impulses produced by the input equipment as it reads the input data normally represent binary 1s and 0s which are to be stored in the computer's memory. Figures 23.1 and 23.2 show different methods of inserting data into a computer.

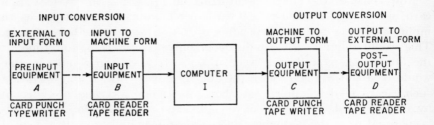

Fig. 23.1 Generalized input-output diagram.

Solid arrows indicate higher speeds of data transfer and direct communication with the machine. These impulses are represented by the solid arrows directly to the left of computer blocks I and II in Fig. 23.1. Blocks B and C serve as data rate buffers. Input and output tape equipment serves as additional data rate buffers. Computer II costs twice as much as computer I and works five times as fast; hence, computer II both justifies and requires the high-speed tape equipment shown in Fig. 23.2.

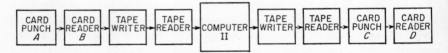

Fig. 23.2 Specialized input-output diagram showing additional buffering.

The form data takes in the memory depends upon the type of memory involved. In almost any case, however, it would be a form distinct from the input form. To cite an example, many current computer installations have punched cards for an input form and magnetic-drum storage for a memory. The particular form the data takes while in the computer can be termed "machine form" since the word "machine" is often used as a synonym for computer. Differences between the input form and the machine form are now examined. It is apparent in the example given that the input data in the form of punched cards represents an opportunity for permanent storage. When punched-card data is processed by the input unit, in this case a punched-card reader, it is translated into electric impulses which become magnetized or nonmagnetized spots on a revolving drum. This machine form differs from the input form in that it is decidedly not adapted to permanent storage. Although the drum would hold the data bits after the power is turned off, the important considerations are that the drum is expensive, difficult to revolve, and limited in size. Consequently, data stored on the drum in all but very specialized applications must be removed after the completion of a problem. The differences between the input form and the machine form described above may now be defined:

1. Data in machine form is immediately electronically accessible to the rest of the computer at regular computer speed, while data in input form is accessible to the computer at a lower speed and only after mechanical handling has taken place in the input equipment.
2. Data in the input form is adapted to long-term storage while data in machine form is not.

On-line and Off-line Operation

In the discussion on data-form conversion just completed, a distinction was drawn between input and pre-input equipment. This distinction is similar to the one that is frequently made in computer terminology between on-line and off-line input and output equipment. Although there are some slight differences between writers as to exact areas to be covered by these two terms, the following definition will be useful. On-line peripheral operation is that which must be carried on concurrently with the computer's calculations in order to obtain the correct solution to the problem in the required time. Consider the situation mentioned in connection with input and pre-input equipment in the previous discussion (see Fig. 23.1). Whether a particular piece of equipment is utilized in an on-line or an off-line capacity depends on the type of problem being solved and the characteristics of other types of equipment in the system.

Assume that in the situation given, the computer's memory has sufficient input-data space available for the contents of one or, at most, a few punched cards. In such a case, the input equipment (Fig. 23.1) will have to operate concurrently with the computer in order to solve the problem in a reasonable amount of time. This is on-line operation. If, however, the computer's memory can hold at once all the input data involved in the problem, the input equipment will be needed before the calculation rather than during it. The pre-input card-punch equipment, on the other hand, will always operate off-line. Even if more than one card punch could be utilized to place additional cards in the card reader during computer operation it would be only an unnecessary coincidence. The same operation could have been carried out while the computer was doing another problem or was inoperative.

In the same situation, the mode of operation of the output equipment will be parallel. Again referring to Fig. 23.1, note the output equipment designated C. If the memory of the computer can store all the final results from a particular problem, the output equipment need not be connected on line. Instead, it will presumably be used after the problem is solved and the final results will be punched out or written on tape. If, on the other hand, the memory cannot hold all the final results to the problem, then it will be necessary for the output equipment to operate on-line so as to receive the final results as they come from the machine. At the completion of the operation of the output card punch or output tape writer, the final results will be available in the form of punched cards or magnetic or paper tape. This output form of the data may then be converted to some external form, like a printed page using post-output equipment. The post-output equipment will always operate off-line for two reasons: First, however essential it may be for the final results to be utilized in external form, the solution of the problem is complete before this conversion takes place. Hence, it cannot be said that the post-output equipment provides an essential link in the solution of the problem. Second, the post-output equipment performs mechanical operations which by their very nature are too slow to keep up with the computer. Hence, post-output operations, where required, are performed off-line after the final results have been accumulated.

Why Input Equipment Is Necessary

The previous discussion pointed out that input-output equipment is necessary in order to utilize effectively high computer speeds. The question can naturally arise as to why such fast and expensive computers are employed. Would it not be more reasonable, in the case of payroll processing, for example, to employ a simpler, cheaper computer so that direct input could be utilized? The answers to this question are both yes and no. In amplifying these answers some basic factors in computer cost and complexity are pointed out.

It may be thought that if a high-speed digital computer costs $200,000, then perhaps a slower computer which could do the same job at a much lower speed could be purchased for around $10,000. This, however, is not the case. The computer desired would cost several times the latter figure. This is because the basic units of an electronic digital computer, namely the memory, arithmetic unit, and control circuits, are inherently complex regardless of the speed of operation. Thus, in dealing with digital computers it is impossible to save more than a certain amount of money by sacrificing speed. On the contrary, if an organization has a high enough data-processing volume, it can save money by buying a faster computer. This is because a faster computer is more efficient in terms of dollar cost. To take a good example from one manufacturer, the Burroughs E 101, a small desk-sized computer, costs about $38,000 and can perform 20 additions per second, while the Burroughs 205 costing $135,000 for a complete system can do 500 additions per second. Here an increase to about 3½ times in cost yields 25 times faster operation-handling capacity. Thus, the small computer is more efficient than the large only in instances where the data volume is comparatively low. In all other cases, indirect-input equipment in spite of its cost more than pays for itself because it allows more efficient high-speed computers to be employed.

The advantages of various types of pre-input and input equipment will now be considered. In this discussion it is well to keep in mind the concept of a file as used in data processing. To simplify slightly, a file may be thought of as a collection of all the related data on a particular subject. For example, the payroll file would contain the names of the employees, their rates of pay, their tax classifications, and other information. The accounts receivable file would contain the names of customers, the amount they owe, and other information. An inventory file would normally include the part number, the amount on hand, and the minimum amount of the item to be carried.

Punched Cards as an Input-data Form

As an input-data form, punched cards have both advantages and disadvantages in comparison with paper and magnetic tapes. Probably the most important advantage of punched cards is that an individual card may be used to hold the data on a significant subdivision of the file. For example, data on a particular employee, customer, or inventory item is usually found on one card. For many purposes this is convenient. For example, if 10 names are to be added to an alphabetical payroll file, new cards may be conveniently punched and inserted. If the same operation is to be performed on a tape, the situation may be more complicated. Even if spaces were left between names, several individuals with similar names may be employed. In this case, the alphabetical tape file would probably have to be rewritten. The advantages of punched cards can be listed as follows:

1. A file of punched cards is easily expanded, contracted, or revised.
2. A file of punched cards may be quickly sorted into subfiles, and cards with special characteristics may be conveniently removed. For example, the cards of "all employees with over 1 year of tool and die experience" can be sorted out of a properly prepared employee file in a few minutes.
3. Punched cards conveniently carry names, numbers, or other visual tags which enable them to be identified quickly and handled manually when necessary. In general, punched cards are often employed

whenever the ability to manipulate individual items conveniently in a data file is important.

Although punched cards are the most widely used input (and output) medium for digital computers, certain limitations to their use must be pointed out. Punched-card pre-input equipment, namely card punches, is usually slower and more bulky than tape equipment of the same cost. This is especially true in high-data-volume applications. The punched cards themselves are heavier and take up more storage space per data bit. As a result, most computer applications which have a high data volume combined with minimum sorting and searching requirements utilize some form of tapes in preference to punched cards.

Punched-card format. The two most widely used punched cards are the Remington Rand Corporation card and the International Business Machines Corporation (IBM) card. Both cards have the same physical dimensions: 7⅜ in. long, 3¼ in. wide, and approximately 0.065 in. thick. The major difference between the two is the number of columns on each: the Remington Rand card has 90 columns whereas the IBM card has 80. Since the IBM card is the most commonly used, its general format is discussed.

The IBM card is a piece of cardboard made of carefully selected stock and checked for defects and thickness. Each card has 80 vertical columns, and within each column there are 12 punching positions. Figure 23.3a shows the general format of an IBM card. Figure 23.3b shows the IBM card with several positions punched. The rows are numbered 0 through 9; in addition, two unnumbered rows can be punched above row 0. This gives a total theoretical capacity of 12 × 80 or 960 bits of information on each card.

The punched card consists of an individual code for each of the digits 0 to 9 and an individual code for each letter of the alphabet, A to Z.

Table 23.1 Typical Code for Alphabetic Punching

Numerical zone	12 zone	11 zone	0 zone
1	12 and 1 = A	11 and 1 = J	
2	12 and 2 = B	11 and 2 = K	0 and 2 = S
3	12 and 3 = C	11 and 3 = L	0 and 3 = T
4	12 and 4 = D	11 and 4 = M	0 and 4 = U
5	12 and 5 = E	11 and 5 = N	0 and 5 = V
6	12 and 6 = F	11 and 6 = O	0 and 6 = W
7	12 and 7 = G	11 and 7 = P	0 and 7 = X
8	12 and 8 = H	11 and 8 = Q	0 and 8 = Y
9	12 and 9 = I	11 and 9 = R	0 and 9 = Z

Numerical coding is a single punch per column in any position from 0 to 9. For example, a 6 would be recorded as a hole in the 6 position.

In alphabetic punching, the 12, 11, and 0 rows are referred to as zones and in combination with numerical punching produce the alphabet as shown in Table 23.1.

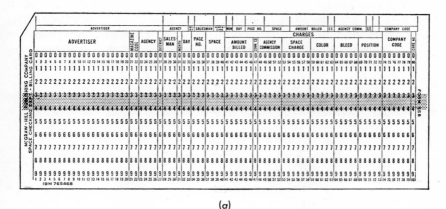

(a)

(b)

Fig. 23.3 (a) Standard IBM card—general format. (b) Card punching positions. (IBM Corporation)

When the cards are prepared on a card-punching machine (which has a keyboard similar to that of a typewriter), the depression of the "A" key will automatically punch two holes in the same column—the 12-zone punch and the 1-zone numerical punch—which form the letter "A." After the information is punched on the card, the card is then verified by another operator to ensure that the information is accurate. An erroneously punched card can cause a computer to miscalculate and propagate erroneous information; therefore, it is simpler to verify the card before it is placed into the card reader than to painstakingly retrace all the steps of a program loop to find the source of error.

Card reading. After the computer instructions and/or data are punched and verified, the cards are arranged in the proper order by the operator and placed into the card hopper (receptacle on a machine in which cards are placed before and during a machine operation). The cards are then chuted one by one into a reading mechanism. There are several methods of obtaining read-out from cards; the two most frequently employed are the brush-contact method and, for higher speed, the use of photoelectric readers.

The brush-type mechanism is shown in Fig. 23.4. In this system, the unpunched portion of the card acts as an insulation and prevents a

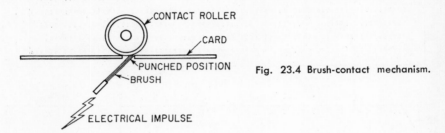

Fig. 23.4 Brush-contact mechanism.

metal brush from making contact with a metal contact roll. However, when the brush falls into a punched hole, contact is made and an electric impulse results. Hence, from any given column or columns of coded information, impulses can be generated to initiate, sort, punch, compare, print, compute, and accumulate operations.

Perforated-paper-tape Input-Output Devices

Perforated paper tape with its holes-and-no-holes coding serves the same purpose as the punched card. As with punched cards, the paper tape may also be prepared by an operator using a manually operated tape-punch keyboard or an automatic tape-punching machine which translates numerical information from one form into coded tape information. Once the tape is punched and verified, it is run through the tape reader of the computer at a rate up to 300 characters per second. The tape is pulled through the tape reader at high speeds by either a friction capstan or a sprocket gear. A capstan-driven tape reader utilizing a photoelectric reader is shown in Fig. 23.5 along with the tape-loading procedure.

Typical paper-tape system. A good example of a flexible paper-tape input-output system is that used in conjunction with the Burroughs 205

DATATRON computer. The DATATRON is a general-purpose, internally programmed electronic computer that accepts data directly from punched cards, punched tape, magnetic tape, or keyboard. The computed results are read out directly on punched cards, punched tapes, magnetic tape, or printed documents. The input-output device which can read or

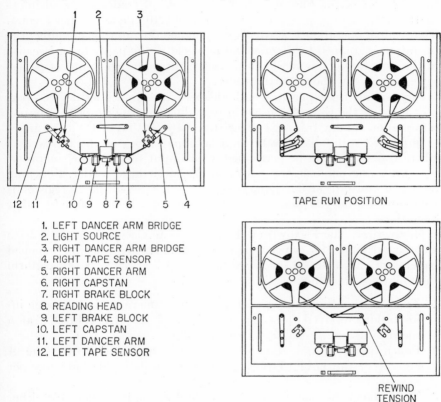

TAPE RUN POSITION

1. LEFT DANCER ARM BRIDGE
2. LIGHT SOURCE
3. RIGHT DANCER ARM BRIDGE
4. RIGHT TAPE SENSOR
5. RIGHT DANCER ARM
6. RIGHT CAPSTAN
7. RIGHT BRAKE BLOCK
8. READING HEAD
9. LEFT BRAKE BLOCK
10. LEFT CAPSTAN
11. LEFT DANCER ARM
12. LEFT TAPE SENSOR

REWIND
TENSION
ARM

TAPE LOAD POSITION   TAPE REWIND POSITION

Fig. 23.5 Capstan-driven perforated-tape reader.

punch perforated paper tape and print out typewritten results is an electric typewriter called the Flexowriter. All input is decimal and all numeric output is decimal. Uppercase and lowercase alphabetic characters, punctuation marks, and all other symbols on the keyboard can be printed out on the typewriter or punched out on paper tape.

Photoelectric tape reader. The DATATRON employs a photoelectric reader which can read information from the paper tape into the computer at a speed of 540 decimal digits per second, or about 45 computer words per second. Operation of the photoelectric reader is under control of commands from the computer, or commands punched in the paper tape. Loading of information from the paper tape may be intermittent.

Mechanical reader. The DATATRON is also equipped with a mechanical reader which is mounted on the output typewriter as an integral part of the Flexowriter. The mechanical reader can read information into the computer at a rate of about 10 characters per second. The reading operation is started by a command from the computer; the operation is stopped by a command punched in the paper tape. Because of the slow rate of the mechanical reader, the preferred means of paper-tape input is the photoelectric reader.

High-speed tape punch. The high-speed tape-punching device operates through the control console to reproduce on paper tape the output information coming from the A register of the DATATRON. The tapes so produced will subsequently serve as input tapes to the typewriter, where translation can be performed, or as input tapes to the computer, by way of the photoelectric reader or the mechanical reader. Punching occurs at the rate of 60 characters per second. Since the A register is being used during the punch operation, the computer is not free for other operations.

Flexowriter. The Flexowriter (Fig. 23.6) is an electric typewriter with an integral punch for paper tape and a mechanical reader for punched paper tape. As modified for use with the DATATRON, it can perform the following functions:

1. Type, or simultaneously punch and type numeric and alphabetic information, received from the A register of the DATATRON, at a speed of about 10 characters per second.
2. Punch numeric and alphabetic information, received from the A register of the DATATRON, at a speed of about 14 characters per second.
3. Type, punch, or simultaneously type and punch information in either the DATATRON or the Flexowriter code, received by way of the mechanical reader, at a speed of about 10 characters per second.
4. Reproduce a paper tape from another paper tape automatically, with or without translation from the DATATRON code to the Flexowriter code, at a speed of about 10 characters per second.
5. Punch a paper tape in either DATATRON or Flexowriter code.

The Flexowriter four-bank keyboard has a total of 51 key lever positions. There are 42 keys for character operation, and the remaining nine are for functional operations. The standard carriage accepts a $9\frac{7}{8}$-in. form with a maximum writing line of $8\frac{1}{2}$ in., with a line spacing of six lines per inch.

A tabular mechanism is provided with a minimum of two letter spaces between tab settings. The type basket shifts to select printing between uppercase and lowercase characters, with two shift keys (one for uppercase and one for lowercase) on each side of the keyboard. Shift-key operation is required for shifting in each direction.

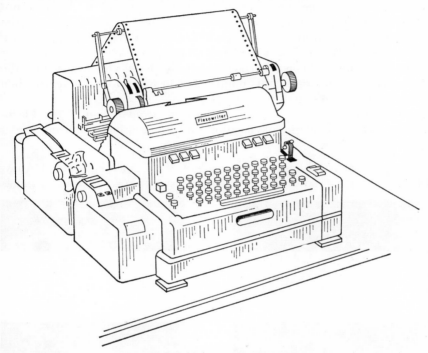

Fig. 23.6 Flexowriter.

There are seven control switches associated with the Flexowriter. Their functions are listed below:

1. START READ. When this switch is depressed, a prepunched paper tape moves through the mechanical reader.
2. STOP READ. When this switch is depressed, the mechanical reader stops operation.
3. PUNCH ON. When this switch is depressed, each character or function typed on the keyboard or read by the mechanical reader is punched in the paper tape by the punch unit.
4. TAPE FEED. When this switch is depressed, blank paper tape feeds through the punch unit, provided the PUNCH ON switch is in the ON position.
5. CODE DELETE. When this switch is depressed, a delete punch is re-

corded in the paper tape, indicating that the associated digit is to be ignored. This punch is an instruction to the Flexowriter *only*, and it is not sensed by the photoelectric reader. When the delete code is read by the mechanical reader, no character or function operation will occur on the typewriter or be punched by the punch unit for that digit. A paper tape containing a delete punch should not be read into the DATATRON via the photoelectric reader since not only will the error remain, but an extra digit will be added to the word.

6. STOP CODE. When this switch is depressed, a stop code is punched in the paper tape. When this code is read by the mechanical reader, the paper tape will stop at this point and will move forward again when the START READ switch is depressed.

7. ON-OFF. This switch, located on the right front corner of the Flexowriter, must be in the ON position for all operations requiring use of the Flexowriter.

Code system. The paper-tape readers communicate to the DATA-TRON through serial-digital information read from six parallel channels

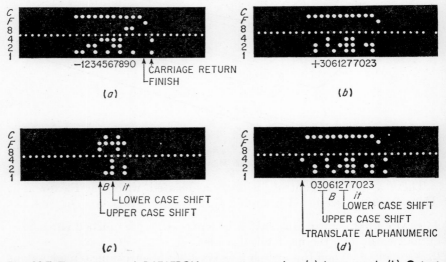

Fig. 23.7 Flexowriter and DATATRON paper-tape codes. (*a*) Input word. (*b*) Output word. (*c*) Translated word (Flexowriter code). (*d*) Untranslated word (DATATRON code).

of a 7/8 in. paper tape. Four tape channels are used for the binary-coded decimal digit, one channel for a clock (C) punch which accompanies each digit of a word, and one channel for the finish (F) punch which furnishes an end-of-word signal to the computer. Each digit of the computer word must be accompanied by a clock punch, since without it the digit will not be read into the DATATRON. The digit value is punched in the lower four channels, the F and C punches in the fifth and sixth channels, respectively. The seventh channel, which is ignored by the photoelectric reader, is used for the delete punch as an instruction to the Flexowriter and for the parity punch when tape is prepared with the tape preparation unit.

Table 23.2 Standard Alphameric Code for DATATRON Input and Flexowriter Output

Lowercase	Uppercase	Alphameric code	Lowercase	Uppercase	Alphameric code
a	A	20	0	)	40
b	B	61	1	½	41
c	C	62	2	&	42
d	D	63	3	/	43
e	E	64	4	$	44
f	F	65	5	%	45
g	G	66	6	?	46
h	H	67	7	!	47
i	I	70	8	*	50
j	J	71	9	(	51
k	K	72	+	=	24
l	L	36	−	—	25
m	M	73	;	:	26
n	N	74	,	,	31
o	O	75	.	.	32
p	P	76	'	"	33
q	Q	77	lowercase		27
r	R	21	uppercase		30
s	S	22	space		34
t	T	23	color shift		35
u	U	52	ignore		00
v	V	53	backspace		01
w	W	54	tab		04
x	X	55	carriage return		05
y	Y	56	stop		07
z	Z	57			

Each standard computer word on the tape occupies 12 digit positions: one for the sign, 10 for the binary-coded decimal digits of the word, and one for the finish punch which follows the last digit.

The form of a typical computer word as it would appear on paper tape for input to the DATATRON is illustrated in Fig. 23.7a. The last digit punched on the tape shown is a carriage-return code which is convenient for listing the contents of a tape. It causes the words to be printed in columnar form on the typewriter. The carriage-return code is not accompanied by a clock punch and is therefore ignored by the photoelectric reader.

The DATATRON uses a four-unit binary code which agrees with the Flexowriter code for purely numeric output. Numeric information

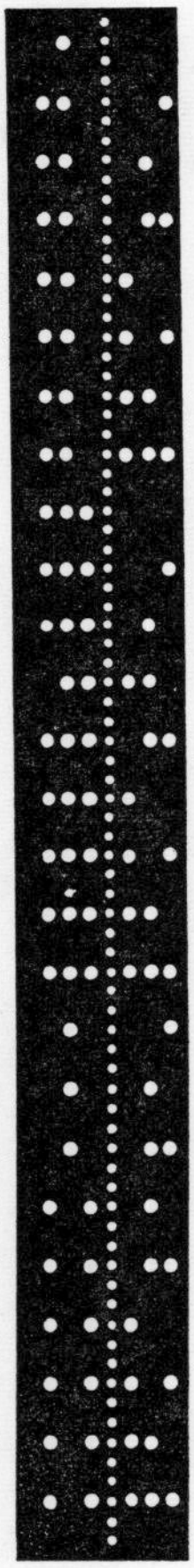

		TYPEWRITER ACTION			TYPEWRITER ACTION	
		L.C.	U.C.		L.C.	U.C.
		a	A	0	)	
		b	B	1	½	
		c	C	2	&	
		d	D	3	/	
		e	E	4	$	
		f	F	5	%	
		g	G	6	?	
		h	H	7	!	
		i	I	8	*	
		j	J	9	(	
		k	K	,	,	
		l	L	.	.	
		m	M	—	—	
		n	N	'	"	
		o	O	;	:	
		p	P	+	=	
		q	Q	TAB		
		r	R	LOWER CASE		
		s	S	UPPER CASE		
		t	T	CARRIAGE RETURN		
		u	U	COLOR SHIFT		
		v	V	BACK SPACE		
		w	W	DELETE		
		x	X	SPACE		
		y	Y	STOP CODE		
		z	Z	SPROCKET HOLES		

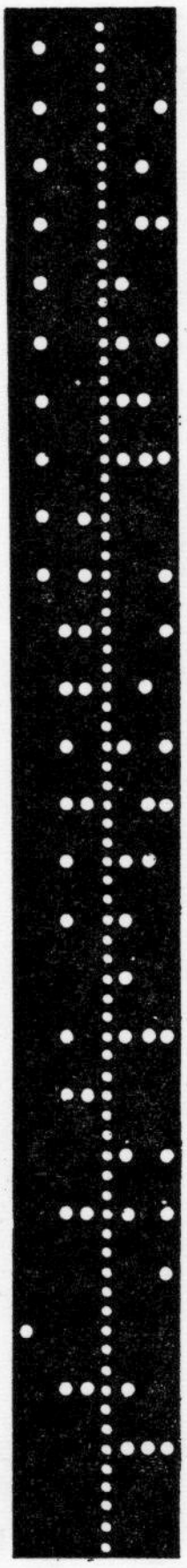

Fig. 23.8 Complete Flexowriter code.

from the DATATRON can be punched or typed on the Flexowriter without requiring translation. A typical word of numeric output as it would appear on paper tape is illustrated in Fig. 23.7b.

The Flexowriter uses a six-unit binary code which provides 63 possible code combinations. The Flexowriter code, as it would appear on perforated paper tape, is shown in Fig. 23.8. A perforated tape which would be produced by the punch unit when operating simultaneously with Flexowriter type-bar operation, or when the punch unit is producing tape after translation from the DATATRON code to the Flexowriter code, is shown in Fig. 23.7c.

For alphameric output, it is necessary to translate the DATATRON four-unit binary code into the Flexowriter six-unit binary code. This requires that two adjacent digits of the computer word be used for the representation of one alphameric character, three binary units from each computer digit being translated on output into one six-unit binary code. This translation is accomplished by the typewriter control. The standard alphameric code for DATATRON paper-tape input and for alphameric Flexowriter output from the computer is given in Table 23.2.

When alphameric output from the DATATRON is punched by the Flexowriter punch unit and the output does not pass through the typewriter control, the information appears on the tape in the untranslated DATATRON code. Tape produced with this arrangement is identical with that produced by the high-speed tape punch. The untranslated code, as it would appear on tape for subsequent alphameric translation, is illustrated in Fig. 23.7d. The complete Flexowriter code is shown in Fig. 23.8.

Paper tape is inexpensive and easy to handle, which makes it well suited for use in a small- or medium-size computer. It can be stored in considerably less space than punched cards, and if it is to be used as an auxiliary storage, it is probably superior in most respects to cards. During actual operation, a reel of paper tape is less likely to suffer damage than would a deck of cards in the same operation. Should physical damage occur, however, or should an error area be encountered, repair or correction of this area on paper tape is somewhat more difficult than it would be in a deck of punched cards.

Magnetic-tape Input-Output Equipment

Magnetic tapes are generally used by computers as supplementary storage devices. The relatively prevalent use of magnetic tape as an external storage medium is justified by the inherently large storage capacity. It is possible to store over 2 million characters on a single $10\frac{1}{2}$-in.-diameter reel of magnetic tape. This large reserve of storage capacity permits storage of permanent records, files, inventories, accounts, and other items of information too bulky to store in the internal memory unit of the computer. The reels of tape are usually arranged in tape bins or single tape-handling units. The average access time to any particular block of information on the tape is in the order of 15 sec. When the computer requires information from the tapes, an advance "search" order is initiated by the computer. The information is then located and read from the tape and applied through buffering equipment to the internal memory of the computer, such as a magnetic drum. The computer then refers to the drum for the requested information, the drum offering faster access to the information. This process is described further in this chapter in a later section, Input-Output Logic.

Typical tape-handling unit. The tape-handling unit (Fig. 23.9) contains the mechanical elements necessary to move the tape and read-write heads which insert and remove information. In the unit shown, movement of the reels is independent of tape movement past the heads and is controlled only by the position of the tape loops in the two vacuum columns (see Fig. 23.9a).

The use of vacuum columns provides several feet of slack tape ready for immediate movement without waiting for the reels to start their independent motion. The start time required for reel movement is in the millisecond range.

The tape is moved on command from the computer. To move the tape forward, the right-hand roller pivots to provide friction between the tape and a constantly rotating shaft. Reverse movement is initiated by the left-hand pinch roller pivoting against the left-hand shaft (see Fig. 23.9b).

Vacuum switches in the upper and lower tape guides sense the beginning or ending of a tape. Perforations at the end of the tape release the seal at one of the tape guides, activating the switch that stops all tape movement. Unperforated tape automatically seals the vacuum switches, allowing normal tape movement.

The gaps between the blocks (interrecord gaps) are required to accelerate the tape to operating speed or to decelerate the tape to a halt. When the tape is stationary, the read-write heads rest in the middle of a gap. This gap varies in width from $\frac{3}{4}$ to 3 in., depending upon the start-stop distance required by the tape-handling mechanism.

The operating rate of typical tape-handling units is about 60,000 characters per second (approximately 50 in. of tape travel per second).

Magnetic-tape system characteristics. Magnetic tape used in the storage unit is similar to that used in home tape recorders. The tape has a nonmagnetic base material such as Mylar or acetate with a magnetic coating on one side onto which the information is recorded. The completed tape is usually several thousandths of an inch thick and from $\frac{1}{2}$ to 3 in. wide. Average tape length is 2,500 ft wound on $10\frac{1}{2}$-in.-diameter reels.

Information is recorded on the tapes in the form of small magnetized areas referred to as bits. The information is divided into channels across the width of the tape and grouped into blocks the length of the tape, each block containing one of several computer words. Each block has an identifying address channel and a parity-checking channel, wherein a digit is carried along with each machine word as a check on the accuracy of the data. For machines using an even-parity-check system, the parity digit is 1 when the total number of 1s in a machine word is odd and 0 when the total number of 1s in a machine word is even (see Fig. 23.10). The read-write head shown in Fig. 23.10 is one of two. The other read-write

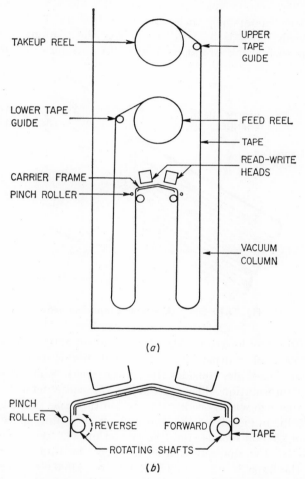

Fig. 23.9 (a) Tape-handling unit. (b) Enlarged view of roller mechanism.

head utilizes the spaces between the channels shown, resulting in an interlacing of the information. In this situation, the tape would have 12 recording tracks.

The storage density is approximately 200 characters per inch distributed in several channels across the width of the tape; hence, if a reel of tape is 2,500 ft in length, then the theoretical storage capacity is 6 million characters per reel (30,000 in. × 200 characters per inch). However, the theoretical capacity of 6 million bits per reel is not feasible because of the interrecord gap required between blocks of information. For example, suppose a block of computer information contained 100 characters. The storage space required for this block at a recording density of 200 characters per inch would be 0.50 in. The start-stop gap preceding each block is 0.75 in. Therefore, the amount of tape space required for each block would be 0.50 + 0.75, or 1.25 in. Dividing this

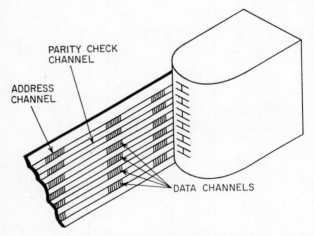

PARITY CHECK CHANNEL

ADDRESS CHANNEL

DATA CHANNELS

Fig. 23.10 Six-track magnetic tape and head.

distance into a reel length of 30,000 in. gives an actual storage capacity of 24,000 blocks of information or 2,400,000 characters per 2,500-ft reel.

As a second example, consider the storage space required on a reel for a computer information block containing 150 characters. A block of information this size would occupy 0.75 in. on the tape. Adding this length to the 0.75 in. required for the gap gives a recording space of 1.50 in. At this rate, 20,000 blocks could be stored on a 2,500-ft reel; however, since there are 150 characters in each block, the total number of characters on the tape is now 20,000 × 150, or 3,000,000, instead of the 2,400,000 in the previous example. Hence, the storage capacity of the tape is directly proportional to the recording density and the size of the recorded blocks of information and is inversely proportional to the gap width. The data blocks on magnetic tape are usually of fixed length for a given system.

Tape searching. Each data block has a specific address or identifying label. When a tape is searched for a specific address, the tape starts to move in a given direction. The sensing mechanism compares the address of the scanned tape with the address wanted. If the difference is increasing, the tape is quickly brought to a halt and reversed to move in the proper direction. When the proper address is found, the information in that data block is read from the tape and put into the internal storage unit of the computer to await further processing.

Summarizing, magnetic tape is a reliable and nonvolatile storage medium. Its main advantage is its ability to store millions of characters per reel. If more character storage is required, the tape units may be operated in parallel. It is also the most economical storage medium since the cost per character averages approximately $0.00001 per character per reel. The large storage capacity of magnetic tape makes the storage of voluminous business records feasible.

High-speed Printers

The desirability of obtaining visible records of computer output at rates compatible with the high internal speeds at which computers operate has resulted in the development of very-high-speed printing devices. Owing to the extremely complex internal mechanisms of these devices, the functions of printers will be treated, in this discussion, in only the most general terms.

Usually, distinction is made between two types of printers: mechanical and electronic. Physical contact between paper and a hard type is the essential characteristic of the mechanical printer. The electronic printer employs a sophisticated electronic character-formation process, with little or no physical contact between paper and print heads.

Mechanical printers

Line-at-a-time Printers. The so-called line printers are in rather wide use in computer installations today. They were originally developed for punched-card tabulators, but they are easily converted to output printers for on-line computer operation. The essential components of the typical line printer are print wheels containing 120 alphabetic, numeric, and special-character print positions. The print wheels are positioned by electric impulses according to characters desired. Special hammers activated by other electric impulses strike the corresponding print wheels. Paper and ink ribbons are guided by rotating sprockets between the print wheels and hammers. At an average speed of about 150 lines per minute, the characters are printed an entire line at a time, up to 120 characters per line. In this fashion, an entire program or any portion thereof may be printed when it is desired.

On-the-fly Printers. An electromechanical version of the line printer, capable of attaining very high speed, is the *on-the-fly* printer. The characters can be on individual wheels or in rows on a solid drum; in either case, they are struck by hammers when in the desired position. The distinctive feature is the continuous motion of the wheels or drum during operation. The movement of hammer and character is so synchronized as to allow them to strike the paper at precisely the desired instant and position. Some high-speed printing systems which incorporate this principle have attained a speed of 1,800 lines per minute.

Electrostatic printers. Electrostatic printers do not employ the principle of physical contact between paper and a hard print surface. Typical operation and characteristics are described in the following coverage of the Burroughs S-203 Electrostatic Printer.

The S-203 is a compact high-speed printer that occupies approximately 15 ft³ of space. The printing capabilities are:

> 72 characters per line
> 10 characters per inch horizontal
> 5 characters per inch vertical
> 100 to 3,000 words per minute

The S-203 requires a special type of paper. This paper is opaque with a plastic coating on one side. The width of the paper is 8½ in. and it comes in 500- and 1,000-ft rolls. A special-formula powdered ink is used to produce an image on the paper.

Print heads for the S-203 are arranged in sticks. Each stick contains a group of nine print heads. The print-head assembly is made up of eight sticks. The total number of print heads is therefore 72. These print heads are so arranged that a line of 72 characters can be printed across the 8½-in. paper. Printed characters have the appearance of capital letters. The active surface of each print head is very small and details can be discerned only under magnification.

Close examination of any print head reveals that it is made up of 35 pins arranged in a 7 × 5 matrix (see Fig. 23.11). These pins are molded in an insulating plastic. In addition to the matrix of pins, five vertical bars are molded into the plastic of the head. The five bars in each print head are electrically tied together. Each pin is completely independent of the other pins on that head and has its own voltage source. Each print head has the capability of reproducing any of the characters that can be printed by the S-203.

Electrostatic printing. Character formation is accomplished by applying a high voltage to a selected configuration of pins on the print head. An equally high voltage of opposite polarity is applied to the bars. Arcing occurs between the selected pins and the bars. This arcing sets up a strong electrostatic field between pin and bar.

During the printing operation, the plastic coating of the paper passes close to, but does not touch, the print head. When the pin-to-bar arcing occurs, the strong electrostatic field existing between pin an bar will cause charges to be deposited on the plastic coating of the paper. In this

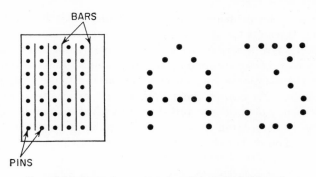

Fig. 23.11 Typical print head and characters formed.

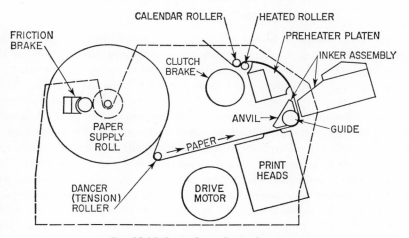

Fig. 23.12 Printer's mechanical system.

manner, the pattern of arcs on the print head is transferred to the paper as a similar configuration of charged areas. After the transfer takes place, the paper is advanced to an inking chamber. The static charges on the paper attract the dry powdered ink. The ink clings only to those areas that are charged. It should be noted that the paper does not physically enter the ink chamber, but passes close to the open port outlet of the ink chamber. This chamber is operated at a low vaccum so that any ink particles attracted by the charged paper must overcome a reverse air flow to reach the paper. Adjusting the vaccum will provide a means of controlling the inking. Characters should be sharp and clear with a minimum of background. The vacuum existing at the inking port would tend to draw the paper against the ink chamber. To offset this tendency, a higher vacuum is applied to the back of the paper as it crosses the anvil (see Fig. 23.12).

To complete the printing process, the print must be "fixed" (made permanent). Without fixing, the characters could be smudged or rubbed off. The characters are permanently fixed by passing the paper over a heated platen and then through a pressure roller. While the paper is over the platen, the plastic coating softens and the ink tends to settle further into the plastic. To ensure the fixing, the paper passes over a heated roller and is subjected to the pressure of a plastic calendar roller. The temperature of the platen and the heated roller is controlled to ensure proper fixing. Too little heat will allow the print to smudge on the roller. Too much heat causes distortion and, in some cases, peeling of the plastic coating.

Input-Output Logic

Some of the basic problems which must be solved in the logical design of input and output equipment can be best illustrated by showing the actual logic which could be formulated to meet a specific situation.

Note the logical diagram of a tape input buffer (Fig. 23.13). This name is appropriate and brings to mind the various meanings of the word "buffer" in connection with input-output equipment. In general, a computer buffer provides for a transfer of data from one computer unit to another in spite of differences in timing and format. Punched cards and magnetic tape have already been referred to as data media used in buffering. The buffer shown in Fig. 23.13 handles differences in both timing and format. Its actual physical location in a computer system would depend on its particular application, but normally it would be located in the input tape-reader unit. In such a case the overall designation "tape reader" would imply both a tape reader and any buffer required. In general, the logic of the tape input buffer will be described in sequential fashion, showing how data moves through the equipment. However, there is so much interaction between various stages of the buffer that an introduction emphasizing certain major functions is useful. Simplifications of the logic are used where appropriate.

The buffer performs the basic function of coupling between a five-channel tape reader and a computer drum memory (see Fig. 23.13). In this hypothetical application the computer receives a block of 16 input words at a time and places this data on a particular drum channel. Each input word contains four 5-bit characters (20 bits). Five bits are distributed across the width of the tape; as a result, only one 5-bit character, a tape character, can be fed to the buffer at any one time.

The difference in format that has to be handled by this buffer is as follows: The incoming data words were derived from a format suitable for human use. This means that the first character coming off the tape will contain the five MSBs of the first word while the fourth character

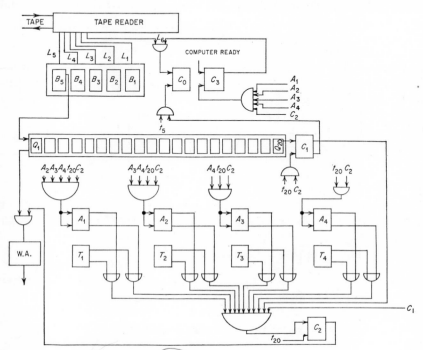

Fig. 23.13 Tape input buffer.

will contain the five LSBs of the same word. For computer drum-storage purposes it is most convenient for the LSB to be written into the input drum channel first and the MSB to be written last. The logic illustrated in Fig. 23.13 is designed to accomplish this format change as explained in the following paragraphs.

Each of the four tape characters which together constitute the first word of a 16-word data block are fed one at a time into the five-bit B register in parallel. After a tape character has been in the B register for a certain period of time it is shifted serially out of the B register into the Q register. The Q register is a 20-bit bidirectional serial shift register with an associated control flip-flop. The first tape character is fed into the Q register with the MSB first. At the appropriate time the second and third tape characters are fed into this register in a similar manner. Finally the fourth and last character is fed into the register with the LSB last. The Q register now contains a complete 20-bit word. When the time comes for this word to be fed into the drum write head, the register shifts out in the opposite direction so that the LSB is the first bit placed on the drum. Note that it will take 20 shift pulses to shift out the entire contents of the Q register. These timing pulses are provided by the computer and

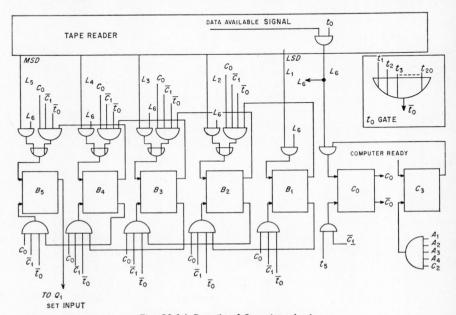

Fig. 23.14 Details of B-register logic.

are designated t_1, t_2, t_3, $\cdots$, t_{20}. They are 3 μsec wide and 20 μsec apart. An additional buffer timing pulse, t_0, is also provided. This pulse falls before t_1. All these pulses taken together provide a continuous 21-pulse cycle starting with t_0 and ending with t_{20}. Whether or not the pulses t_1 to t_{20} will actually be used to shift out the Q register depends on whether the register is full and on other conditions.

The overall purpose of the B register is to hold each tape character until it is time to shift it into the Q register (see Figs. 23.13 and 23.14). The five bits of a tape character are shifted out of the B register by timing pulses t_1 to t_5. It will be noted that there are six input lines (L_1 to L_6) to the B register. The five lines L_1 to L_5 contain the data read from the tape reader. L_6 is an input gating line. At t_0 time when data is present at the tape reader, a transfer pulse is gated onto line L_6 (see Fig. 23.14). This pulse in turn gates the data on lines L_1 to L_5 into the B-register flip-flops

B_1 to B_5. The t_0 gate in the tape reader is used to prevent external data from entering the B register while it is shifting out. It may be thought that the data itself could be used as an indication of its presence on the data lines. This approach has several disadvantages, however. One is that in certain cases it may be difficult to distinguish between a tape character of all zeros and a blank space on the tape.

In simplified form the purpose of control flip-flop C_0 associated with the B register is to indicate the presence of data in the B register. One of the inputs to C_0 is, of course, L_6.

Control flip-flops C_0, C_2, and C_3. The drum address registers and their associated control flip-flop C_2 comprise an important area of the logic (see Fig. 23.13). One of these registers is the T register. This is composed of four flip-flops and indicates which of 16 possible addresses the drum write head is passing over at the moment. The first location is 0000 and the sixteenth is 1111. The A register has a different function. Rather than indicating where the write head actually is, this register indicates the drum address into which the word in the Q register is to be written.

It will be noted that the T register changes its contents much faster than the A register does. Since the drum makes one revolution in 8 msec and the input channel contains 16 addresses, the T register will advance one count each $\frac{1}{2}$ msec. On the other hand, the A register advances each time a word from the incoming data block is written in the input drum channel. Thus, several advances of the T register will take place between each advance of the A register. The next coincidence of the A and T registers following a filling of the Q register with a word is the signal to write that word at the specified location at that time. Figure 23.12 shows some aspects of this logic. The eight wires leading from the A and T registers into the AND gate above flip-flop C_2 constitute a comparator circuit. These eight wires will all be high only if the A and T registers both contain the same number. This may be verified by trying various combinations and noting the results of the gating.

The C_2 flip-flop, which allows the contents of the Q register to be written on the drum, is set by the AND gate referred to in the preceding paragraph. The logic diagram shows that C_1 is an additional input to this gate. C_1 is set when the Q register is filled. Thus, it can be seen that in addition to a coincidence of the A and T registers, a full Q register is also necessary before writing on the drum can begin. It is assumed that advances in the T register are exactly synchronized with the t_0 pulse. The general logic of the buffer will now be described in sequential fashion. The computer indicates that the buffer should commence loading a 16-word block of data by providing the "computer ready" signal. This signal sets control flip-flop C_3. Since the first tape character is presumably being sensed by the tape reader, the "data available" signal will go high. This signifies to the buffer that data is available on the five input lines L_1 to L_5. At the beginning of the next cycle (t_0 time) a pulse will be gated onto L_6. This pulse will have two effects. It will gate data on the input lines into the B flip-flops. At the same time it will set C_0. At t_1 time the data in the B register will begin to shift out. The C_0 set equation and an explanation of its terms follows:

$$C_0: \quad 1 = (L_6 t_0) C_3$$

The L_6 input to the SET side has already been referred to. The C_0 flip-flop is to signal to other areas of the logic that data is in the B register and is ready to be shifted to the Q register. The t_0 condition is present so that C_0 can be set only at the beginning of a timing cycle. The C_3 condition ensures that no shift out of the B register can take place until the computer is ready to accept a block of data from the buffer. It can be noted from the B-register logic that the initial tape character of a new data block can be clocked into the B register without the presence of C_3. This does no harm, as the absence of C_3 will prevent this character from leaving the register.

Because of the complexity of the logic under discussion, it will be constructive to review what has been covered thus far. First, a buffer was described as providing for transfer of data from one computer unit to another in spite of differences in timing and format. The requirements for a hypothetical input-tape-reader buffer were then laid out. The input of this buffer is a five-bit-wide tape and its output is the write head of a drum channel. The buffer has to cope with typical differences in format between input and output data. It does so by utilizing the Q shift register which shifts data in and then out in the opposite direction. Twenty-one timing pulses, t_0 through t_{20}, make up a basic timing cycle. These pulses occur 20 μsec apart. At certain times, five of these pulses (t_1 to t_5) are used to shift tape characters into the Q register. When the Q register is full, 20 pulses (t_1 to t_{20}) are used to shift the binary word in this register to the drum channel by way of the drum write head.

Second, additional points of detail were covered. It was pointed out that the input storage or B register is fed by five data lines (L_1 to L_5) and one control line (L_6). This last line indicates the presence of data on the other five lines. The A and T registers were described. The T register indicates the particular address which is passing under the write head at any given moment. The A register shows where on the drum the word in the Q register should be written. When both registers contain the same number and the Q register is full, it is time to begin shifting the word in the Q register into the drum. This condition sets the C_2 flip-flop. Since this flip-flop allows the contents of the Q register to be written, it may be designated the *drum write flip-flop*. The timing cycle during which C_2 is high may be called the *drum write cycle*.

The four control flip-flops as a group may now be compared:

C_0 = input data transfer flip-flop (B register full)
C_1 = Q register full flip-flop
C_2 = drum write flip-flop
C_3 = computer ready flip-flop

The relationship between these four flip-flops may be summarized as follows: The "computer ready" signal sets C_3. C_3 allows L_6 and t_0 to set C_0. C_0 allows data to be shifted out of the B register into the Q register. At the end of the fourth shift, the 20-bit Q register will be full. When the Q register is full, C_1 will be set. After C_1 has been set, the next coincidence of the A and T registers will set C_2, initiating the drum write cycle. During the sixteenth drum write cycle, C_3 will be reset and will remain in this condition until the next "computer ready" signal.

Details of B-register logic. Figure 23.13 shows the general aspects of tape-input-buffer logic which have been described. The parallel shifting of data into the B flip-flops at t_0 time has also been discussed. Now Fig. 23.14 will be utilized to explain the details of the B-register shift-out.

This shift-out is controlled by flip-flop C_0. Note that as long as C_3 is set, C_0 will receive a SET input with the first timing pulse of each cycle (t_0). Further, as long as the Q register is not yet filled, C_0 will be reset by t_5. The C_0 RESET gate in Fig. 23.14 shows this. Thus, $\bar{C}_1$, when present, shows that the Q register is not filled. It has the function of preventing the contents of the B register from being shifted into a full Q register. Taken together, these three inputs allow data in the B flip-flops to shift to the left only under certain conditions, namely, during the timing pulses t_1, t_2, t_3, t_4, and t_5, provided the Q register is not filled.

A specific example of a B-register shift-out will now be given. The incoming tape character is 00001. Therefore, L_1 (the LSD line) has a 1 output. At t_0 time this information is gated by L_6 into the B register. B_1 will now contain a 1. No further information can enter the B register from the tape reader until the next t_0 time.

Notice the $\bar{t}_0$ gate insert in Fig. 23.14. It can be seen that a $\bar{t}_0$ pulse will be produced coincident with each timing pulse except t_0. There will therefore be 20 $\bar{t}_0$ pulses in a complete timing cycle. The first $\bar{t}_0$ pulse will be produced at t_1 time. At this time the four-input AND gates leading into the B flip-flops will be primed. In the case at hand, B_1, which was set at t_0 by data on L_1, will be reset at t_1. At the same time, however, the high output from B_1 leading into the four-input SET gate at B_2 will set this flip-flop. Thus, the 1 in B_1 is shifted to B_2. Since this action occurs simultaneously in several flip-flops, it will be well to review it in some detail. An examination of the inputs to flip-flops B_2 through B_5 shows that each of these flip-flops has $C_0\bar{C}_1\bar{t}_0$ gates leading to both its SET and RESET sides. As a result, if the timing pulses last long enough, each flip-flop will be set or reset to the configuration of the flip-flop on its right. Ultimately, all flip-flops would assume the state of B_1. This is not the objective of the B-register logic. It is therefore necessary to limit the timing-pulse duration to half or less than half of the switching time of the flip-flops. If a switching time of 8 μsec is assumed, a timing-pulse duration of 3 μsec would be satisfactory.

Now consider the five gates which lead into B_1 and B_2. At t_0 time, a 1 is gated into B_1 and a 0 remains in B_2 because L_2 is assumed low for this particular tape character. At t_1 time the two-input gates are inhibited. At the same time the four-input SET gate at B_2 and the B_1 RESET gates have high outputs. As a result, 1 μsec after the upclock of t_1, the following situation will occur: B_1 will begin to reset and B_2 will begin to set. Although the level of the ONE-side output of B_1 is dropping, it is still sufficient to initiate setting action in B_2. At the same time, the ZERO-side output of B_1, although rising, is not sufficient to influence B_2 through its RESET input gate. Seven microseconds later, the process will be complete and the 1 from B_1 will have been shifted into B_2.

At t_2 time the action in B_1, B_2, and B_3 will be as follows: B_1 will receive an input to its ZERO side and will remain in that state. B_2 will receive no inputs to its SET side. It will, however, receive a RESET input gated in from the ZERO side of B_1. This input will cause B_2 to begin to reset. In the meantime, B_3 will set because of an input from the ONE-side output of B_2. At an interval of 8 μsec later, the 1 originally in B_1 and then in B_2 will be in B_3. By the same process, t_3 will shift this 1 into B_4 and t_4 will shift it into B_5. Finally the next timing pulse, t_5, will shift the 1 into flip-flop Q_1 in the Q register.

It can be seen by retracing the logic that if the series of five gated timing pulses have shifted the contents of B_1 into Q_1, they will likewise shift the contents of B_2 into Q_2 and so on. Therefore 8 μsec after the t_5 pulse, the contents of the B register will lie in the first five flip-flops of the Q register. Pulse t_5 will also reset C_0 so that no more shifting of the B register will be possible during this timing cycle.

At the next t_0, C_0 will be set and another five-bit tape character will be shifted into the Q register. The original 1 from B_1 will now be in Q_{10}. During the next two timing cycles, two more tape characters will be shifted into the Q register. By t_5 time of the fourth cycle, the Q register will be full, containing the 20-bit word of the current data block. By logic to be explained later, the C_1, or "Q register full," flip-flop will go to the ONE state (see Fig. 23.13).

The setting of C_1 will have two effects. One is that the B-register shift gates will be inhibited by the absence of signal $\bar{C}_1$. The other is that the input from the C_1 ONE-side output to the comparator (C_2) gate will go high. This means that the C_2 flip-flop will be set by the next A and T register coincidence at t_0 time. Thus, it may be said that setting of the C_1 flip-flop inhibits additional inputs to the Q register and prepares for the transfer of the Q register's contents to the drum.

Q-register logic. The Q-register shift-in is now discussed in detail. Each Q-register element is a 20-μsec delay line (see Fig. 23.15). Because of space limitations, delay lines Q_4 through Q_{18} are not shown. Note that each delay line shown in the figure is fed by either two, three, or four AND gates as well as two OR gates. To simplify the explanation of the logic, the following two conventions will be used in designating the gates feeding any delay line:

1. The expression "input OR gate" refers to any $\bar{C}_0 + C_1$ gate shown in the diagram.
2. AND gates will be designated numerically from the left. For example, the $B_5 C_0 \bar{C}_1$ gate is the first AND gate of delay line Q_1. The $Q_4 C_2$ gate is the third AND gate of delay line Q_3.

Note that the output of delay line Q_1 terminates in three gates: AND gate 2 of delay line Q_1, AND gate 1 of delay line Q_2, and the drum write gate. (To save unnecessary words, AND gates in Fig. 23.15 will be designated in shortened form. For example, "$GA2$ of Q_1, means AND gate 2 of delay line Q_1.) The three outputs of Q_1 are utilized at three different times: The output leading to $GA2$ of Q_1 is used to recirculate the data bit, if any, in delay line Q_1. (Delay-line amplifiers necessary to compensate for losses in the circuit are not shown.) The output leading to $GA1$ of Q_2 is used to transfer a data bit coming out of Q_1 to Q_2 under certain conditions. An inspection of $GA1$ of Q_1 will show that the conditions for shift-in to Q_1 are $B_5 C_0 \bar{C}_1$. The $\bar{C}_1$ term means "Q register not full" while the C_0 term means data is available in the B register. The terms $C_0 \bar{C}_1$ in $GA1$ thus control when data may be shifted into the Q register. An examination of Fig. 23-15 will show that all No. 1 gates have the same terms. Therefore, these No. 1 gates may be termed shift-in gates.

Delay lines Q_3 through Q_{18}, which are missing from Fig. 23.14, have the same input and output configurations as the gates shown. It should be apparent, therefore, that when the $C_0 \bar{C}_1$ term is high, data will move into the Q register at a 20-μsec-per-bit rate. In other words, since the delay is 20 μsec, it will require 100 μsec for a bit entering Q_1 to reach Q_5. This transfer can only take place when C_0 and $\bar{C}_1$ are both present at the various No. 1 gates concerned.

Figure 23.14 shows that C_0 is reset by $t_5 \bar{C}_1$. This means that C_0 will go low after five timing pulses. This limits the number of data bits shifted into the Q register to five at a time. As the discussion of the B register pointed out, these shifts will take place during times, t_1, t_2, t_3, t_4, and t_5.

After t_5 time the No. 1 gates will be closed. If it were not for the recirculating gates (No. 2 gates), the information in the Q register would expire at t_6 time. However, the recirculating gates prevent this from happening. Notice any No. 2 gate—No. 2 of Q_1, for example. The terms

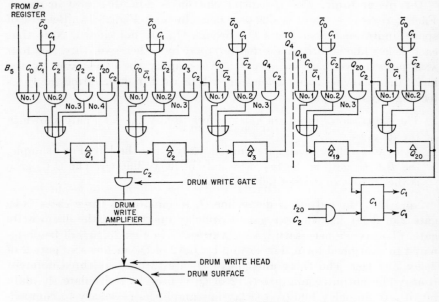

Fig. 23.15 Details of Q-register logic.

(other than Q_1) are $(\bar{C}_0 + C_1)\bar{C}_2$. It will be observed that these terms spell out the conditions under which data in Q-register delay lines can recirculate. First $\bar{C}_2$ must be present (see Fig. 23.14). From this diagram it should be apparent that when C_2 is present the Q register should be emptying. Thus, recirculation should be impossible at this time. The $\bar{C}_2$ condition, then, ensures that the recirculation gates will be inoperative during shift-out.

The $\bar{C}_0 + C_1$ term selects the two situations during the $\bar{C}_2$ period in which recirculation is indicated. $\bar{C}_2$ has to do with shift-in. It will be observed .that although the t_5 pulse resets the C_0 flip-flop, the $\bar{C}_0$ level will not actually develop at $GA2$ until just after t_5 time. Thus, during shift-in the recirculation gates (No. 2 gates, Fig. 23.15) will be inhibited from t_1 to t_5 and enabled from t_6 to t_0. This is, of course, consistent with correct functioning of the Q register at this time. The C_1 allows the Q register to recirculate while it is full until the drum write cycle begins. The logic of the recirculating gates is summarized by the following statement: The $(\bar{C}_0 + C_1)\bar{C}_2$ gates at the inputs to the Q-register delay lines serve the function of allowing the Q-register information bits to recirculate, except during shift-in and shift-out times.

Before the shift-out of the Q register is discussed, the "Q register full" function will be explained. It has been previously noted that flip-flop C_1 goes to the ONE state when the Q register fills. However, the method of getting this indication has not been explained. Figures 23.13 and 23.15 both show that C_1 is set to the ONE state by an output from delay line Q_{20}; that is, C_1: $1 = Q_{20}$.

For purposes of this discussion the bit which leaves Q_{20} and sets C_1 may be termed the *traveling control bit*. The insertion and progress of the bit through the Q register are examined. Note $GA4$ of delay line Q_1 in Fig. 23.13. This gate is used to insert the bit under discussion; the terms of the gate are $t_{20}C_2$. Signal C_2 is high only during the drum write period, thus, a traveling control bit can be inserted in Q_1 only once for each word written on the drum. Therefore, it may be stated that the function of $GA4$ of Q_1 is to insert a bit into Q_1 at the last bit time of the drum write period.

This bit will be shifted to the right and will eventually serve the function of setting C_1 as the Q register fills. In order to understand how this is accomplished, it will be useful to reexamine the situation in the Q register immediately following the insertion of the traveling control bit. Insertion time ($t_{20}C_2$) will be followed by the condition $t_0\bar{C}_2$. At this time the bit which entered delay line Q_1 at $t_{20}C_2$ time will recirculate, reentering Q_1 by way of its No. 2 gate. (Although it is set by the t_0 pulse, flip-flop C_1 will not be in the ONE state until a few microseconds after the leading edge of t_0 passes. This is because of circuit delays. Therefore, at $t_0\bar{C}_2$ time $\bar{C}_0$ will still be present to enable $GA2$ of Q_1.) At t_1 time this same bit will be entering Q_2 through its No. 1 gate. At t_5 time this bit will enter delay line Q_6. However, at t_6 time when it leaves Q_6 it will not be able to enter Q_7 through its $GA1$. Instead, it will be recirculated during times t_6 through t_0. This is consistent with the previously described recirculating gate logic. During t_1 to t_5 times of the next shift-in cycle the traveling control bit will move five delay lines to the right, landing in Q_{11}. During the next shift-in cycle it will land in Q_{16}. During the fourth and last shift-in cycle the bit will be shifted into C_1, signifying that the Q register is full.

As has been previously mentioned, the C_1 flip-flop will remain set until the end of the bit time of the last bit of the drum write cycle (consult Figs. 23.13 and 23.15). Under typical conditions the drum is not ready to receive the word in the Q register immediately following the loading of the register. In other words, a drum write cycle does not normally directly follow the fourth loading cycle. The reason for this is that the drum cannot be loaded until the proper data location is about to come under the drum write head. This condition is indicated by the coincidence of the A and T registers (see Fig. 23.13).

It will be recalled from the introduction to this section that the T register shows the actual drum location under the drum write head (which also can function as a read head). The purpose of the A register is to indicate the location at which the word in the Q register is to be stored. There are 16 such locations on the data input drum channel. They are consecutively numbered from 0000 to 1111. Each location holds one 20-bit word.

The A register will function correctly if it follows this pattern: When the first word of a data block is in the Q register, the A register should show 0000. When this word has been transferred to the drum, the A register should show 0001. When the next word has been transferred to the drum, the A register should show 0010. This process should continue until the sixteenth (and last) word of the data block has been transferred. At this time the A register should recycle to 0000. The logic for bringing about these conditions will now be introduced.

Note the A-register logic shown in Fig. 23-13. This register consists of four complemented flip-flops with the LSD on the right. Each gate, except the one feeding A_4, receives one or more inputs from other A-register flip-flops. Assume the register contains all zeros. Then at the last bit time (t_0) of the first drum write cycle of a data block, C_2 will be high and A_4 will be set. The register will then contain a 1. At the last bit time of the second drum write cycle, A_4 (being a complemented flip-flop) will be reset and thus indicate a 0. At the same time the gate to flip-flop A_3 will set it to the ONE state. It will be apparent that the register has received two inputs and has counted from 0000 to 0001 and then to 0010. Further, an examination of the A-register logic will show that it will continue to advance one count each $t_{20}C_2$ time, thus satisfying the requirements specified above.

The actual drum write cycle is initiated by the setting of flip-flop C_2. As was previously mentioned, the OR and AND gates feeding the SET side of C_2 form a detector of coincidence between the A and T registers. The additional condition C_1 ensures that C_2 can be set only when the Q register is full. Thus, it may be stated that when C_2 is set, the Q register contains a word and it is time to write this word in the drum channel (A and T register coincidence). It is therefore logical to expect C_2 to play an important part in Q-register shift-out logic.

Q-register shift-out and drum write will now be described (consult Fig. 23.15). Notice particularly the No. 3 gates leading to the delay lines. At C_2 time the bits which have been recirculating in anticipation of the correct location appearing under the drum write head will now begin to shift out of the register and into the drum. If it is assumed that the T register shows each new drum position at t_0 time, it will not be until just before t_1 time of the drum-write cycle that C_2 output voltages will be at full SET value. Thus, the first shift left in the Q register will be at $t_1 C_2$ time. There will be, in effect, no $t_0 C_2$ time at all. Note that bits shifted out of Q_1 are gated into the drum by the drum write gate. At $t_{20} C_2$ time the Q_1 delay line will be "busy." At its output the last data bit is being gated into the drum. At its input the traveling control bit is being gated in. As the t_{20} pulse develops, these C_2 levels will begin to fall off, but not fast enough to prevent the desired gating. However, a few microseconds after the downclock of t_{20}, the C_2 flip-flop will be firmly in the RESET condition.

The final steps of the tape input buffer in handling a data block will now be described. When the A and T registers indicate drum-write coincidence for the sixteenth word in a data block C_3, RESET conditions will be satisfied (see Figs. 23.13 and 23.14). This means that C_0 cannot be set again until the computer is ready for another data block. The B register can still load on the condition of L_6, but it cannot shift out without C_0.

The logical functioning of the tape input buffer may now be summarized. The computer initiates the loading of a 16-word block of data by generating the "computer ready" signal. This signal permits the development of C_0. C_0 allows data gated into the B register by L_6 to be shifted into the Q register. Five such bits are shifted per timing cycle. At the end of four complete timing cycles following the "computer ready" signal, the Q register will be full. At this time C_1 is set and the data in the Q register will recirculate until the drum write cycle. During the drum write cycle the Q register will shift out into the drum. This cycle begins when the proper drum location is about to come under the drum write head. This condition is signaled by a coincidence of the A and T registers. The four-flip-flop A register indicates the drum location into which the next word will go. It goes through a complete 16-count cycle once for each data block loading. The T register indicates which drum location is passing under the write head. It goes through a complete 16-count cycle every drum revolution. Once the Q register is full, a coincidence of the A and T registers allows the generation of C_2, which enables the shifting out of the Q register. At the last drum write cycle, C_3 will be reset and the buffer will await another "computer ready" signal.

QUESTIONS

23.1 List the forms of direct input and indirect input.
23.2 Differentiate between on-line and off-line equipment.
23.3 What type or types of information can be represented on a punched card?

23.4 What type or types of information can be represented on punched paper tape?

23.5 Between punched card and punched paper tape, which medium is more easily modified or updated? Explain your answer.

23.6 Which method of punched-card and punched-paper-tape reading offers highest speed?

23.7 In magnetic-tape systems, what factors determine the size of the interrecord gaps?

23.8 Why is interlacing of the information necessary in magnetic-tape systems?

23.9 Why are high-speed output printing devices desirable?

23.10 In the tape-input-buffer diagram shown in Fig. 23.12, what dictates the pulse recurrence rate of the t_0 to t_{20} timing pulses?

23.11 What is the function of the C_0 flip-flop in the tape-input-buffer diagrams? Briefly describe how this flip-flop accomplishes its function.

23.12 What other logical element or elements can be used to replace the Q-register delay-line elements?

23.13 What is the purpose of the traveling control bit?

Chapter 24

Programming the Computer

Since it is beyond the scope of this chapter to give a complete course in programming, the bulk of it is devoted to a general discussion of those topics that are fundamental to the art. Coding fundamentals are introduced and discussed in general terms. Finally, coding operations will be illustrated by means of a simplified computer and a sample problem.

History

Early in the nineteenth century, the British mathematician Charles Babbage designed the forerunner of the modern automatic digital computer. Babbage's first machine, the "difference engine," was designed to compute mathematical tables. Then in 1833 Babbage designed a general-purpose computer called the "analytical engine," the first machine to permit automatic control over the sequencing of arithmetic operations. Attempts to build efficient working models of Babbage's machines were unsuccessful, however, because of financial difficulties and the impossibility at that time of fabricating the parts with sufficient precision.

Babbage's idea of automatic sequential control was first incorporated into the automatic sequence-controlled calculator, or Mark I, designed by Dr. Howard Aiken of Harvard University and later built by the university in cooperation with the International Business Machines Corporation. It went into operation in 1944, and its basic component is the electromechanical relay.

Another advance in computer technology was made when Dr. J. W. Mauchly and Mr. J. P. Eckert of the University of Pennsylvania designed the electronic numerical integrator and computer (ENIAC). It was completed in 1946, and it was the first computer to be entirely electronic in its internal operation. It is sequence-controlled by a combination of switches, externally wired plugboards, and punched cards.

Perhaps the greatest advance in automatic computing came in 1945 when Dr. John von Neumann introduced the idea of storing computer instructions internally, instead of controlling a computer by means of plugboard wiring or instructions stored in some external medium such as punched paper tape or cards. In the United States this idea was first used in the design of the electronic discrete variable automatic computer (EDVAC). Today every general-purpose digital computer in operation is of the stored-program type, with the exception of a few older models and those small computers that cannot accommodate a stored program. The stored-program idea not only increased the speed of the computer but also revolutionized programming. Storing the computer instructions internally in the form of numbers enables a computer to perform arithmetic operations on its own instructions. Internal storage of instructions enables the programmer to program the computer to alter its instructions automatically. This is called *instruction modification*, and it has become a routine part of the programming process.

Since the computer can store and execute commands, it is said to have its own language, and it is the programmer's primary task to translate the problem language into computer language. The process of translating the problem into computer instructions is called *coding*, and it can be difficult because of the great difference between the two languages. Therefore, the computer itself is nearly always used to help the programmer perform the translation. This is called *automatic coding*.

Because of the ability of the computer to operate on its own instructions logically and arithmetically, it is possible to construct an intermediate language with which the programmer is more familiar to code the problem. This intermediate language is inserted into the computer; the computer translates it into computer instructions by means of a program. This makes coding easier, since much of the translating burden is shifted from the programmer to the computer.

The intermediate language and a program written in that language have been given various names. They have been given the names *pseudo-code* and *pseudo-coded program*, respectively. They have also been given the names *source language* and *source program*, respectively. Programmers sometimes refer to them as the *symbolic language* and the *symbolic program*, respectively, because the intermediate language employs alphameric symbols (symbols consisting of some combination of alphabetic and numeric characters) instead of the actual operation codes and addresses of the computer. The language of the computer is then called either the *target language* or the *object language*, and the computer language program is called either the *target program* or the *object program*. A program that will translate a source program into computer language is called an *assembly program* or *compiling program*, because it assembles or compiles computer instructions by using the source program as a reference.

Great advances have been made in recent years in the field of automatic coding. A typical example in the field of scientific computing is the mathematical formula translation system, or FORTRAN system, developed by the International Business Machines Corporation for its 704 computer. The FORTRAN compiler went into use in January, 1957, and it performs the function its name implies. It will translate complex algebraic formulas into computer instructions, and like all other compilers of the same type it is called an *algebraic compiler*. FORTRAN also simplifies input-output programming and the handling of one-, two-, and three-dimensional arrays of data. FORTRAN II, a recently improved version, also has a subprogramming feature which makes it easier for programmers to code sections of a problem independently and then combine the sections into one program. Many other compilers have similar features.

Applications

General-purpose digital computers have their widest application in the scientific and business data-processing fields. Mathematical problems arising in the fields of science and engineering are grouped under the former heading, and clerical and accounting problems arising in the fields of business administration and finance are grouped under the latter heading. The computation of missile trajectories to determine the efficiency of missile designs might be an example of the former type of application; and the computation of a monthly bank statement, an example of the latter. General-purpose computers are also used for research purposes. For example, the IBM 704 computer has been programmed for research purposes in the field of logic, to play chess. Special-purpose digital computers also have many applications. For example, they may be used for air traffic control, for computing racetrack odds, for the automatic aiming of missiles, and for controlling numerous industrial processes. These are only a few of the many applications of modern digital computers.

Computer applications may also be classified as either the repetitive type or the one-shot type. In the repetitive type of application, the same program is used again and again, with different input values each time. For example, once a program has been written to compute missile trajectories, the same program may be used repeatedly in the design of future missiles having similar design parameters. The computation of a table of prime numbers is an example of a one-shot application, because the prime numbers never change, and hence a program to compute a table of such numbers would need to be used only once. One-shot problems are programmed for a computer only when necessary, for reasons of economy.

The Computer

Although computers differ widely in their particulars, they are similar in general. Most modern computers employ either a magnetic drum or bimagnetic cores as a main memory device. The larger computers may employ bimagnetic cores as a main memory device and use magnetic drums as an auxiliary storage medium. Most modern computers employ punched cards, magnetic tapes, and some type of printing device for input or output, although some may also use punched paper tape as well as other types of input or output media. Magnetic tapes also serve as an auxiliary storage medium.

An operating console with its buttons, switches, and indicators is used for external control of the computer. It is used to start and stop the computer, display the contents of a particular register or memory location, stop the computer at some predetermined point in the program for code-checking purposes, and so on. Most computers also have other special switches and indicators that may be used for programming purposes.

Also of concern to the programmer are the various registers in the computer and their functions. Most modern computers have three arithmetic registers and various control registers such as an instruction register, operation register, address register, and perhaps an instruction counter. The arithmetic registers are used in performing arithmetic and various logical operations. The control registers are used by the computer to select, interpret, and execute instructions. The computer may also have one or more indexing registers.

In addition to its speed and freedom from error, the computer has two capabilities that make it such a powerful tool. It can alter its own instructions automatically, and it can choose between two or more paths in the program, depending on conditions existing within itself. That is, every computer will have *conditional jump* commands included in its language. In general, the commands enable the computer to choose one of two paths in the program, depending on whether a number stored internally is plus or minus, zero or nonzero, and so on. These conditional jump commands and the capability of the computer to alter its own instructions are the building blocks used by the programmer in the coding of any problem.

The Programmer

Since the programmer's primary task is to translate the problem language into computer language, he must have an intimate knowledge of both languages. He must also have a detailed knowledge of the components of the computer and how they function singly and in relation to each other from a programming point of view. He need have no knowledge of electronic or circuit logic, although that additional knowledge would certainly not be harmful.

It has been truthfully said that programming is not a science but an art, and hence the programmer is as much an artist as he is a technician. This is because each problem consists of two different but related parts, the arithmetic and the logic involved. Although the arithmetic may remain essentially the same, the logic of each new problem is usually entirely different from any of its predecessors. The programmer must work out an entirely new logical sequence for each new problem, and in doing so he is thrust upon his own resources. He must, then, use his imagination and ingenuity in the coding of each new problem to arrive at an efficient program.

Steps in Problem Solving

The following five steps are involved in the solution of any problem with the aid of a computer:

1. Analysis
2. Planning
3. Coding
4. Code checking
5. Production

Analysis. Scientific problems are analyzed to determine the best method of solution from the point of view of computing time and accuracy. Most scientific problems consist of a number of interrelated but separate mathematical problems. For example, in solving any single scientific problem, it may be necessary to solve a system of differential equations, solve a system of simultaneous algebraic equations, solve trigonometric and other transcendental equations, solve an algebraic equation of high degree, perform matrix manipulations, perform table interpolations, and so on. Each of these mathematical problems, and others not mentioned, may be a part of the total problem. There are various reasons why each part must be analyzed. Scientific problems frequently give rise to differential, integral, or integrodifferential equations having no known formal solution. The problem must then be analyzed to determine the best numerical method of approximating the solution to any desired degree of accuracy. In other instances, such as in solving an algebraic equation of the fourth degree, a formal solution may be known, but a numerical method may be employed because it is easier to program. In still other instances, such as in performing table interpolation, many methods may be available; and they may all be easy to program, but some analysis is still necessary because one method may be more nearly accurate than another, depending on the data involved. These problems, and others not mentioned, are solved by using the methods of numerical analysis. Numerical analysis is the concern of mathematicians, and they have formulated various methods of solving the problems mentioned above. Extensive analysis is still necessary in most instances, however, because these methods differ widely as far as accuracy and computing time are concerned and because the accuracy of the method may depend on the results to be obtained.

The programmer sometimes performs the analysis, if it is not too difficult, but usually the services of a highly trained mathematical analyst are required.

It is also necessary to analyze business problems, but less from a mathematical and more from a procedural point of view. Business problems are less self-contained, and hence various procedural methods must be analyzed to arrive at an efficient solution. This is no less difficult, and the services of an experienced systems analyst are usually required.

Planning. Planning is more properly called *programming*, but the term programming is popularly used in reference to the overall problem-solving process. Since the term is used here in its popular sense, the term planning has been used for this step of the problem-solving process. An important part of the planning step is the drawing of a flow chart. Planning also includes such things as allocating blocks of memory locations to instructions, data, intermediate results, subroutines, final results, and other miscellaneous items. It might also include such things as choosing input-output media and preparing input-output formats.

Coding. Once the analysis and planning have been completed, the programmer can start writing actual computer instructions, either in source language or in computer language. The process of writing computer instructions is called coding; and in whatever language the programmer uses, coding can be a time-consuming process because of the complexity of most problems and the detail involved.

During the coding process the programmer searches either his own memory or a programmer's manual to determine what computer commands are available which will cause the computer to perform each of the logical and arithmetical processes required by the problem; and by combining these commands in the proper sequence, he contrives the complete program.

The programmer's skill may be measured by the size of his program and the computing time that it requires, because he should strive to minimize computing time and the number of commands required. In practice these factors frequently oppose each other, and the programmer should then strive to either minimize one and stress the other or arrive at a good compromise between the two, his choice dictated by the problem.

The coding step is perhaps the greatest source of error in the entire problem-solving process since coding mistakes are easily made, even by experienced programmers, owing to the complexity of the logic and the detail involved.

Code checking. Code checking is the process of locating and correcting mistakes in coding. It is also called *debugging*.

Since coding mistakes are easily made and sometimes difficult to locate, the programmer has many ways of code checking. There are methods that do not involve the computer, and one or more of these methods should be applied first because they are less expensive.

For example, the programmer may visually check the finished program, instruction by instruction. This has a disadvantage associated with it in that the programmer in following the same train of thought has a tendency to repeat the same mistakes he made originally. This could be circumvented by having another person check each instruction. This also has a disadvantage associated with it, however, in that the other person would have to be briefed on the details of the problem unless he were already familiar with them.

Punched cards may also be used as an aid in code checking. That is, the program might be punched in cards, and these cards might then be machine-sorted and listed in various ways to facilitate the checking of the validity of operation codes and addresses. Although this method is relatively quick and easy, it is also superficial, since the operation codes and addresses may be valid but may be incorrect as used in the program.

Another method of code checking is to translate the computer instructions back into flow-chart form. The resultant flow chart may then be compared with the original, with a discrepancy between the two indicating a coding mistake. This method has the same disadvantages as the first method mentioned above, although it is a good method in that it would detect any mistake in the logic of the program.

Experience has shown that a few coding mistakes go undetected in spite of any prechecking that may be done and that the code-checking phase really begins when the first "check run" is made on the computer. The programmer then has two main methods of debugging. He may look for a coding mistake by watching the console display indicators as he steps through the instructions in a section of his program. Programmers call this "debugging at the console." It is very expensive, and hence experienced programmers employ this method only as a last resort. A second main method of debugging is to use a computer program written for that purpose. These programs are of two types: a *dump routine* or a *tracing routine.* A dump routine is a program that is used to print out (or dump) all or part of the contents of the memory of the computer while another program is running, after it has stopped, or perhaps both. Similar dump routines are used to print the contents of auxiliary storage devices such as magnetic tapes or drums. In addition to these prepared dump routines, the programmer may write his own dump routines as an integral part of his program. That is, he may program the computer to print out results at strategic points in his program for debugging purposes. Then after the program has been checked out, he may remove these special instructions from his program or he may leave them in his program as dead weight and bypass them by means of switch settings at the console.

If dumping fails to locate a coding mistake, the programmer may use a tracing routine. A tracer is essentially a program that takes over the program to be checked and interprets and executes each of its instructions, while at the same time it records the location of each instruction, the instruction itself, the contents of the various registers, and the status of the various indicators and switches on the console. This gives the programmer a detailed map of what is happening in the computer as each of his program instructions is being executed. However, a tracing routine is expensive from the point of view of computer time, and hence it is also something of a last resort.

In conjunction with dumping and tracing, a hand calculation should be used as an aid in debugging whenever possible. That is, final or intermediate results should be computed by hand for one set of inputs, and these results should be compared with results obtained from the program. The hand calculations are usually performed on a desk calculator, and they not only indicate the correctness of the results obtained from the program but also are a definite aid in locating a coding mistake.

In spite of these various aids, debugging is frequently a time-consuming process. It is time-consuming because most programs are so large that they contain a number of coding mistakes, and any two or more coding mistakes may influence each other in such a way as to disguise each other. In other instances, some detail is involved that is so minute that it is repeatedly overlooked by the programmer as he scans the program instructions.

Production. Once a program has been checked out, it may be used to obtain results; it is then said to be in the production stage. Production runs may be made by the programmer; but once the program has reached the production stage, it is usually given to a production group. It is the responsibility of the production group to convert input data to the proper form and format and make production runs whenever they are requested by the originator of the problem. This relieves the programmer of any further responsibility so that he may devote full time to the programming of future problems.

Although the above five steps have been listed in the order of their performance, at any stage of the problem-solving process the programmer may have to reexamine and perhaps change what has been done previously, and he may have to do this a number of times.

The time required to get a program into production varies over a wide range. There are problems that can be programmed in a week or less, but in most scientific and business applications it takes anywhere from a month to more than a year to complete the five steps listed above.

Flow Charting

A flow chart is a block diagram that graphically illustrates the sequence of steps to be taken in the solving of a problem, and there are many different types. For example, in business applications there are systems charts and computer block diagrams, and other levels of flow charting may be employed between these two extremes. A systems chart is used to present a general picture of the overall problem, and it is mainly of interest to management. A computer block diagram illustrates the detailed steps to be taken by the computer, and it is mainly of interest to the programmer.

This section is concerned with computer block diagrams, and since the term "flow chart" is popularly used in reference to computer block diagrams, it will be used in that sense.

In addition to the existence of many different types of flow charts (computer block diagrams can also be broken down into various subtypes), a wide variety of symbols is used (Fig. 24.1). When a flow chart is drawn, a symbol shaped like a punched card is often used to represent an input or an output operation involving punched cards. A rectangular symbol, sometimes called a *computing box*, is usually used to represent a sequence of arithmetic operations. A truncated ellipse, sometimes called a *decision box*, is usually used to represent a conditional choice that is to be made by the computer. Other symbols are sometimes used to represent these and other computer operations. These symbols are usually connected by arrows to indicate the logical sequence of operations.

No two computer installations necessarily adopt the same set of flow-chart symbols, and the same can be said of any two programmers. Hence only a few of the more common symbols that are used in the drawing of a typical flow chart will be listed. A sample flow chart will be found in Fig. 24.2.

A flow chart is used as a guide by the programmer as he codes the problem. It also serves as a valuable reference if another programmer

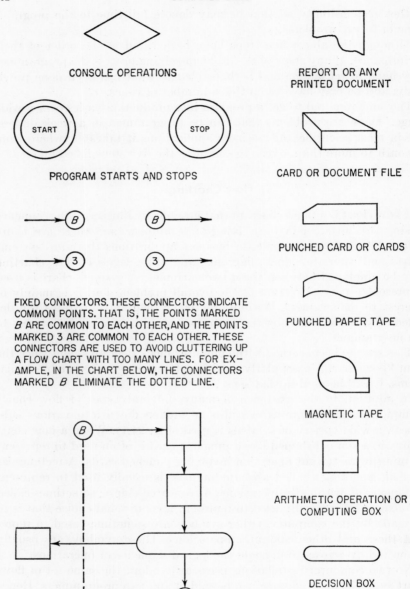

CONSOLE OPERATIONS

REPORT OR ANY
PRINTED DOCUMENT

PROGRAM STARTS AND STOPS

CARD OR DOCUMENT FILE

PUNCHED CARD OR CARDS

PUNCHED PAPER TAPE

FIXED CONNECTORS. THESE CONNECTORS INDICATE
COMMON POINTS. THAT IS, THE POINTS MARKED
B ARE COMMON TO EACH OTHER, AND THE POINTS
MARKED 3 ARE COMMON TO EACH OTHER. THESE
CONNECTORS ARE USED TO AVOID CLUTTERING UP
A FLOW CHART WITH TOO MANY LINES. FOR EX-
AMPLE, IN THE CHART BELOW, THE CONNECTORS
MARKED *B* ELIMINATE THE DOTTED LINE.

MAGNETIC TAPE

ARITHMETIC OPERATION OR
COMPUTING BOX

DECISION BOX

Fig. 24.1 Flow-chart symbols.

takes over the problem at any stage of the programming process. The originator of the problem might also use it to familiarize himself with the generalities of the program.

Computer Instructions

To enable the computer to locate instructions and data, each memory location has a numerical address. Each number stored in a memory location, or any number consisting of the same number of digits, is called a *word*. The number of digits that make up a word defines the *word length* of the computer.

Regardless of the number system used in a computer or the word length, each instruction word will consist of at least two parts, an operation code and an address. The operation code tells the computer what action to perform and the address tells the computer where to get the data to perform the action. That is, the computer will break down each instruction word into various digit groups for interpretation. One digit group will be interpreted as an operation (add, subtract, etc.), and one or more digit groups will be interpreted as reference addresses. If the computer has index registers, each instruction word may also contain digit groups for calling in these registers. Index registers are discussed later in this chapter.

The manner in which a computer breaks down its instructions into digit groups is called its *instruction format*. A single-format machine breaks down all its instruction words into the same digit groups. A multiformat machine will break down some of its instruction words into different digit groups depending on the type of instruction. (In addition to multiformat machines, there are variable-word-length computers.)

There are also one-, two-, and four-address machines. In these machines each instruction word has one, two, three, or four address parts, respectively. In addition there are computers that use the one-plus-one addressing system. These are called *modified single-address* computers. In this system each instruction word has two address parts; but instead of each address being that of an operand, as is the case in a two-address machine, one address is that of an operand and the other address tells the computer where to locate its next instruction.

In a single-address computer successive instructions are stored in sequentially numbered memory locations, and the computer locates its successive instructions by means of a counter termed either a *program counter* or an *instruction counter*. In a modified single-address computer, no program counter is needed since each instruction word contains an address which tells the computer where to locate its next instruction. These two types of computers also differ from a programming point of view. In a single-address computer, the programmer must store his successive instructions in sequentially numbered memory locations, but in a modified single-address computer, he may store his successive instructions at random relative to memory locations. Another minor difference is that the modified single-address computer does not require an unconditional-jump instruction in its set of operation codes since the address part of each instruction word that tells the computer where to locate its next instruction is effectively an unconditional-jump command.

Although no two computers have the same set of operation codes, certain types are required in any machine. There must be operation codes for performing arithmetic operations, transferring words from one location to another, performing input-output operations, making conditional choices, and miscellaneous operation codes such as a stop command, and so on. Along with these codes there will be other operation codes peculiar to a particular machine. (Some computers have 150 or more operation codes.)

Program Loops

A loop may be defined as a sequence of instructions that is executed repeatedly by the computer, and any program will consist of a network of these loops. For example, in a banking problem the input to the program might be a list of checks. The programmer would then write a sequence of instructions to process the first check. He would then program the computer to alter one or more of the instructions in the sequence to enable it to locate the next check. He would then program the computer to repeat the sequence, and he would put some type of conditional-jump instruction (or test) in his program at that point to tell the computer when to stop repeating the sequence. This entire sequence of instructions, including the instruction modifications and testing, would then be repeated by the computer until all the checks had been processed. The conditional-jump instruction would then cause the computer to jump to another sequence of instructions, perhaps to print out the results.

Basically, the writing of a loop requires two steps, modifying instructions and testing; however, sometimes a third step is required. After a sequence of instructions has been repeated by the computer a number of times and one or more of the instructions in the sequence has been altered, it sometimes becomes necessary to repeat the sequence again with the altered instructions restored to their original form. The computer must then be programmed to perform this restoration. This is called *initializing* a loop.

Instruction modification, testing, initializing, and looping are fundamental to the art of programming. Hence, these things will be illustrated by a discussion of the construction of a simple computer and the coding of a sample problem.

Simplified Computer

The simplified computer is a modified single-address decimal machine having a word length of 10 digits preceded by a sign bit. It will have an output unit, a memory unit, an arithmetic unit, and a control unit. The control unit will contain the necessary registers for interpreting and executing instructions, and it need not be described in further detail. The output unit will be a printer. The memory unit will be a magnetic drum capable of storing 4,000 words in memory addresses 0000 through 3999. The arithmetic unit will contain two registers called the A and R registers, each capable of containing one word, with the R register having no sign position. The A register will be used for adding and subtracting, and the R register will be used as a right-hand extension to the A register for performing shift operations.

The computer will have an instruction format of the form $+$CC DDDD NNNN. The first two digits (CC) of each instruction word will be the operation code. The next four digits (DDDD) will be the address of an operand. The last four digits (NNNN) will be the address of the next instruction to be executed. These addresses will be called the D and the N addresses, respectively.

The computer will operate in the basic two-phase cycle: an execute phase and a fetch phase. During the execute phase, the operation code and D address will be interpreted and the instruction will be executed. During the fetch phase, the N address will be interpreted and the next instruction will be fetched into the appropriate control register in preparation for the next execute phase. These phases will occur alternately during the execution of the program.

The computer will have the operation codes listed below. The two numerical digits in the first column represent the actual operation code as it would appear in the computer. The two capital letters that follow are an abbreviation of the operation code. The words in parentheses are a brief description of the operation code. The last column contains a detailed description of the operation code. These operation codes, which would normally be listed in a programmer's manual, are as follows:

01 CA (Clear and add)	Clear the A register to $+0$ and then add to it the contents of the D address.
02 AD (Add)	Add the contents of the D address to the contents of the A register and leave the sum in the A register.
03 SU (Subtract)	Subtract the contents of the D address from the contents of the A register and leave the remainder in the A register.

04 SR (Shift right)	Shift the contents of both the A and the R registers right the number of places specified by the D address and insert a 0 into the high-order position of the A register for each place shifted. The sign of the A register is not shifted. It remains unchanged.
05 SL (Shift left)	Shift the contents of both the A and the R registers left the number of places specified by the D address and insert a 0 into the low-order position of the R register for each place shifted. The sign of the A register is not shifted. It remains unchanged.
06 SC (Store and clear)	Store the contents of the A register in the location specified by the D address and then clear the A register to $+0$.
07 ST (Store)	Store the contents of the A register in the location specified by the D address, leaving the contents of the A register unchanged.
08 CN (Change control on nonzero)	If the A register does not contain $+0$ or -0, go to the D address for the next instruction. If the A register contains $+0$ or -0, go to the N address for the next instruction.
09 PR (Print)	Print the sign and the contents of the A register. Print the number of digits specified by the D address, beginning with the highest-ordered digit of the A register.
10 SP (Stop)	Stop executing instructions. The D and the N addresses are not used.

Sample Problem

A manufacturing company maintains a stock of 999 different replacement items, and no more than 1,250 of each are kept in stock at any time. Each item has a four-digit nonzero identification number. The inventory of the previous month is stored in memory locations 1000 through 1998. Each item is represented by one word. The first four digits of each word are the item number, and the last four digits are the number of items on hand after the inventory of the previous month. Location 1999 contains $+0000000000$ to mark the end of the file. The used items

Table 24.1 Storage Location Assignments

0000 through 0029:	Program instructions
0901 through 0904:	Temporary storage locations
0910:	$+01\ 2000\ 0008$ Programming constant
0911:	$+00\ 0001\ 0000$ Programming constant
1000 through 1998:	$+PPPPOONNNN$ Inventory of previous month. PPPP is the item number, and NNNN is the number on hand after the inventory of the previous month
1999:	$+0000000000$
2000 through 2998:	$+PPPPOOUUUU$ Used items. UUUU is the number used since the last inventory. $+0000000000$ follows the last word in this file

are stored in locations 2000 through 2998. Again, each item is represented by one word. The first four digits of each word are the item number, and the last four digits are the number of items used since the inventory of the previous month. There may be any number of words in this file of

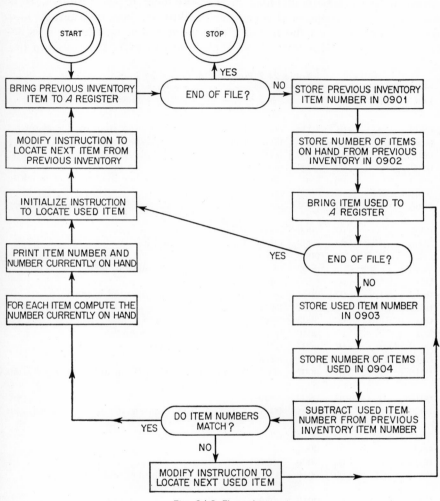

Fig. 24.2 Flow chart.

used items (up to 999), and the location following the last word in the file contains +0000000000 to mark the end of the file. The words in each file all have a plus sign, and they are not stored in sequence according to their identification numbers. It is desired to write a program to update the inventory of the previous month and print only those items used and the number currently on hand. Storage locations are assigned as in Table 24.1.

Since it is not the purpose of this chapter to illustrate how a problem is analyzed or planned for a computer, the analysis and planning are assumed to have been included in the statement of the problem. It is also beyond the scope of this chapter to illustrate how instructions and data are entered into the memory of the computer, and hence it is assumed that there is a way of accomplishing this after the program has

Table 24.2 Program for Figure 24.2

LOC	AB	OP	D	N	Remarks
0000	CA	+01	1000	0001	Bring previous inventory item to A register
0001	CN	+08	0003	0002	End of file for previous inventory?
0002	SP	+10	0000	0000	Stop
0003	SR	+04	0006	0004	
0004	SC	+06	0901	0005	Store previous inventory item number in 0901
0005	SL	+05	0006	0006	
0006	ST	+07	0902	0007	Store number of items from previous inventory in 0902
0007	CA	+01	2000	0008	Bring item used to A register
0008	CN	+08	0009	0025	End of file of used items?
0009	SR	+04	0006	0010	
0010	SC	+06	0903	0011	Store used item number in 0903
0011	.SL	+05	0006	0012	
0012	ST	+07	0904	0013	Store number of items used in 0904
0013	CA	+01	0901	0014	
0014	SU	+03	0903	0015	
0015	CN	+08	0016	0019	Do item numbers match?
0016	CA	+01	0007	0017	
0017	AD	+02	0911	0018	
0018	ST	+07	0007	0007	Modify instruction to locate next used item and jump
0019	CA	+01	0902	0020	
0020	SU	+03	0904	0021	Compute the number of items currently on hand
0021	SR	+04	0006	0022	
0022	CA	+01	0901	0023	
0023	SL	+05	0006	0024	
0024	PR	+09	0010	0025	Print used item number and the number currently on hand
0025	CA	+01	0910	0026	
0026	ST	+07	0007	0027	Initialize instruction to locate used item
0027	CA	+01	0000	0028	
0028	AD	+02	0911	0029	
0029	ST	+07	0000	0000	Modify instruction to locate next item from previous inventory and jump

been written. The problem of loading a program into the memory of the computer is discussed superficially later in the chapter. The flow chart and the program are shown in Fig. 24.2 and Table 24.2, respectively. The first instruction in the program is in memory location 0000, and it is also assumed that the computer jumps to that location after the program is loaded.

In Table 24.2, the symbol LOC means the location of the instruction in the memory of the computer. AB is the abbreviation of the operation code, and it is used merely as a reference in reading the program; it is not entered into the memory of the computer. OP, D, and N signify the operation code and the D and N addresses, respectively, as they would appear in the memory of the computer.

The instruction in location 0000 will bring the previous inventory item to the A register. The instruction in location 0001 tests for the end of that file. If the end of the file has not been reached, the computer will go to location 0003 for its next instruction. The instructions in locations 0003 through 0006 merely store the previous inventory item number and the number of items on hand from the previous inventory in separate memory locations. The instruction in location 0007 brings the used item to the A register. The instruction in location 0008 tests for the end of that file. If the end of the file has not been reached, the computer will go to location 0009 for its next instruction. The instructions in locations 0009 through 0012 merely store the used-item number and the number of items used in separate memory locations. The instructions in locations 0013 and 0014 compute the difference between the previous inventory item number and the used item number. The instruction in location 0015 then tests for a zero difference to determine whether or not the item numbers match. If the difference is nonzero, or the item numbers do not match, the computer will go to location 0016 for its next instruction. At this point, the computer is to match the next used item number against the previous-inventory item number already stored. This would be done by instructing the computer to jump back to location 0007 if it were not for the fact that the computer would then bring the used item in location 2000 to the A register instead of the next used item in location 2001. Hence the computer can be instructed to jump to location 0007 if the D address of the instruction in location 0007 is increased by 1. The instructions in locations 0016 through 0018 accomplish this modification of the instruction in location 0007. The instruction in location 0016 brings the instruction in location 0007 to the A register. The instruction in location 0017 then adds the constant $+00\ 0001\ 0000$ to the contents of the A register. This addition increases the D address of the instruction in the A register by 1. The instruction in location 0018 then stores this instruction back in its original location, 0007. The N address of the instruction in location 0018 is used to tell the computer to jump to location 0007 after it has stored the contents of the A register. Thus, the next used item in location 2001 is brought to the A register, and this operation will continue until the computer reaches the end of the file of used items or until the item numbers match, whichever occurs first. In the former case the computer will jump to location 0025; and in the latter case, the computer will jump to location 0019 for its next instruction. This description of a portion of the program explains how an instruction is modified when no index register is available and how a typical test is made to cause the computer to stop executing a loop at the proper time.

Observe that the program consists of three interconnected loops, as shown by the flow chart in Fig 24.2. Also note that the instructions in locations 0025 and 0026 and the constant in location 0910 are used to initialize the instruction in location 0007. The instructions in locations 0027, 0028, and 0029 and the constant in location 0911 are used to modify the instruction in location 0000.

Like all programs, the above could have been written many different ways. The preceding program may not be the best possible; however, this particular problem with its program was chosen because it best illustrated the programming points that needed emphasis.

Index Registers

It has been noted that a program consists of a network of loops and that these loops involve instruction modification and testing. When an instruction is modified it is nearly always the address part of the instruction that is altered, and testing often involves nothing more than programming the computer to count the number of times it has executed a loop. These processes of instruction modification and counting increase the tedium of programming, and they are wasteful storagewise in a computer that does not have index registers, because of the additional instructions that are required to perform these bookkeeping processes. Therefore, most modern computers have one or more index registers to facilitate these processes. An index register is used by the programmer for combined address modification and counting or for performing either of these operations alone. Although these are the primary functions of an index register, it may also be used in some computers to link a subroutine with a main program. This is discussed in the next section.

Index registers are called into play by various digits in the instruction word. For example, the one index register of the Burroughs 205 computer is called into play by giving a minus sign to the instruction to be modified. The contents of the index register are then added to the address part of the instruction word as it passes through the adder on its way to the control register. As a second example, the IBM 704 computer has three index registers; if a binary 1 appears in the eighteenth, nineteenth, or twentieth digit position of the instruction word, then the contents of the appropriate index register are subtracted from the address part of the instruction prior to its execution. Both of these computers employ what is called *effective address modification;* that is, the instruction is modified just prior to its execution but it is not altered as it appears in the computer's memory.

The index registers function differently in different computers, but they serve the same purposes. To accomplish these purposes, the computer must have commands for loading, storing, and testing the contents of the index registers.

As an example of how an index register is used, consider the Burroughs 205 computer. Its index register is called a *B* register, or *B* box, and it can contain four decimal digits. The address part of each instruction word is also four decimal digits in length. The computer also has a *set B* and a *decrease B* command. The *set B* command is used to place a number in the *B* box, and the *decrease B* command performs two functions: it first decreases the contents of the *B* box by 1 by adding 9999 to its contents, and it then tests the contents of the *B* box. If the *B* box contains 9999, the computer continues on to the next instruction in sequence. If the *B* box contains anything other than 9999, the computer jumps to the location specified by the address part of the *decrease B* command for its next instruction. Hence if a programmer wanted to write a loop, he would place a number in the *B* box by using the *set B* command. He would then give a minus sign to the following instructions whose address parts he wished to modify. Then at the end of the loop, the programmer would write a *decrease B* command, which would decrease the contents of the *B* box by 1 and cause the computer to jump back to the beginning of the loop. Then the next time through the loop each modified instruction would have 1 less added to its address part, or each of these instructions would again be modified. This would continue until the contents of the *B* box were reduced to 0. Then the *decrease B* command would be executed again; but instead of jumping back to the beginning of the loop, the computer would leave the loop and continue on to the next instruction in sequence.

It can now be seen that the use of an index register not only makes coding less tedious but also affords saving in a storage space. In the above example, it was still necessary to store one constant (the number to be placed in the *B* box) and write two instructions (the *set B* and *decrease B* instructions) in order to modify other instructions. The additional instructions that would normally have been required for counting were eliminated, since the *B* box combined the counting process with that of instruction modification. If the worst programming case is assumed, seven storage locations were actually saved in this instance because without the use of an index register three constants and seven instructions would have been required to modify instructions and count.

Index registers have been found to be so useful that the trend today is to place more of them on the newer computers.

Subroutines

In any computer application, there are many logical and mathematical processes that occur again and again, such as computing a square root. Essentially the same sequence of instructions is required to perform any one of these processes no matter where the process may occur in the program. Hence, to decrease the tedium of programming and conserve storage space, the necessary instructions are written once and then permanently stored and recorded in such a way that the programmer can insert them into his program wherever needed. These specialized programs are called *subroutines* and are so labeled because they are routine and are a subordinate part of the programmer's main program.

A subroutine may be defined as a relatively short program designed to perform one specific function independently of any other program. There are two types, called *open subroutines* and *closed subroutines*. The open type of subroutine has no built-in method of linking itself with another program; that is, an open subroutine is an integral part of a main program in that it must appear in the main program at every point at which it is to be used. This type of subroutine relieves the programmer of the chore of coding the same sequence of instructions over and over at various places in his program, but it does not save any storage space. The closed type, however, affords a saving in storage space, and it is equally convenient to use. Hence, nearly all the subroutines that are written are of the closed type, and this section will be confined to a discussion of these.

A closed subroutine has a built-in method of linking itself with another program; that is, the subroutine is written in such a way that a programmer can link it with his main program without disturbing his main program. This linking process affords a saving in storage space because the subroutine need appear only once in the main program, and it may be stored anywhere in the memory of the computer. The subroutine is an independent program, but it may be called into play by the main program whenever needed.

Linkage methods vary from computer to computer. In general, however, these linkage methods fall into two main categories. The linkage may be accomplished with or without an index register. In either case, the same problems are involved. There must be some way of calling in the subroutine. This can be accomplished by using any jump command. There must also be some way of furnishing the subroutine with the data upon which it is to operate, and a convention is adopted among programmers for this purpose; that is, the programmer will place the data in prearranged locations before he calls in the subroutine so that the writer of the subroutine will know where to locate the data that is to be processed. The writer of the subroutine also has to have some way of telling the programmer where to locate the results obtained from the subroutine, and prearranged locations are again used to accomplish this. However, the writer of the subroutine must also have some way of returning the programmer to the proper point in his main program. If no index register is available, this may be accomplished by using some prearranged sequence of jump commands.

There is one general method called the *Wheeler method*. Using this method, the programmer writes an instruction that is placed in an arithmetic register. This can be accomplished by writing a clear-and-add instruction (or its equivalent) whose address part corresponds to the memory location in which the clear-and-add instruction itself is stored. The programmer then writes an add instruction, which adds a stored constant to the instruction in the arithmetic register. The constant is such that it modifies both the operation-code part and the address part of the instruction in the arithmetic register. It modifies the operation-code part in such a way that it converts the clear-and-add instruction in the arithmetic register to an unconditional-jump instruction, and it modifies the address part to correspond to the desired return address in the programmer's main program. The programmer then calls in the subroutine. The writer of the subroutine stores the jump instruction in the arithmetic register in some location known to him; after the subroutine has performed its function, he performs a jump to that location which returns the programmer to the proper point in his main program.

Another general method, which is simpler but not quite so economical, might be employed. That is, the programmer might write an unconditional-jump instruction as part of his main program and store it in some prearranged memory location prior to calling in the subroutine. The address part of this jump instruction would correspond to the desired return location in his main program. Then after the subroutine has performed its function, the writer of the subroutine might perform a jump to that prearranged location, which would return the programmer to the proper point in his main program. As far as is known, this latter method is not used, but it is both a simple and a general method that could be used in any computer not having index registers.

If the computer has an index register, a special command is usually used for subroutine linkages. For example, the IBM 704 computer is a single-address machine, and it takes its successive instructions from sequentially numbered memory locations. When it modifies addresses, it subtracts the contents of the index register from the address part of the instruction word being modified. It also has a *transfer and set index* command, which places the complement of its location in the index register; then the computer performs an unconditional jump to the address specified by the address part of this *transfer and set index* command. In calling in a subroutine, the programmer would write a *transfer and set index* command, which would set the index register as described above and cause the computer to perform an unconditional jump to the subroutine. Suppose, then, that the programmer wished to be returned to a memory location which is three locations beyond the location of his *transfer and set index* instruction. The writer of the subroutine would be aware of this by prearrangement, and he would return the programmer to his main program by writing an unconditional-jump instruction having an address of 3 and then call in the index register. The location of the programmer's *transfer and set index* instruction would then be effectively added to the address part of this unconditional-jump instruction, which would return the programmer to the proper point in his main program.

Certain conventions must be adopted whatever linkage method is employed; that is, every subroutine has a *calling sequence*, which is the sequence of steps that must be followed by the programmer when calling in the subroutine.

Every subroutine also has what are called *specifications*. These written specifications tell the programmer all he needs to know in order to use the subroutine, such as the details of the calling sequence, the computing time required by the subroutine, the storage space required by the subroutine, the limitations of the subroutine as far as input data is concerned, and the accuracy of the results to be obtained from the subroutine.

Arithmetic

When a number is written on paper, the radix point is placed either in its true location or in any location; the resultant number is then multiplied by an appropriate power of the base. In computer terminology the former is referred to as a *fixed-point* number and the latter as a *floating-point* number.

Floating-point arithmetic is necessary in solving virtually all scientific problems because of the magnitudes of the numbers generated. To facilitate the programming of floating-point arithmetic operations, most modern computers have a built-in floating point. That is, the circuits are designed so that the computer can perform floating-point arithmetic operations automatically, and the appropriate commands are included in the language of the computer.

In those computers that do not have a built-in floating point, it may still be possible to perform floating-point arithmetic operations. If the necessary commands are available, it is possible to write subroutines to perform a floating add, subtract, multiply, and divide. (In actual practice, the floating add subroutine is used to perform a floating subtract operation by changing the sign of the subtrahend before calling in the floating add subroutine.) This is more expensive from the point of view of storage space and computing time, however, because a computer with a built-in floating point can perform a floating-point arithmetic operation much faster than it can perform the same operation by executing a relatively long sequence of subroutine instructions. The subroutines themselves take up additional storage space.

Floating-point arithmetic operations are always slower than fixed-point operations, even though the computer may have a built-in floating point. Hence, floating-point arithmetic is employed only when necessary.

In performing floating-point arithmetic, the computer keeps track of the radix-point location automatically; but when fixed-point arithmetic is performed, the programmer must do this. There are simple rules for doing this in any given computer, but they are not of sufficient interest to be described here.

Load Routines

The problem of entering a program into the memory of the computer is separate from those problems involved in inserting data or printing out results under the control of an already stored program. This section is concerned with the problem of entering a program into the memory of the computer when it is empty of any instruction that might be used to accomplish this. No two computers solve this problem in the same way; hence, only one of them will be discussed.

The IBM 650 computer has STORAGE ENTRY switches on the console, and they have an address of 8000. It also has a COMPUTER RESET and a START button. The COMPUTER RESET button clears all the arithmetic and control registers and inserts 8000 into the address register, the control register used by the computer to locate its next instruction. The START button causes the computer to start executing instructions. To enter his program into the memory of the computer, the programmer sets a *card-read* instruction in the STORAGE ENTRY switches. He then presses the

COMPUTER RESET button. This inserts 8000 into the address register of the computer. He then presses the START button. Since 8000 is in the address register of the computer, the computer goes to that address for its next instruction. The card-read instruction set in the STORAGE ENTRY switches is thus sent to the appropriate control of the computer and executed. This instruction actuates the card reader and causes the computer to read the contents of the first input card. The address part of the card-read instruction in the STORAGE ENTRY switches may be used by the programmer to transfer control to one of the memory locations into which the contents of the first card have been read. In addition to the program information to be stored, this first card may contain other instructions for storing this program information in any desired locations. These additional instructions may also transfer control back to the STORAGE ENTRY switches to read the next card, or the first input card may contain another card-read instruction and the other necessary instructions for the reading and storing of the program information contained in succeeding cards. That is, the first block of one or more input cards may not contain any program information. Instead, it might contain the necessary instructions for storing a subroutine in the memory of the computer with a subsequent transfer of control to the subroutine. The subroutine might then cause the computer to read and store the program information contained in succeeding input cards. This type of subroutine is called a *load routine*.

Load routines may be combined in cascade fashion, or a relatively simple load routine may be used to load another load routine of a more sophisticated nature. For example, with the IBM 650 computer, the STORAGE ENTRY switches might be used to enter the first card-read instruction into the appropriate control register. The first two input cards might contain the necessary instructions for loading a four-word-per-card load routine into the memory of the computer. This four-word-per-card load routine might be used to read and store four words of program information from each succeeding card; or, instead, it might be used to read and store a seven-word-per-card load routine in the memory of the computer. This seven-word-per-card load routine would be read into the memory of the computer at the rate of four words per card from a block of succeeding input cards. This seven-word-per-card load routine might then read and store seven words of program information from each succeeding card. This entire loading sequence would be automatic, and it would be initiated by the single instruction obtained from the STORAGE ENTRY switches. This is sometimes called the "bootstrap method" of loading a program. In this example, the first load routine in the sequence (the four-word-per-card routine) would have to be what is called a self-loading routine; that is, it would have to be capable of loading itself without the aid of any other load routine stored in the memory of the computer. Any following load routine, however, would not have to be of the self-loading type.

Automatic Programming

Although the terms "automatic programming" and "automatic coding" have different definitions, almost all automatic coding systems have one or more automatic programming features. Hence, for purposes of this section, these terms are synonymous.

As mentioned previously, if the computer is used to aid the programmer in translating the problem language into computer language, the process is called automatic coding, and a program written for this purpose is called an assembler or compiler.

The need for assemblers and compilers arose because of the inherent difficulty in translating problem language into computer language because of the nature of the computer language itself. For example, imagine writing thousands of instructions in computer language for a binary machine having a word length of 36 digits. Even if these instructions were written in octal notation, it would be a formidable task.

Assemblers and compilers allow the programmer to use what is called *relative address coding*. This idea arose because of the difficulty in making coding corrections. That is, if the program is written in computer language, a specific memory location must be assigned to each instruction, and the address parts of these instructions must also correspond to specific memory locations. This makes it hard to insert or delete instructions if a coding mistake is discovered, because it may be necessary to change the memory locations of all the instructions that follow. It may also be necessary to change the address parts of many instructions to correspond to these new locations. This correcting process can, because of these many changes, be an additional source of error. Relative address coding overcomes this difficulty because the programmer does not assign specific memory locations to instructions or their address parts. He uses some alphameric symbol to represent an instruction location or instruction address. It is called relative address coding because these symbolic addresses are relative to some origination address. For example, in a computer that takes its successive instructions from sequentially numbered memory locations, the location of any program instruction may be completely defined in terms of the first (or any other) instruction in the program. When relative address coding is used in this type of computer, a specific memory address is usually assigned to the first instruction in the program after the coding has been completed, and this specific address is called the *origin*.

If relative address coding is used, it is unnecessary for the programmer to assign a symbolic address to all the instructions in his program. He would have to assign a symbolic address only to the originating instruction and those other instructions to which reference is made in the program. That is, there would be long sequences of instructions in his program having no addresses, either specific or symbolic, assigned to them. This enables the programmer to insert or delete instructions without changing any addresses, or by changing at most one or two symbolic addresses. Relative address coding also allows the programmer to choose symbols that have high memory value.

In addition to relative address coding, assemblers and compilers have other features. For example, the share assembly program written for the IBM 704 computer allows the programmer to use fixed three-letter abbreviations for the operation-code parts of his instructions, instead of the actual numerical operation codes used by the computer. This makes coding easier because these abbreviations are also chosen for their high memory value. This assembler also provides the programmer with what is called a "library" of subroutines. It also provides for the insertion of data in decimal or octal form and for the automatic conversion of this data to binary form. The necessary conversion subroutines are included in the subroutine library, as is also the case with other assembly and compiling programs.

Before an assembly program can perform the assembly process, it must be given certain information by the programmer. It must know the origin in order to assign memory locations, how many memory locations to reserve for various blocks of data, the subroutines the programmer needs in his program so that it may obtain them from the library, and so on. These items of information are supplied to the share assembly program by pseudo-instructions. A pseudo-instruction may be defined in this instance as a symbolic instruction that has no counterpart in computer language. It is used exclusively by the assembly program as a reference during the assembly process.

There are one-pass and two-pass assemblers. A one-pass assembler will translate a source program into computer instructions by making only one pass through the source program. A two-pass assembler will construct a table of symbolic addresses for purposes of reference and determine what subroutines are needed in the program during the first pass. It will then assign memory addresses and insert the subroutines in the program during the second pass.

Assemblers and compilers are distinguished by the type of symbolic language they employ. An assembler employs a symbolic language that is very closely related to the computer's language. For example, when using the share assembly program, the programmer writes symbolic instructions having much the same form as computer instructions, and each symbolic instruction will give rise to one computer instruction when the program is assembled. If this one-to-one correspondence exists between symbolic and computer instructions, the program that does the translating is called an assembler. If this correspondence does not exist, then the translating program is called a compiler. It is sometimes difficult to classify a given translating program since it may be a combination of both types.

Although an assembly program is of great help to the programmer, it still has a disadvantage associated with it in that its symbolic language is closely related to the computer's language and hence very different from the problem language. A compiling program is an even greater aid in that its symbolic language is more closely related to the problem language. This enables the programmer to code the problem in a more nearly human language.

The FORTRAN system mentioned at the beginning of this chapter is a good example of a compiler. When coding a problem using this compiler, the programmer writes a sequence of very general statements. Any single statement may be a complex algebraic formula, a format statement telling the compiler how to arrange input-out data and what number conversions must be performed, a statement that indicates some type of decision is to be made by the computer, or some other general statement. These general statements are then translated into computer instructions by the compiling program. Any single statement will give rise to an indefinite number of computer instructions.

A compiler usually translates the general program statements into some type of assembly language during the first pass. During the second pass, it translates this assembly language into computer language. For example, the FORTRAN compiler translates the general program statements into share assembly program language during the first pass. Then it translates this share assembly program language into computer instructions during the second pass. It performs both passes during a single run on the computer.

In addition to performing the translation and having the advantages heretofore mentioned, an assembler or compiler usually performs other clerical duties that aid the programmer. For example, it will punch the object program in a deck of cards or write the object program on a magnetic tape in such a way that the object program can be run immediately on the computer by using this deck of cards or tape. It will also print out a list of both the source program and the object program, which the programmer may use as a reference when debugging his program. In addition, most assemblers and compilers have a built-in diagnostic routine. In using an assembler or compiler, the programmer must adhere to certain rules when writing his program. These rules are determined by the writer of the assembly or compiling program. The programmer may also make typographical errors when coding his problem, such as omitting a parenthesis or transposing the characters in a symbolic operation code. Any rule violations or typographical errors will be detected by the diagnostic routine and printed for the benefit of the programmer.

Thus far those programs have been discussed which translate a source program into an object program before the object program is run on the computer. This is called *pretranslation*. Programs have also been written which perform a running translation. These are called *interpretive programs*. An interpretive program is written in something other than computer language, and each instruction is interpreted just prior to its execution during the running of the program. Interpretive programs are usually written for computers that do not have sufficient memory capacity to accommodate an assembly or compiling program. They have a disadvantage associated with them in that many of the program instructions will have to be interpreted many times over during the running of the program. This repetitive interpretation of the same instructions takes additional computer time and hence adds to the expense of the program.

Although assemblers, compilers, and interpretive programs have greatly facilitated the programming of computers, they have not constituted a complete solution to the programming problem. There are, as well as differing problem languages, as many computer languages as there are computers, and with very few exceptions a compiling program is compatible with only one problem language and one computer language. Hence, if the number of problem languages is L and the number of computer languages is C, then $L \times C$ compiling programs must be written in order to conveniently program all existing computers. This presents a problem because it takes approximately 20 to 25 man-years (or it takes a group of programmers 2 to 3 years) to write a compiling program. The amount of time required to write a compiling program makes it difficult to keep pace with computer production. To help solve this problem, it has been suggested that the computing industry adopt a universal computer-oriented language called UNCOL. The original UNCOL concept required a program called a generator for each problem language and a program called a translator for each computer language. In practice, the appropriate generator would transform a given problem language into UNCOL and the appropriate translator would transform UNCOL into a given computer language, or a total of $L + C$ instead of $L \times C$ programs would be required to translate all problem languages into all computer languages. More recently it has been suggested that the computer industry adopt a common business-oriented language called COBOL for business applications and an algorithmic language called ALGOL for scientific applications. An alternative solution to the problem would be to write a universal compiler of compilers, or a program that would produce a compiling program for any given problem language and any given computer. While this latter solution appears at the moment to be the more ideal, the former solution or some modification thereof appears to be the more practical because no one presently has any idea of how to write a universal compiler of compilers.

This discussion of automatic programming presents some idea of the advanced state of the art at present. In spite of these advances, however, many problems remain. The subject of automatic programming is still undergoing intensive study, and greater advances will be made in the future in seeking solutions to these problems. The ultimate in programming will have been reached when the programmer can give the computer verbal and printed information in human language form and have it compute results.

QUESTIONS

24.1 List the advantages of a stored program.
24.2 What is the function of the operating console?
24.3 Can a computer automatically modify its program or instructions? Explain.
24.4 What is the purpose of flow charting?
24.5 What methods are used to check programs before they are entered into the machine?
24.6 What is a subroutine?
24.7 Given the quadratic equation $ax^2 + bx + c$, complete the following program table to solve the equation, using the memory locations, operational codes, and pre-stored constants in corresponding locations shown below:

Instruction	Operation code	Instruction	Operation code
Add	01	Store	05
Subtract	02	Transfer	06
Multiply	03	Jump	07
Clear and add	04	Stop	08

The constants are stored at the following addresses:

Location	Constant
0015	a
0016	b
0017	c
0018	x

Program Table for $ax^2 + bx + c$

Location	Operation	Address	Result
0000	04	0015	Places a into the accumulator
0001	03	0018	Accumulator now contains ax
0002	01	0016	Accumulator now contains $ax + b$
0003			
0004			
0005			
0006			
0007			
0008			
0009			
0010			
0011			
0012			
0013			
0014			
0015			
0016			
0017			
0018			
0019			
0020			

Appendix I

Digital Symbology

The symbols on the following charts were compiled from the manufacturers' literature and the references listed below:

1. Proposed Symbology for Digital Systems, Paper No. 60-1224, *Trans AIEE*, Oct. 28, 1960.
2. Graphical Symbols for Logical Diagrams, MIL-STD-806 (U.S.A.F.), Apr. 11, 1960.

The "Proposed American Standard" column is a compilation of the symbols set forth in the references above.

The "Preferred by A.F." column is the standards set forth in Air Force Contract No. A.F. 19 (604)-1863.

DIGITAL SYMBOLOGY

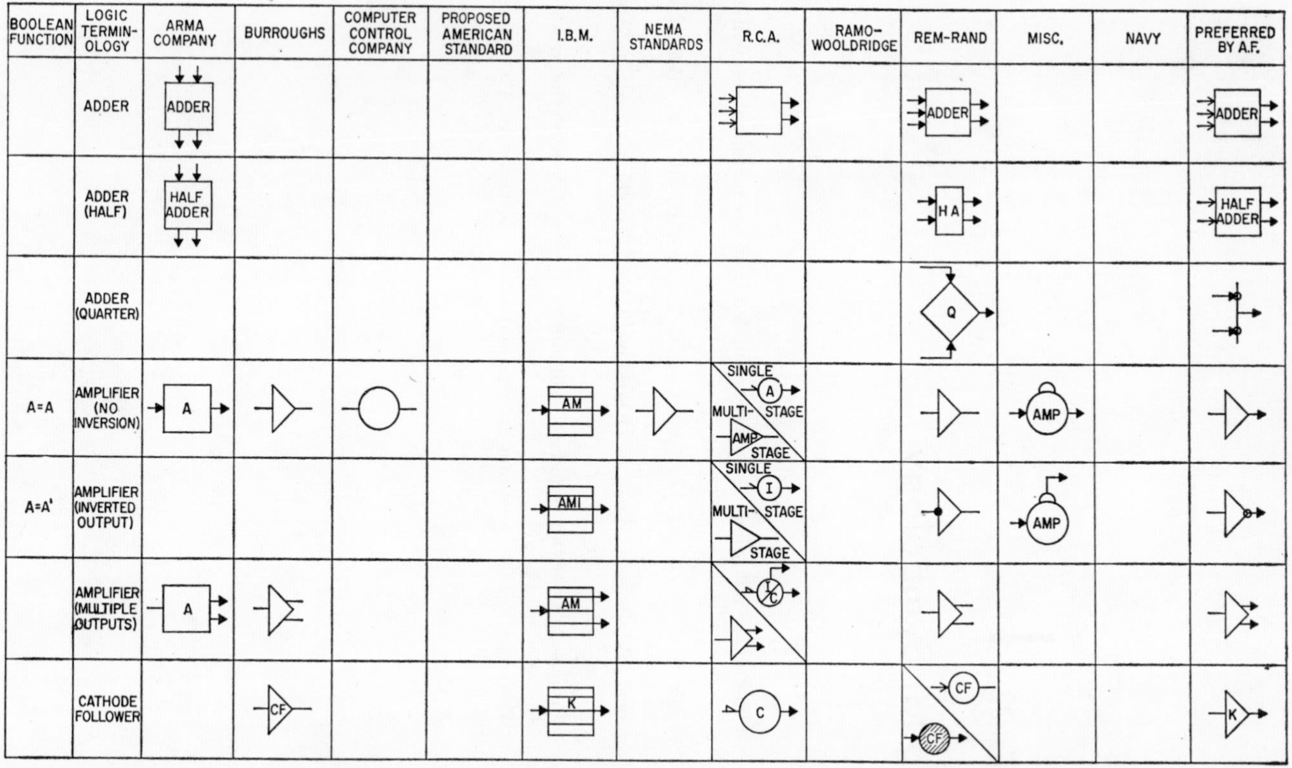

BOOLEAN FUNCTION	LOGIC TERMIN- OLOGY	ARMA COMPANY	BURROUGHS	COMPUTER CONTROL COMPANY	PROPOSED AMERICAN STANDARD	I.B.M.	NEMA STANDARDS	R.C.A.	RAMO- WOOLDRIDGE	REM-RAND	MISC.	NAVY	PREFERRED BY A.F.
	ADDER	ADDER								ADDER			ADDER
	ADDER (HALF)	HALF ADDER								H A			HALF ADDER
	ADDER (QUARTER)			○						Q			
A=A	AMPLIFIER (NO INVERSION)	A				AM		SINGLE A / MULTI-STAGE AMP			AMP		
A=A'	AMPLIFIER (INVERTED OUTPUT)					AMI		SINGLE I / MULTI-STAGE			AMP		
	AMPLIFIER (MULTIPLE OUTPUTS)	A				AM							
	CATHODE FOLLOWER		CF			K		C		CF / CF			K

484

BOOLEAN FUNCTION	LOGIC TERMINOLOGY	ARMA COMPANY	BURROUGHS	COMPUTER CONTROL COMPANY	PROPOSED AMERICAN STANDARD	I.B.M.	NEMA STANDARDS	R.C.A.	RAMO-WOOLDRIDGE	REM-RAND	MISC.	NAVY	PREFERRED BY A.F.
A·B=X	AND GATE					A			AND	G436	AND	A	
A'·B=X	AND GATE (INHIBITED INPUT)					AG			AND				
A·B=X'	AND GATE (INVERTED OUTPUT)					AI				G436		N	
A·B=X	AND THYRATRON					ATH				TG			
	BINARY SWITCH (FLIP-FLOP)	FF	S R		S R FF	T		S FF R		R FF S	FF	S F R F	S FF R
	BINARY COUNTER	BC	S C R					S T CTR R		BC STEP TO 1 STEP TO 0		S F R F	S T R
	DELAY LINE		DL		0.5µSEC	D		5D		D5			5µSEC

485

DIGITAL SYMBOLOGY
(CONT.)

BOOLEAN FUNCTION	LOGIC TERMINOLOGY	ARMA COMPANY	BURROUGHS	COMPUTER CONTROL COMPANY	PROPOSED AMERICAN STANDARD	I.B.M.	NEMA STANDARDS	R.C.A.	RAMO-WOOLDRIDGE	REM-RAND	MISC.	NAVY	PREFERRED BY A.F.
	DELAY (FLIP-FLOP)		DMV		OS 1 0 .5	SS		OS 1 N R O		DF 4MS		1/S	S R 5μSEC
A = A'	INVERTER	I	I			I		I	NOT	I	NOT	I	I
	MAGNETIC AMPLIFIER									A			
	MAGNETIC CORE (BINARY)		1 0										
	MAGNETIC HEAD				WRITING ONLY / READING ONLY / ERASURE ONLY			READ OR WRITE / READ AND WRITE / ERASE		HEAD			READ / WRITE / ERASE
	MATRIX (DE-CODER)												
	MATRIX (EN-CODER)												

486

DIGITAL SYMBOLOGY
(CONT.)

BOOLEAN FUNCTION	LOGIC TERMIN- OLOGY	ARMA COMPANY	BURROUGHS	COMPUTER CONTROL COMPANY	PROPOSED AMERICAN STANDARD	I.B.M.	NEMA STANDARDS	R.C.A.	RAMO- WOOLDRIDGE	REM-RAND	MISC.	NAVY	PREFERRED BY A.F.
	OR CIRCUIT												
	OR CIRCUIT (INVERTED OUTPUT)												
	OSCIL- LATOR												
	PULSE TRANS- FORMER												
	PULSE TRANS- FORMER (INVERTED OUTPUT)												
	NOT OR (NOR)	SAME AS	INVERTED OR !										
	NOT AND (NAND)	SAME AS	INVERTED AND !										
	INHIBIT SYMBOLS	O PLACED INSIDE SYMBOL											

Appendix II

General Bibliography

BOOKS

Berkeley, E. C.: "Giant Brains," John Wiley & Sons, Inc., New York, 1949.

Boole, G.: "An Investigation of the Laws of Thought," Dover Publications, New York, 1951 (reprint of the 1854 original).

Burroughs Corporation MFSD Instructor Staff: "Computer Fundamentals," rev. no. 1, Radnor, Pa., 1959.

————: "Introduction to Digital Techniques," Radnor, Pa., 1957.

Coblenz, A., and H. L. Owens: "Transistors: Theory and Applications," McGraw-Hill Book Company, Inc., New York, 1955.

Dawes, C.: "A Course in Electrical Engineering," vol. I, "Direct Currents," 4th ed., McGraw-Hill Book Company, Inc., New York, 1952.

Engineering Research Associates: "High-speed Computing Devices," McGraw-Hill Book Company, Inc., New York, 1950.

Fahnestock, J. D.: "Computers and How They Work," Ziff-Davis Publishing Company, New York, 1959.

"General Electric Transistor Manual," 4th ed., General Electric Company, Syracuse, New York, 1959.

Grabbe, E. M., S. Ramo, and D. E. Wooldridge: "Handbook of Automation, Computation and Control," vol. II, John Wiley & Sons, Inc., New York, 1959.

Hunter, L. P.: "Handbook of Semiconductor Electronics," McGraw-Hill Book Company, Inc., New York, 1956.

Mandl, M.: "Fundamentals of Digital Computers," Prentice-Hall, Inc., Englewood Cliffs, N.J., 1958.

"Manual of Digital Techniques," Control Engineering Publishing Co., New York, 1959.

McCormick, E. M.: "Digital Computer Primer," McGraw-Hill Book Company, Inc., New York, 1959.

McCracken, D. D.: "Digital Computer Programming," John Wiley & Sons, Inc., New York, 1957.

————, H. Weiss, and T. Lee: "Programming Business Computers," John Wiley & Sons, Inc., New York, 1959.

Millman, J., and H. Taub: "Pulse and Digital Circuits," McGraw-Hill Book Company, Inc., New York, 1956.
Murphy, J. S.: "Basics of Digital Computers," vol. II, Rider Publishing Company, New York, 1958.
Phister, M.: "Logical Design of Digital Computers," John Wiley & Sons, Inc., New York, 1958.
Pressman, A. I.: "Design of Transistorized Circuits for Digital Computers," Rider Publishing Company, New York, 1959.
Puckle, O. S.: "Time Base Scanning Generators," 2d ed. John Wiley & Sons, Inc., New York, 1955.
Reintjes, J. F., and G. T. Coate: "Principles of Radar," 3d ed., McGraw-Hill Book Company, Inc., New York, 1952.
Richards, R. K.: "Arithmetic Operations in Digital Computers," D. Van Nostrand Company, Inc., Princeton, N.J., 1955.
———: "Digital Computer Components and Circuits," D. Van Nostrand Company, Inc., Princeton, N.J., 1955.
Riddle, R. L., and M. P. Ristenbatt: "Transistor Physics and Circuits," Prentice-Hall, Inc., Englewood Cliffs, N.J., 1958.
Stibitz, G. R., and J. A. Larrivee: "Mathematics and Computers," McGraw-Hill Book Company, Inc., New York, 1956.
U.S. Department of the Air Force: "Radar Circuit Analysis," AF Manual 52-8, 1951.
U.S. Department of the Army: "Basic Theory and Application of Transistors," TM 11-690, 1959.
U.S. Department of the Army: "Radar Electronics Fundamentals," TM 11-466, 1944.
Williams, S. B.: "Digital Computing Systems," McGraw-Hill Book Company, Inc., New York, 1959.

ARTICLES AND PAMPHLETS

Burroughs Corporation: Product Improvement Bulletin No. 17, Detroit, Michigan, July, 1958.
———: Third Interim Technique Report 04(625)-23, Detroit, Michigan, May, 1957.
Hurley, R. B.: Designing Transistor Circuits, Part 2, *Electronic Equipment Eng.*, October, 1958.
Moll, J. L.: Junction Transistor Electronics, *Proc. IRE*, vol. 43, December, 1955.
Miehle, W., J. Paivinen, J. Wylen, and D. Leov: Bimag Circuits for Digital Data Processing Systems, Burroughs Corporation Research Center, Paoli, Pennsylvania, 1956.
Philco Corporation: The Crystal Oscillator, Philco Tech Rep Bulletin, Philadelphia, Pennsylvania, September, 1953.
Shannon, C. E.: Symbolic Analysis of Relay and Switching Circuits, *Trans. AIEE*, vol. 57, 1938.
Williams, B.: Transistor Physics, *Semiconductor Products*, vol. 1, no. 1, January/February, 1958.

Glossary of Computer Terms

access time The time interval which is characteristic of a storage unit, being a measure of the time required to locate information in a storage position and make it available for processing or to return information from the processing unit to a storage location.

accumulator A device or register used for temporary storage of data in an arithmetic or logic operation. The accumulator usually stores one quantity and, upon the receipt of another quantity, forms the sum of the two quantities and temporarily stores the result.

accuracy The quality of freedom from error in computer operations. Accuracy is distinguished from precision in the following example: A six-place table of logarithms is more precise than a four-place table of logarithms; however, if there are errors in the six-place table, the four-place table may be more accurate.

adder A device which forms the sum of two or more numbers or quantities.

address The specific location where data is stored in a memory; a numerical or alphabetical designation of the storage location of data or machine unit to be used.

analog Using physical variables, such as distance or voltage, to represent a quantity.

AND gate A gate which has an output when, and only when, all inputs are present.

arithmetic operation A machine operation in which numerical quantities are manipulated.

arithmetic unit That portion of the hardware of a digital computer in which arithmetic and logical operations are performed.

automation The use of electronic computing equipment either by itself or in conjunction with other types of equipment to accomplish the functions of control or performance of one or more procedures, processes, or operations.

base A number, the powers of which are assigned as the unit value of columns in a numeric system; for example, 2 is the base in binary notation, 8 is the base in octal notation, and 10 is the base in decimal notation.

bimag A magnetic core possessing two stable states of magnetization. The core consists of a thin metallic ribbon of high retention properties wound spirally on a ceramic bobbin. Bimags are used principally as shift register elements.

binary Involving a choice or a condition in which there are but two alternatives.

binary cell A device having two stable states or conditions used to store one digit of binary information (1 or 0).

binary code A code in which each element may be either of two distinct values, for example, the presence or absence of a pulse.

binary-coded decimal A coded decimal number represented by a group of binary digits. A four-bit binary coding is normally used to represent the 10 decimal digits.

binary number system A positional number system in which the successive digits are interpreted as coefficients of the successive powers of the base 2. For example, the binary number 100 is equivalent to $1 \times 2^2 + 0 \times 2^1 + 0 \times 2^0$, or 4.

binary point In positional notation, the character or symbol which separates the integer part of a numerical expression from the fractional part. The binary point in binary notation is equivalent to the decimal point in decimal notation.

biquinary code A seven-bit binary code with the weights of 5, 0, 4, 3, 2, 1, 0, respectively. Each code group representative of a decimal digit contains only two binary 1's. For example, decimal 7 is represented as 1000100; decimal 4 is 0110000. The biquinary code notation for decimal digits 0 through 9 is shown in Table A.1.

Table A.1

Decimal Number	Biquinary Equivalent
	5043210 Position value
0	0100001
1	0100010
2	0100100
3	0101000
4	0110000
5	1000001
6	1000010
7	1000100
8	1001000
9	1010000

bit Contraction of *binary digit*. A basic symbol in the binary system (0 or 1); a unit quantity of information.

block A group of computer words considered or transported as a unit, an item, or a message. In flow charts, an assembly of boxes with each box representing a logical unit of programming.

blocking oscillator A relaxation oscillator using inductive feedback with its period of oscillation determined by the time constant of the grid resistor-capacitor combination.

Boolean algebra An algebra of logic which deals with rules for operating upon logical conditions rather than numbers.

Branch A point in a program at which the machine will proceed with one of two or more possible routines as determined by instructions and existing conditions.

breakpoint A point in a routine at which the computer may be stopped for a visual check of progress.

buffer amplifier A device used for circuit isolation and/or signal amplification.

buffer storage Storage equipment in computers used to compensate for differences in the speed of the various components of the system.

byproduct Data in some form developed without additional effort from a device whose basic purpose is to perform some other operation.

capacity The maximum number of digits that can be handled or processed by a computer unit; also, the upper and lower limits of the numbers which can be handled by the computer.

capstan The rotating shaft on a magnetic-tape-handling unit which is used to impart uniform motion to the magnetic tape when engaged.

card See **punched card**.

card column One of a number of columns on a punched card into which data is entered in the form of holes and no holes.

card feed A mechanical device which moves cards singly into a processing device.

card programming The use of cards as an instruction medium for computers.

card punch A device that punches information on cards under the guidance of a human operator or a program. Sometimes referred to as a key punch.

card reader A mechanism that converts the information on cards to another form, usually electric impulses.

card stacker A mechanism that stacks cards in a bin or pocket after they have passed through a card reader.

carry In the process of addition, the digit produced when the sum of two digits in the same digit position exceeds the base of the number system used. The carry is usually added to the next higher digit position.

chad The piece of paper removed when a hole is punched in a card or paper tape.

channel A path or strip along which information, usually in the form of bits, may flow or be stored.

character One of a set of elementary marks which may be combined to express information. For example, a decimal digit (0 to 9); a letter (A to Z); a symbol (comma, plus, minus, etc.); or, in digital computers, 1s and 0s.

check A process of partial or complete testing of machine operations; verification of the existence of certain prescribed conditions within the computer, or the verification of results produced by a routine.

check digits One or more digits carried along with a machine word (or information grouping) to verify that the information is correct. The bits are tallied for an odd or even amount of 1s before and after transmission; and if the number of 1s is not the same in both instances, a programmed error alarm is given. See **parity check**.

clear To restore a storage or memory device to a prescribed state, usually that state which denotes zero in the number system used.

clock The primary source of synchronizing signals, usually a crystal-controlled oscillator.

closed loop A routine in which a group of instructions is repeated for an indefinite period.

code To prepare problems in computer language or a pseudo-language for processing by a computer.

coded decimal digit A decimal digit expressed in a code, usually a four-digit binary code. See **binary-coded decimal**.

coder A person who translates a sequence of instructions into the precise code acceptable to a specific computer.

collate To produce a single sequence of items according to some rule from two or more other sequences of items. The final sequence of items may or may not contain all the data available in the original items.

command   1. A pulse, signal, or set of signals that steps the computer in the execution of a computer operation. 2. A machine instruction.

compiler   An automatic programming routine which processes a source program written in a pseudo-code and produces a machine-language routine to solve the problem defined by the source program.

complement   A number derived from the finite positional notation of another number by one of the following methods:

1. True complement: Subtract each digit from one less than the base; then add 1 to the least significant digit, executing all carries required. For example, the 2's complement of binary 10110 is:

$$\begin{array}{r} 11111 \\ -10110 \\ \hline 01001 + 1 \text{ or } 01010 \end{array}$$

2. Base-minus-one complement: Subtract each digit from one less than the base. (This is equivalent to changing every 1 to 0 and every 0 to 1 in the binary system.)

NOTE: In many machines, a negative number is represented as the complement of the corresponding positive number.

computer   A machine which can calculate or perform reasonable arithmetic and logical operations and transform the results of these operations into a usable form.

conditional transfer   An instruction which interrupts the normal process of obtaining the instructions in an ordered sequence and specifies a different instruction address if certain programmed conditions occur.

control unit   That portion of a computer that directs the sequence of operations by storing, interpreting, and producing signals from the coded instructions.

counter   1. A device capable of changing from one to the next of a sequence of distinguishable states upon each receipt of an input signal. 2. A device that counts input pulses, producing an output pulse each time it receives some predetermined number of input pulses.

cycle   A complete process of action required to perform a recurring chronological sequence in a computer operation.

data   Figures, words, or other forms of information used to describe some item or situation.

data processing   An ordered system for the collection, verification, recording, accumulation, evaluation, and presentation of statistical and related data.

data processor   A system designed to operate with large quantities of actual information upon which extensive calculation is usually not required but which must be sorted or otherwise manipulated.

data reduction   The use of arithmetic, mathematical, or statistical techniques to obtain or extract only needed information from a larger mass of related information.

debug   To develop a procedure to test the completeness, correctness, and adequacy of a program and to try out such procedures on the computer.

decoder   A network in which a prescribed combination of simultaneous inputs produces a single output.

delay line   A device which introduces a specified time delay in the passage of a pulse or string of pulses. Computers use real or artificial transmission lines, columns of mercury, or monostable multivibrators to accomplish signal delay. The output signal of the delay line is distorted and therefore must be amplified and reshaped before it is again usable.

density   The closeness of space distribution on a storage medium such as a magnetic drum, magnetic tape, or cathode-ray tube.

diagnostic routine   A routine specifically designed to locate either a fault in computer operation or a mistake in coding.

digit   A single symbol or character representing an integral quantity.

digital computer   A computer used to process data consisting of clearly defined numbers. A programmed machine capable of performing sequences of internally stored instructions.

drum, magnetic   See **magnetic drum**.

dump   1. To remove all power accidentally or intentionally. 2. To transfer all or part of the contents of one section of the computer memory into another section or type of storage.

Eccles-Jordan trigger circuit   A bistable-multivibrator circuit in which the output of one amplifier is direct-coupled to the input of the other amplifier. It has two conditions of stability, remaining in one of its stable conditions until some action causes the nonconducting tube to conduct, at which time the functions of the amplifiers reverse.

edit   To rearrange information. Editing may involve the deletion of unwanted data, the selection of pertinent data, or the insertion of symbols.

encoder   A network in which only one input is excited at a time and each input produces a combination of outputs.

end-around carry   A carry digit from the highest order of digits which is added to the lowest order of digits.

erase   1. To replace all digits in a storage device by zeros; equivalent to clearing. 2. To remove old information from a storage location, leaving the location empty for the insertion of new information.

error   The difference between the true value and a calculated or observed value. The amount of deviation from the original quantity. (A quantity, equal in absolute magnitude to the error, added to a calculated or observed value to obtain the true value is called correction.)

excess-3 code   A number code in which the decimal digit n is represented by the four-bit binary equivalent of $n + 3$. For example, decimal 0, 1, and 2 appear as 0011, 0100, and 0101 in the excess-3 code.

execute phase   1. The part of the computer operating cycle wherein a command in the program register is carried out upon the address indicated. 2. The act of performing a command.

external storage   Storage media separate from the machine but capable of retaining information in a form acceptable to the machine, for example, decks of punched cards or reels of magnetic tape.

fetch phase   The alternate part of the computer operating cycle wherein the instruction is brought from the memory into the program register prior to the execute phase.

field   1. In a computer, a set of one or more characters which is treated as an item of information. 2. In a punched card, a set of one or more columns consistently used to record similar items of information.

file A collection of items of information sequentially arranged for easy reference by some classification.

fixed-cycle operation A synchronous computer operation wherein a fixed amount of time is allotted for the completion of an operation.

fixed-point calculation Arithmetic calculation wherein the digit positions to the right and the left of the decimal or binary point are always occupied by coefficients of the same power of the base.

flip-flop A device having two stable states, two input terminals, and two output terminals, such that output exists from the side to which the last input was applied. See **Eccles-Jordan trigger circuit.**

floating-point calculation Arithmetic calculation wherein a number is written by specifying its sign, its coefficient, and the exponent to which the base is raised. For example, in floating-point calculation the number $+341,628,000$ may be recorded as $+3.41628,8$, meaning that it is equal to $+3.41628 \times 10^8$.

flow chart A graphical representation of a program or routine in a computing system.

format An arrangement of information on a form or in storage.

functional unit A combination of logical and nonlogical elements grouped to perform an elementary computer function, such as adding, complementing, or pulse generation.

gang-punch To automatically copy punched information from a master card onto one or more other cards.

gate A circuit having two or more input terminals and one output terminal, such that an output is present when and only when prescribed inputs are present.

general-purpose computer A computer possessing a flexible programming arrangement which enables it to solve a variety of problems.

half-adder An electronic circuit having two inputs for binary signals arbitrarily labeled X and Y and two outputs labeled S and C for sum and carry, respectively, the output of which is related to the input according to Table A.2.

Table A.2

Input		Output	
X	Y	S	C
0	0	0	0
0	1	1	0
1	0	1	0
1	1	0	1

hardware Computer elements; the magnetic, mechanical, electric, and electronic devices or components from which a computer is constructed.

hole site The position on a punched card where a hole may or may not appear.

hysteresis loop A graphical representation centered around the origin of rectangular coordinates, depicting the two values of magnetic induction for each value of magnetizing force: one when the magnetizing force is increasing and one when the magnetizing force is decreasing.

ignore In output devices such as the Flexowriter, a character indicating that no action is to be taken.

information Any facts or data which can be used, communicated, or transferred.

inhibit pulse A pulse applied to magnetic storage cells that prevents flux reversal.

input equipment That portion of computer hardware used for accepting information into a computer.

instruction A command plus one or more addresses in the form of a word which causes and directs computer operation to be performed on the indicated data.

internal storage Storage facilities that are an integral part of and directly controlled by the computer.

jump To conditionally or unconditionally cause the next computer instruction to be selected from a specified storage location.

karnaugh map A tabular arrangement which facilitates combination and elimination of duplicate logical functions by listing similar logical expressions.

library A collection of tested programs, routines, and subroutines by which problems and parts of problems of various types can be solved.

line printer A printer which is capable of printing an entire line of characters simultaneously.

load program A set of instructions used in conjunction with the console to enter a program (normally on punched cards) into computer storage.

logical comparison The consideration of two items with regard to some characteristic, to obtain a symbol or signal representing a Yes if they are the same and a No if they are different.

logical design The planning of the mathematical and logical interrelationships of a computer or a data-processing system prior to its detailed engineering design.

logical operations Computer operations of comparing, selecting, mixing, or taking alternative action.

logical symbol A symbol used to represent a logical device.

loop A conditional routine in which a group of instructions is repeated.

machine language Information in a form which the computer can interpret as data.

machine word A unit of information consisting of a fixed number of bits or characters for computers of fixed word length. In other computers, the number of characters per word may vary.

magnetic core A small doughnut-shaped piece of material made of a magnetizable substance possessing bistable properties for reliable retention of information. The information is stored in the form of flux lines traveling in a given direction around the core to represent a 1 and in the opposite direction to represent a 0. The larger metallic-ribbon variety is termed bimag and is normally used in shift registers. The smaller ferrite-compound variety is used in the computer memory.

magnetic drum A storage device consisting of a rotating cylindrical drum surfaced with a magnetic coating. Data is stored as small magnetized spots arranged in tracks or channels around the drum. A read-write head is associated with each channel so that the channel can be selected by electronic switching.

magnetic tape A storage medium consisting of metal, paper, or plastic tape coated with magnetic material. Information is stored as small magnetized spots, usually arranged in columns across the width of the tape, with each column representing a tape character. A read-write head is usually associated with each row of magnetized spots so that one column can be read or written at a time as the tape is moved relative to the head.

malfunction A failure or fault in the operation of the hardware of a machine.

marginal checking   A preventive-maintenance procedure in which the supply voltage of the electronic circuits is varied above and below its normal value to detect and locate circuits which are becoming defective.

matrix   A switching network which has an output line corresponding to each possible combination of inputs.

memory   A computer unit or device into which information can be stored and then withdrawn at a later time. Synonym for storage.

memory capacity   The maximum amount of information that can be stored in a memory, usually expressed in words containing a specified number of bits.

message   A group of words which are handled and transferred as a unit.

mistake   A human error in coding or in manual operation.

multiplicand   The quantity which is multiplied by each digit of the multiplier in the process of multiplication.

multivibrator   A type of relaxation oscillator for the generation of nonsinusoidal waves in which the output of each of two stages is coupled to the input of the other to sustain oscillations.

nor element   A gate that produces an output only when all inputs are absent.

octal notation   A number system in which the successive digits are interpreted as coefficients of successive powers of the base 8. For example, octal number 324 is equivalent to $3 \times 8^2 + 2 \times 8 + 4 \times 1$, or $192 + 16 + 4$, or decimal 212; octal 324 is equal to 011 010 100 in binary notation.

off-line equipment   Auxiliary equipment used with a computing system which operates independently of the main processing equipment, so as not to hamper the computer speed. Typical off-line equipment includes punched-card, punched-paper-tape, and magnetic-tape units.

on-line equipment   Major processing equipment of compatible computer speed which is directly connected to the main processing unit.

operand   Any one of the quantities being used for or resulting from a computer operation.

operation code   That part of a computer operation which designates the basic arithmetic, logical, or transfer operation to be performed.

operational unit   A combination of logical and nonlogical elements which perform a complete computer operation or process, such as storage or input processing.

or gate   A gate which produces an output when one or more inputs are present.

order   A defined, successive arrangement of numbers, elements, or events.

output   The results of computer operations in the form of punched cards, magnetic tapes, or printed documents, or otherwise transferred out of the computer.

output unit   That portion of the computer which is used to deliver information from the inside to the outside of the computer.

overflow   That condition in which the result of an arithmetic operation exceeds the capacity of the register to hold that result.

paper tape   A specially treated strip of paper in which a pattern of holes is punched; this pattern, in combination with blank spaces, represents numbers and letters.

parallel transfer   The simultaneous transfer of all specified characters from one part of the machine to another.

parity check   A summation check, in which the bits in a character or word are totaled before and after transporting and the sum is checked against a previously computed quantity—reduced to either an odd or an even count. The parity check prevents errors from occurring because of lost or spuriously gained bits.

patch   A section of coding inserted into a routine (usually by transferring control from the routine to the patch and then back again to the routine) to alter the routine or correct a mistake.

patchboard   A removable board, containing hundreds of terminals into which patch cords (short wires) are connected, which determines the different programs for the machine. To change the program, the wiring pattern on the patchboard or the patchboard itself must be changed.

peripheral equipment   Equipment separate from the main computer; off-line equipment such as punched-card and punched-tape units.

plotter   A device which provides a visual display of an object or operation under surveillance, usually in the form of a graph.

plug-in unit   A subassembly of electronic components forming matrices, flip-flops, buffer circuits, etc., so designed that connections to the device can be made by inserting its terminals into a suitable socket or receptacle.

precision   The degree of exactness with which a quantity is recorded or specified, usually in terms of the number of significant digits used.

program   A plan for the computer solution of a problem, including plans for the transcription of data, coding, and the absorption or distribution of the results into the system.

program tape   A tape, usually magnetic, upon which is written a complete sequence of instructions required for solving a problem.

programmer   An analyst responsible for originating, in complete detail, the steps necessary to give a digital computer instructions for each minute step in a data-processing operation.

programming   The science of translating a problem to terms and instructions that a machine can understand and obey.

program register   A register located in the control unit which stores the instruction currently governing the operation of the computer.

pseudo-code   An arbitrary coding used in writing programs and later translated into computer code.

pulse repetition rate   The number of pulses occurring per unit of time (usually given in pulses per second).

punch card   A card of standard size and shape upon which data may be stored in the form of holes and no holes. The hole positions (hole sites) are arranged in columns; a given pattern of holes in a column represents one character. The holes may be sensed mechanically, electrically, or photoelectrically.

punched tape   See **paper tape**.

punching position   One of the 12 divisions of a card column into which a hole may be punched.

quantization   A process by which analog information is converted to digital information.

random access   A method of information selection wherein equal or nearly equal access time is required for selection and procurement of any article of information.

random processing   The processing of data which is in no predetermined order when it enters the computer system.

read   To copy or sense information, usually from one form of storage to another.

read in   To place data in storage at a specific address.

read out   To copy data from a specified address in the computer's memory to an external storage medium.

real-time operation Solving problems as fast as they occur so that the results can be used to guide the operation.

register The hardware in the arithmetic and control units used for storing portions of or a complete computer word. The register is used to hold the word while it is being manipulated as either data or instructions.

reset 1. To place a binary device in the zero, or initial, state. 2. To restore a storage device to a prescribed state.

ring counter A loop of interconnected bistable elements such that only one is in a specified state at any given time and such that, as input signals are counted, the position of the one specified state moves in an ordered sequence around the loop.

routine A set of instructions arranged in proper sequence to cause a machine to perform a desired operation.

scaling Shifting the decimal point of a quantity in the relationship to the machine decimal point so that (1) the quantity remains within the capacity of the machine; (2) two or more quantities are in the correct relationship to each other for arithmetic operations; or (3) the results are computed with the actual decimal point of the quantity in the desired location.

sense To detect the presence or absence of a binary 1 in a binary device.

sequential processing The processing of data that has been operated on prior to its entry into the computer system and placed in a definite and prescribed order.

serial digital computer A machine in which the digits are handled in a serial manner, especially the arithmetic unit.

set 1. To insert a specified number into a counter or register. 2. To place a flip-flop in the ONE state.

shift To displace an ordered set of bits one or more places to the right or left.

sign digit The digit in a computer word which is used to designate the algebraic sign of a quantity, either positive or negative, with the use of a 0 or 1.

signed magnitude The form of a number consisting of an initial sign bit followed by true (not complemented) magnitude bits.

significant digit Any digit in the expression of a quantity except a zero in an order higher than the highest nonzero digit and in a lower order than the lowest nonzero digit.

special-purpose computer A computer designed for solving a specific type of problem, usually containing a built-in program.

storage The components which enable the computer to retain data internally by electromechanical, magnetic, or electronic devices until it is needed.

subroutine A short sequence of instructions with which the computer will carry out a well-defined mathematical or logical operation or will solve a well-defined part of a large problem. A subsection of a routine.

tabulator A machine which copies specified fields of information, usually from punched cards or tapes, and types or prints the information on continuous paper or special forms.

tape, magnetic See **magnetic tape.**

tape reservoir That part of a magnetic-tape-handling unit in which several feet of slack tape is held to allow rapid start-stop operations.

tape-wound core A magnetic core consisting of a plastic or ceramic toroid around which is wound a strip of thin magnetic tape possessing a squire-hysteresis-loop characteristic. Also known as a bimag, a tape-wound core is used principally as a shift-register element.

ternary notation   A number system using the base 3 and employing three distinct characters.

transfer   To convey or copy information from one location to another.

transistor   A small solid-state semiconductor device composed of germanium or silicon that performs nearly all functions of an electron tube, especially amplification.

translate   To convert information from one language or code to another without significantly altering the meaning.

troubleshoot   To search for a coding mistake or, in the case of a computer malfunction, to locate and remedy the faulty device.

truth table   A tabular listing of a logical element or function showing the output for all combinations of inputs.

unconditional branch   An instruction which interrupts the normal process of obtaining instructions in an ordered sequence and specifies the address from which the next instruction is to be taken.

unpack   To separate a machine word into parts according to fields of operation.

variable-cycle operation   A synchronous computer action wherein operations may be of varying length.

verify   To check a data transcription against the original information or against another transcription.

volatile   A computer storage medium which is incapable of retaining information without continuous power dissipation.

word   A set of digits which occupy an addressable storage location and are treated by the computer as a unit.

word length   The number of bits that constitute a word.

word time   In reference to words stored serially, the time required to read one word from the main or central memory.

write   To record information into a storage medium or copy information from one type of storage device to another.

zero suppression   The removal of nonsignificant zeros to the left of the integral part of a quantity before print-out.

zone punch   A punch in one of the three top positions of a punched-card column (12, 11, 0) which, when combined with a punch in one of the numeric positions, will form an alphabetical character.

Index

Abacus, 3
Acceptor atom, 99
Access time, 385–387
Adder, 338–342
  DCTL, 345–346
  parallel, 340–341
  RTL, 346
  serial, 341–342
  truth table for, 338–340
  (*See also* Full adder; Half-adder)
Adding machine, 4–5
  Burroughs, 5
  first desk type, 4
  stepped reckoner, 4
Addition, binary, 42–44, 338–342,
    366–368
  excess-3, 54–55
  ternary, 58–59
Address, 351
Address modification, 471–472
Address register, 351–355
Algebraic compiler, 455
Alpha, 116
  relation to beta, 119–120
Amplifier, buffer, 256–259
  neon, 259–261
  pulse, 252–256
  relay, 261–262
  transistor, 115–120
Analog computer, 2
AND as logical connective, 64
AND gate, bimag, 279–280
  diode, 24
  switch equivalent of, 16
  symbol for, 24–25, 31

AND gate, transistor, 25
  vacuum tube, 26
Arithmetic unit, 8, 358–380
  components, 359–364
  instructions, 364–380
Associativity, 65
Atom, covalent force, 95
  crystal lattice structure, 96
  shell arrangements, 94–95
  structure, 93–96
Atomic number, 94

Babbage, Charles, 5
Base of number system, 36
  (*See also* Radix conversion)
Beta, 118
  relation to alpha, 119–120
Bimag core, 91, 264–283
  AND circuit, 279–280
  dot notation, 267
  exclusive-OR circuit, 278
  half-adder circuit, 282–283
  inclusive-OR circuit, 278–279
  magnetic shift register, 269–272,
    280–281
  ping-pong circuit, 281–283
  single-diode transfer loop, 274–278
  split-winding transfer loop, 274–
    278
  symbol for, 31, 267
Binary addition, 42–44
  with full adder, 339–342
  with half-adder, 338–339
  table, 43, 338, 340
Binary arithmetic, rules for, 43–51